Lories and Lorikeets

The Brush-Tongued Parrots

Rosemary Low

Distributed in the U.S. by T.F.H. Publications, Inc., 211 West Sylvania Avenue, P.O. Box 427, Neptune, N.J. 07753; in England by T.F.H. (Gt. Britain) Ltd., 13 Nutley Lane, Reigate, Surrey; in Canada to the book store and library trade by Clarke, Irwin & Company, Clarwin House, 791 St. Clair Avenue West, Toronto 10, Ontario; in Canada to the pet trade by Rolf C. Hagen Ltd., 3225 Sartelon Street, Montreal 382, Quebec; in Southeast Asia by Y.W. Ong, 9 Lorong 36 Geylang, Singapore 14; in Australia and the South Pacific by Pet Imports Pty. Ltd., P.O. Box 149, Brookvale 2100, N.S.W., Australia; in South Africa by Valiant Publishers (Pty.) Ltd., P.O. Box 78236, Sandton City, 2146, South Africa; Published by T.F.H. Publications, Inc., Ltd., The British Crown Colony of Hong Kong.

First published 1977 in Great Britain by
Paul Elek Limited
54–58 Caledonian Road, London NI 9RN

CONTENTS

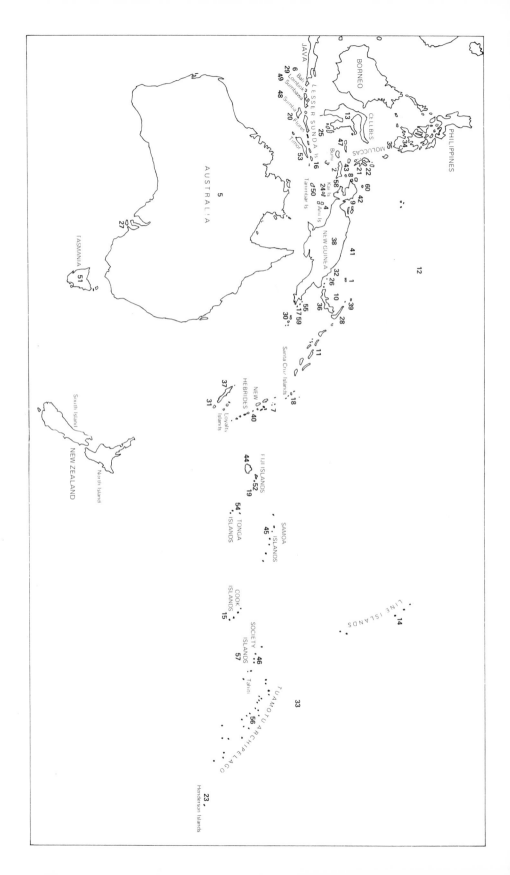

Key to distribution map

ADMIRALTY ISLANDS (Bismarck Archipelago) – **1**
Trichoglossus haematodus flavicans

AMBELAU (southern Moluccas) – **2**
Charmosyna p. placentis

AMBOINA (AMBON) (Indonesia) – **3**
Eos b. bornea
Trichoglossus h. haematodus
Lorius domicellus
Charmosyna p. placentis

ARU ISLANDS – **4**
Chalcopsitta sintillata rubrifrons
Trichoglossus haematodus nigrogularis
Charmosyna p. placentis

AUSTRALIA – **5**
Trichoglossus haematodus moluccanus
Trichoglossus haematodus rubritorquis
Trichoglossus chlorolepidotus
Glossopsitta concinna
Glossopsitta pusilla
Glossopsitta porphyrocephala
Glossopsitta versicolor

BALI – **6**
Trichoglossus haematodus mitchellii

BANKS ISLANDS (New Hebrides) – **7**
Charmosyna palmarum

BATANTA – **8**
Chalcopsitta a. atra
Eos s. squamata or Eos wallacei
Lorius l. lory

BIAK (Geelvink Bay, West Irian) – **9**
Eos cyanogenia
Trichoglossus haematodus rosenbergii
Lorius lory cyanauchen
Chamosyna rubronotata kordoana

BISMARCK ARCHIPELAGO (see also Feni Island,
New Britain, New Ireland and Woodlark Island) – **10**
Trichoglossus haematodus massena
Lorius hypoinochrous devittatus
Charmosyna placentis pallidior

BOUGAINVILLE (Solomon Islands) – **11**
Charmosyna placentis pallidior

BURU, Indonesia – **3**
Eos bornea cyanonothus
Trichoglossus h. haematodus
Lorius domicellus (introduced)
Charmosyna toxopei

CAROLINE ISLANDS – **12**
Trichoglossus rubiginosus

CERAM (SERAM) Indonesia – **2**
Eos bornea rothschildi
Eos semilarvata
Trichoglossus h. haematodus
Lorius domicellus
Charmosyna p. placentis

CELEBES – **13**
Trichoglossus ornatus
Trichoglossus flavoviridis meyeri

CHRISTMAS ISLAND, Line Group – **14**
Vini kuhlii
COOK ISLANDS – **15**

Vini peruviana

DAMAR ISLAND, Indonesia – **16**
Eos reticulata

D'ENTRECASTEAUX ARCHIPELAGO – **17**
Lorius hypoinochrous devittatus

DJAMPEA ISLAND, FLORES SEA
Trichoglossus haematodus djampeanus

DUFF ISLAND (Santa Cruz) – **18**
Charmosyna palmarum

FANNING ISLAND, Line Group – **14**
Vini kuhlii

FEAD, Solomon Islands – **15**
Charmosyna p. pallidior

FENI ISLAND – **10**
Chalcopsitta cardinalis

FIJI (See also Ovalau, Taveuni and Viti Levu) – **19**
Phigys solitarius

FLORES ISLAND – **20**
Trichoglossus haematadus weberi

GEBE (Western Papuan Islands) – **21**
Eos s. squamata or Eos wallacei
Charmosyna placentis intensior

HALMAHERA, Moluccas, Indonesia – **22**
Lorius g. garrulus

HENDERSON ISLAND, Pitcairn Group – **23**
Vini stepheni

JAPEN ISLAND (JOBI) (Geelvink Bay) – **9**
Pseudeos fuscata
Lorius lory jobiensis

KAI (KEI) ISLANDS, Indonesia – **24**
Eos reticulata
Eos bornea bernsteini
Trichoglossus haematodus nigrogularis
Charmosyna p. placentis

KALAO TUA, Flores Sea – **25**
Trichoglossus haematodus stresemanni

KANGAROO ISLAND, Australia – **27**
Trichoglossus haematodus moluccanus
Glossopsitta concinna
Glossopsitta prophryrocephala

KARKAR ISLAND (off N.E. New Guinea) – **26**
Charmosyna rubrigularis krakari

LAU ARCHIPELAGO, Fiji – **19**
Phigys solitarius
Vini australis

LAVONGAI ISLANDS – **28**
Chalcopsitta cardinalis

LOMBOK – **29**
Trichoglossus haematodus mitchellii

LOUISIADE ARCHIPELAGO (eastern Papuan
Islands) – **30**
Lorius h. hypoinochrous

LOYALTY ISLANDS – **31**
Trichoglossus haematodus deplanchii

MANAM ISLAND – **32**
Trichoglossus haematodus intermedius

MARQUESAS ISLANDS – **33**
Vini ultramarina

MINDANAO, Philippine Islands – **34**
Trichoglossus johnstoniae

MIOS NUM ISLAND (Geelvink Bay) – **9**
Eos cyanogenia
Lorius lory jobiensis

MISIMA ISLAND, Louisiade Archipelago – **30**
Trichoglossus haematodus micropteryx
Lorius h. hypoinochrous

MISOOL, (MISOL, MYSOL), Western Papuan
Islands – **8**
Chalcopsitta atra bernsteini
Eos s. squamata
Lorius l. lory

MOROTAI, Moluccas, Indonesia – **22**
Lorius garrulus morotaianus

NENUSA (NANUSA) ISLAND, Indonesia – **35**
Eos histrio challengeri

NEW BRITAIN (Bismarck Archipelago) – **36**
Charmosyna rubrigularis

NEW CALEDONIA – **37**
Trichoglossus haematodus deplanchii
Charmosyna diadema

NEW GUINEA (mainland) – **38**
Chalcopsitta atra
Chalcopsitta duivenbodei
Chalcopsitta s. sintillata
Chalcopsitta s. chloroptera

Pseudeos fuscata
Trichoglossus h. berauensis
Trichoglossus h. haematodus
Trichoglossus h. intermedius
Trichoglossus h. micropteryx
Trichoglossus h. caeruleiceps
Glossopsitta goldiei
Lorius hypoinochrous devittatus
Lorius lory erythrothorax
Lorius lory lory
Lorius lory somu
Lorius lory salvadori
Lorius lory viridicrissalis
Charmosyna multistriata
Charmosyna r. rubronotata
Charmosyna p. placentis
Charmosyna placentis ornata
Charmosyna placentis subplacens
Charmosyna pulchella pulchella
Charmosyna pulchella rothschildi
Charmosyna j. josefinae
Charmosyna j. sepikiana
Charmosyna j. cyclopum
Charmosyna p. papou
Charmosyna p. stellae
Charmosyna p. goliathina
Charmosyna p. wahnesi
Charmosyna wilhelminae
Oreopsittacus a. arfaki
Oreopsittacus a. major
Oreopsittacus a. grandis
Neopsittacus m. musschenbroekii
Neopsittacus m. medius
Neopsittacus m. major
Neopsittacus p. pullicauda
Neopsittacus p. alpinus
Neopsittacus p. socialis

NEW HANOVER – 39
Trichoglossus h. flavicans

NEW HEBRIDES – 40
Charmosyna palmarum

NININGO GROUP (west of Manus Island) – 41
Trichoglossus haematodus nesophilus

NISSAN ISLAND (Solomon Islands) – 11
Chalcopsitta cardinalis

NUMFOOR ISLAND (Geelvink Bay) – 42
Eos cyanogenia

OBI (northern Moluccas) – 43
Eos squamata obiensis
Lorius garrulus flavopalliatus
Charmosyna placentis intensior

OVALAU (Fiji) – 44
Charmosyna amabilis

PANJANG (southern Moluccas) – 58
Charmosyna p. placentis

PHILIPPINE ISLANDS – See Mindanao

PONAPE (Caroline Islands) – 12
Trichoglossus rubiginosus

ROSSEL ISLAND (Louisiade Archipelago) – 30
Lorius hypoinochrous rosselianus

SALAWATI (Western Papua Islands) – 8
Chalcopsitta atra atra
Pseudeos fuscata
Lorius lory lory
Charmosyna r. rubronotata
Charmosyna p. placentis

SAMOA (Polynesia) – 45
Vini australis

SANGHIR (SANGIR) ISLAND
Eos h. histrio

SANTA CRUZ – 18
Charmosyna palmarum

SAPARUA (Indonesia) – 3
Eos b. bornea

SCHILDPAD ISLANDS – Western Papuan Islands – 60
Eos s. squamata

SOCIETY ISLANDS – 46
Vini peruviana

SOLOMON ISLANDS   15
Chalcopsitta cardinalis
Trichoglossus haematodus massena
Lorius chlorocercus
Charmosyna p. placentis
Charmosyna placentis pallidior
Charmosyna rubrigularis
Charmosyna margarethae
Charmosyna meeki

SULA ISLANDS (Indonesia) – 47
Trichoglossus f. flavoviridis

SUMBA – 48
Trichoglossus haematodus fortis

SUMBAWA – 49
Trichoglossus haematodus forsteni

TAGULA ISLAND (Louisiade Archipelago) – 30
Lorius h. hypoinochrous

TALAUD ISLANDS (Indonesia) – 35
Eos histrio talautensis

TANIMBAR (TENIMBER) (Indonesia) – 50
Eos reticulata

TASMANIA – 51
Trichoglossus haematodus moluccanus
Glossopsitta concinna
Glossopsitta pusilla

TAVEUNI (Fiji) – 52
Charmosyna amabilis

TIMOR – 53
Trichoglossus haematodus capistratus
Trichoglossus euteles
Glossopsitta iris

TONGA (Polynesia) – 54
Vini australis

TROBRIAND ISLAND – 55
Lorius hypoinochrous devittatus

TUAMOTU ISLANDS – 56
Vini peruviana

TUBUAI ISLANDS – 57
Vini kuhlii

VITI LEVU (Fiji) – 44
Charmosyna amabilis

WAIGEO (WAIGEU) (Western Papuan Islands) – 60
Lorius l. lory
Eos s. squamata or Eos wallacei

WASHINGTON ISLAND (Line Group) – 14
Vini kuhlii

WATUBELA ISLANDS (Indonesia) – 58
Eos bornea
Trichoglossus h. haematodus

WETAR ISLAND (near Timor) – 16
Trichoglossus haematodus flavotectus
Glossopsitta iris wetterensis

WOODLARK ISLANDS (Bismarck Archipelago) – 59
Lorius hypoinochrous devittatus
Charmosyna placentis pallidior

Foreword

Lories and lorikeets, which comprise the subfamily Loriidae, are widely distributed throughout south-eastern Asia, Papua New Guinea, Australia and Polynesia. Almost all are of extremely bright plumage, perhaps the most brilliantly coloured of all the parrots.

In size, there is considerable variation. Some of the smaller New Guinea lorikeets are no larger in body size than an African Lovebird; others, particularly the lories of the genus *Lorius* (*Domicella*), reach the proportions of a small Amazon Parrot.

In this subfamily, the tongue is specially adapted with a brush-like tip. This structure, composed of elongated papillae, enables the lories and lorikeets to collect pollen and nectar within the flowers rich in carbohydrates, particularly those of eucalyptus trees. These birds are also very fond of fruit and buds. As a result of their feeding habits, lories and lorikeets play a major role in the pollination of trees and other flowering plants.

Rosemary Low's comprehensive treatise of this specialised group of psittacines, the Loriidae, will prove invaluable for recognition purposes as it contains descriptions of all the species and subspecies.

Emphasis is given to information relating to each species both in its natural habitat and in aviculture, especially regarding the experiences of aviculturists the world over in breeding these birds.

I hope this splendid book will have the success it deserves and help to encourage even more aviculturists to dedicate themselves to working with this group.

Kenton C. Lint
Curator Emeritus
San Diego Zoo
California

ACKNOWLEDGEMENTS

I am indebted to the aviculturists and curators of zoological societies who replied so helpfully to my requests for information, especially my friends at the Zoological Society of San Diego, K. C. Lint, Curator Emeritus, and Dr J. M. Dolan, Curator of the San Diego Wild Animal Park. My grateful thanks are due to my husband for photographing lories, also to G. A. Smith, MRCVS, for his ready help in all matters relating to my lories. I should also like to thank Ken Denham of Elek for his invaluable assistance in the publication of this book. Finally, thanks are due to Lansdowne Press for permission to quote from *Parrots of the World* and to the secretaries of the Avicultural Society and the Foreign Bird League for permission to quote from the *Avicultural Magazine* and *Foreign Birds*.

The publishers especially wish to thank The Parrot Society for the use of copyright material from their magazine.

Introduction

Lories can be described, without any fear of contradiction, as being among the most beautiful of the world's birds; some also rank among the most intelligent. The aviculturist who requires colour *and* character is unlikely to find more appealing subjects.

There is a fast-growing awareness that merely keeping birds is not enough; in order to justify their existence aviculturists must make every effort to breed from the birds they keep. Fortunately, lories nest more readily than many parrots, and during the past few years aviary breeding successes have increased substantially in number. One reason is that, dating from the late 1960s, the numbers (of species and individuals) available to aviculturists rose steeply but, in some countries, soon fell off because of various import and quarantine regulations.

In the early 1970s a number of lories which had been strangers to aviculture for 50 years or even longer, were exported from New Guinea, thus arousing the interest of aviculturists who had never previously kept lories. Those who already had lories in their collections found the appeal of tiny gems such as Fairy Lorikeets or exquisitely coloured Yellow-streaked and Dusky Lories, too great to resist.

This came at a time when there was, in any case, an upward trend in the number of people keeping and breeding parrots, many of whom had previous experience with other foreign birds, while others were directly attracted to aviculture by the parrot family—and probably initially by parrakeets.

However, there is one important difference between keeping lories and other parrots. Lories feed entirely or almost entirely on liquid food. The resulting 'droppings' prevent them being kept permanently in cages; the aviary is the only form of accommodation suitable. Seedeating parrots can, if absolutely necessary, be provided with enough food to last for more than one day. Lories are fed on 'nectar' which should be made fresh daily. It is therefore not possible to leave them unattended for more than 24 hours and, according to the weather conditions, attention to their food may have to be more frequent than once daily. In hot weather fresh nectar should be supplied twice daily and, in cold weather, the nectar may freeze and must then be replaced.

These facts must be given careful consideration by the prospective purchaser of lories. Those who feel these birds may be too much trouble or that they are unable to give them sufficient attention, will be able to obtain parrots which need less surveillance. Those who decide, however, that lories are for them, will be privileged to have in their aviaries some of the loveliest and most desirable birds in the world.

All lories, with one single exception, are brightly coloured, and many are very striking indeed with red and blue or red and green predominating in their plumage.

Some exhibit an amazing combination of colours and a few have peculiarities of form, such as greatly lengthened tail feathers, as in the Papaun Lory, or unique narrow feathers, which give the head a spiky appearance (*Chalcopsitta* species) or the collar of elongated feathers of the Solitary or Collared Lory.

Lories vary in size from the diminutive Wilhelmina's Lorikeet from mainland New Guinea, which measures 13cm (5in) to several members of the genera *Chalcopsitta*, *Eos* and *Lorius* which attain a length of over 30cm (12in).

Generally speaking the term 'lory' is applied to short-tailed birds and 'lorikeet' to those with long tails but not all birds fall neatly into either category, thus the terms, like the allied 'parrot' and 'parrakeet', are not precise ones.

Just as the term 'parrot' is used to embrace all psittacine birds, I have used the term 'lory' in its broader sense to include all members of the Loriidae, rather than repeatedly refer to 'lories and lorikeets.'

It is my hope that this book will be of value to the aviculturist since only one other treatise on the subject has been published. Mivart's beautifully illustrated *Monograph* (1896) is now a rare and valuable collector's item. Published at a time when aviculture as we know it was in its infancy, it contains little information of relevance to present-day aviculturists.

NOTE ON CLASSIFICATION

Classification in the main follows Forshaw (1973); however, I have used my own arrangement for the genus *Glossopsitta*, including three species which were formerly placed in the genus *Psitteuteles*. Forshaw does not recognise the genus *Psitteuteles*, classifying all its members (*flavoviridis, johnstoniae, goldiei, versicolor* and *iris*) with *Trichoglossus* while, in my opinion, only the first two belong in that genus.

I believe that *flavoviridis* is a typical *Trichoglossus*, closely related to the Perfect and Scaly-breasted Lorikeets. The display of the Meyer's Lorikeet (*T. f. meyeri*) is typical of that of *Trichoglossus* species: it puffs out the body feathers, sways from side to side and bobs its head up and down, dilating the pupils and simultaneously warbling, or sometimes beak clicking. According to descriptions of its display, this also applies to *T. johnstoniae* (which I have not had the opportunity to observe in display).

The display, voice and general behaviour of the Iris Lorikeet is totally unlike that of any *Trichoglossus* species. Its display resembles that of the Varied Lorikeet which has been described (Mitchell, 1966) as follows:

'. . . both birds made a "zrr-zrr' sound and bobbed up and down on the perch, continually swaying away from each other in a circular fashion as if their feet were anchored to the spot.'

There are very few Musk Lorikeets in captivity. An aviculturist and zoologist who is familiar with the behaviour of this species and who keeps Iris and Meyer's Lorikeets in his private collection, is Dr J. M. Dolan of San Diego Wild Animal Park. In reply to my query regarding the display of the Musk Lorikeet, he stated: 'It is very unlike the *Trichoglossus* lorikeets and parallels that of the Iris.' He agreed that the birds look as though they had been 'nailed to the perch,' and stated that the Musk and Iris are very similar in voice.

Dr W. D. Russell of Bryanston, South Africa, who has bred the Little and Iris Lorikeets and also keeps the Musk, agreed that the behaviour of the Iris is similar in many respects to that of the Little and Musk, rather than to that of *Trichoglossus* species (pers. comm, January 1977).

Goldie's Lorikeet is an interesting example of the confusion which has surrounded the classification of these small lorikeets. It was placed in the genus *Glossopsitta* by Salvadori (1891) and retained there by Mivart (1896). It was included in the genus *Psitteuteles* by Peters (1937). Forshaw (1973) included it with *Trichoglossus* but wrote: 'I am not convinced that *T. goldiei* belongs here and suspect that further investigation with fresh material could result in it being placed in a monotypic genus.'

The late Alan Lendon, an ornithologist and aviculturist who knew Goldie's Lorikeet in life, believed that it should be classified as a *Glossopsitta*.

The comments of Amadon (1942) on the classification of lories and lorikeets are worth repeating here and will indicate the arbitrary nature of any system of classification:

'Peters recognised fifteen genera* in the subfamily Loriinae. Examination of skins of the type species of all these, and of the more important literature, indicates that many of these genera are based upon slight, intergrading structural characters, or upon colour pattern alone. Indeed, of the fifteen genera, four are monotypic, while five or six others are composed of a few closely related species which seem still to replace each other geographically (superspecies). This has resulted from two factors: (1) the species concept has been broadened, and many forms once believed to be good species are now rightly considered to be subspecies; (2) the genus concept has not been broadened. Modern ornithologists have retained most of the old narrowly defined genera, or even set up new ones.'

Amadon wrote: 'I believe it necessary to unite *Charmosyna* with *Vini*. This is probably true of at least *Glossopsitta* also.' While there would seem to be every justification for uniting *Charmosyna* and *Vini*, in behaviour and form, the *Glossopsitta* species are totally different and, in my opinion, must be retained in a separate genus.

*He included the Fig Parrots *Psittaculirostris* and *Opopsitta* and the monotypic *Lathamus* (Swift Parrakeet).

xii

I

Some aspects of keeping lories

Lories have long been kept in captivity but, until comparatively recently, because their food requirements were not fully understood, they had a reputation of being 'difficult' birds to cater for. Death at an early age, said to be due to fits, was common because their diet was unsuitable. Now that their needs are better understood, the nectar-feeding parrots prove just as hardy and long-lived as the seed-eating species but, in the minds of a few, they are perhaps still considered as birds for the specialist. If the 'specialist' is one who is especially conscientious concerning the care of his birds, then there may be some truth in this. Lories are no more difficult to care for than other parrots but, as pointed out in the introduction, they *must* have fresh food daily. With other parrots it is quite acceptable to 'top up' the seed container each day (after removing husks) and to offer fresh fruit and/or greenfood, but with lories the food needs careful attention daily. This, one hopes, is true whatever species of birds are kept. Many lories exist on nectar only, in captivity, while others eat considerable quantities of fruit, seed, greenfood and insects.

Because of the liquid nature of their droppings and the difficulties this fact creates (this aspect is fully discussed in chapter 3), it is not possible to keep lories satisfactorily indoors. Having accepted this fact, the aviculturist will find that keeping lories presents no problems not associated with any other birds—except that of the nectar becoming sour or being consumed by insects in very hot weather, and nectar freezing when the temperature falls well below freezing. However, in a temperate climate, the number of days in any year when either of these problems arise is actually very few.

Obtaining lories. The sources of supply can be divided into three categories: the exporter overseas, the importer dealer in one's own country, and the private aviculturist. Because of the expense of importing a small number of birds, only dealers or private aviculturists who are especially anxious to obtain a species on an overseas dealer's list, will obtain birds from this source. The quarantine regulations enforced in some countries make it difficult or impossible for the private aviculturist to import his own birds.

By far the greater majority of lories are obtained by private individuals through dealers; all of these birds will be newly imported. It is rarely that a dealer can offer aviary-bred birds and if he does this fact is certain to be pointed out in his advertisement, as such birds are, of course, usually more expensive than newly imported ones.

Some of the latter are in immaculate feather; others are not but in many cases all they need is to bathe. Feather condition, unless abnormally poor, is of little importance when buying lories. Occasionally one comes across a lory which has plucked itself, usually on the breast, but this usually occurs in lories which have been in captivity some time. Some newly imported lories, usually the larger species, have had their flight feathers cut on one or both wings. This is a disadvantage if it is intended to place the bird immediately into an aviary because, until it moults, it will only be able to climb about.

On the whole, however, feather condition is much less important than health. The birds to be avoided on dealers' premises are those which sit fluffed up, on two feet, with the head resting on the back. A lory in good health which is merely resting will, unless it is extremely young, normally rest on one foot with the head on its back and it will not have a fluffed appearance. Eyes are an excellent indication of health; in a fit bird they will be bright but in one which is sick they will appear dull, even sunken, and the bird may close its eyes frequently.

Very thin birds should be avoided at all costs; the area to examine is the breast. If the breast bone is very prominent the bird is obviously under-nourished and may be difficult to establish in captivity.

Observe carefully any bird in which the head feathers are matted and sticky. This may merely be a sign of overcrowding when a number of lories have been kept in one cage; on the other hand it could mean that the bird is ill and has been vomiting. If the latter is the case its dull eyes will betray its state of health. A newly imported lory which is seen to vomit needs immediate and very careful treatment if it is to survive.

After purchase, lories which look healthy and lively can, during warm weather, be placed immediately in an outdoor aviary of which they are the only occupants. Those obtained during the colder months will need to be acclimatised.

Any whose health gives cause for concern must be kept indoors, preferably in a flight rather than a cage. Close observation, especially regarding the food taken, is essential.

Those handling lories for the first time must be aware that they are capable of inflicting an extremely painful bite; most parrots can bite hard but that of a lory can be particularly severe. If the birds are handled correctly, the handler will not be bitten. The first essential for catching lories in an aviary is a padded net which can be bought from the larger shops and bird farms which sell birds and accessories.

Most lories will enter their nest-box at the first sign of danger and it is very difficult to remove them. The nest entrance should therefore be covered before any attempt is made to catch the bird. Catching a lory in flight presents no problems; the bird can be transferred immediately to an empty cage that has been taken into the aviary for that purpose. If the net is placed over a lory as it clings to wire netting it may be extremely difficult to persuade the bird to release the grip which its feet and beak have on the wire. On no account should one use one's free hand to achieve this as a severe bite will almost certainly be the result. With a little patience, it is usually possible to manoeuvre the bird into the lower part of the net. If this is not possible, it may be advisable to let the bird go, wait until it drops to the floor of the aviary and then, before it can reach anything to cling to, quickly drop the net over it.

Once netted, many lories will turn on their backs, often shrieking loudly. Care must still be exercised because they may prove reluctant to leave the net and can easily inflict a nasty bite *through* the net. The larger lories, particularly in my experience, *Chalcopsitta* species, resent being netted and will struggle inside the net, unlike some parrots which stay quite calm and still.

If it is necessary to transfer a bird from one aviary to another, resist the temptation to carry the bird in the net; the only safe method is to use a cage.

If a lory has to be transferred from one cage to another, it may be possible to do this by opening the doors, placing the cages together and gently coaxing the bird inside the other cage. If a lory has to be removed from a cage for treatment, or for some other reason, unless the cage is large it will not be possible to use a net. In this case a folded hand towel should be placed firmly over the bird.

One of the most delightful aspects of lories as aviary birds is their tameness. Some are tame when imported, perhaps hand-reared; others quickly become fearless and, of the remainder, very few fail to achieve some degree of *rapport* with their owner. This is in direct contrast to many Australian parrakeets, for example; when one walks along a row of aviaries containing the latter, more often than not, they fly away from one, into the shelter. Lories seldom do this, unless newly imported, and most will fly towards one, rather than away. Indeed, they can become embarrassingly tame, descending on the container of fresh nectar before one has a chance to withdraw one's hand.

Most lories soon become used to their owners, although they may react quite differently towards strangers. If they are slow to lose their fear when first imported, it may help to house them in an aviary near the dwelling house or in the busiest part of the garden or property. Lories become tame more quickly in small aviaries without enclosed shelters. A pair of Edwards's Lorikeets housed for eight years in a 4.8m (16ft) aviary, which included a 1.2m (4ft) enclosed shelter, were rarely seen, rushing into the shelter whenever the aviary was approached. When moved to a 2.4m (8ft) long aviary with an open-fronted shelter, they quickly became steady, remaining perched a few inches from the wire when approached. A pair of Black Lories, temporarily housed in the same range of small aviaries, was almost impossible to view, for they retired into the open-fronted shelter in the presence of people, where their plumage blended with the background. As it matured, one bird became very beautiful, becoming gradually pied with red. In order to observe it better, I moved it to an aviary with a 3m (10ft) frontage on the main garden path. Within a few weeks it and its mate had become very steady and my pleasure in them had increased many times. Careful thought should therefore be given to the situation of all pairs.

Enclosed shelters are not necessary for lories unless they are kept in an inhospitable climate. Nest-boxes must be left in position throughout the year and very few lories will not use them for roosting. It is not necessary to position the nest-box in the shelter but this does provide extra protection during the winter months.

Those who do not keep birds invariably express surprise that lories and other parrots are kept outdoors throughout the year in unheated aviaries. They fail to realise that in the tropics, at a high altitude, the temperature drops steeply at night, so many parrots are not strangers to low temperatures. Also, it is a simple matter to acclimatise birds provided that a little common sense is used and that the birds are placed outdoors for the first time during the warmer part of the year.

There are few parrots which cannot be kept outdoors at all times. In my experience, the only lory not hardy enough to winter outdoors, unless provided with a heated shelter, is the tiny Fairy Lorikeet; presumably this would apply to the other small *Charmosyna* species, were they available. It is possible that they could be wintered without heat outdoors but as they show signs of distress during cold weather I am not prepared to take the risk. The slightly larger lories, such as the small *Trichoglossus* species are very hardy and will even breed during the winter. No problems should be experienced in acclimatising the larger species (see page 10).

One factor which must be considered before buying lories—or any parrots—is that of noise. Generally speaking the strength of a lory's voice can be judged by its size. The small lorikeets have voices which are not loud enough to constitute a nuisance to near neighbours. In my opinion, this also applies to *Trichoglossus* species, but all those larger, especially *Lorius* and *Chalcopsitta* species, have decidedly loud, harsh voices which can be annoying, unpleasant and persistent. It is better that the prospective purchaser should realise this before making a purchase. If near neighbours are likely to complain, provision should be made to keep the birds where they will cause least annoyance; alternatively, quieter birds should be obtained.

Lories seldom have prolonged periods of shrieking but may do so if disturbed by a cat or some other predator. They may also become more noisy and active shortly before they start to breed. If the larger species are noisy during the early hours of the morning, it is advisable to house them in an aviary with an enclosed shelter, in which the nest-box is placed, so that they can be shut in for the night.

Lories as pets. There are few more enchanting pets than a hand-tame lory. However, the difficulties involved in keeping a lory indoors will be sufficient to deter most people from doing so.

For a single bird it is worth going to some trouble to construct a cage which will help to eliminate the problems created by the liquid droppings of a lory. Most suitable is a large box cage, made from formica or some other easily cleaned material, with glass that slots into the lower half of the cage (in much the same way as in cages for pet Budgerigars). Lories are very active birds and it would be cruel to confine one permanently in a parrot cage of the normal type or one of similar size. For a medium-sized lory the cage should be a minimum of 91cm (3ft) long—preferably longer.

Tame lories which are gentle are truly delightful; one which I looked after for a short while would explore my face with the brushes on its tongue. Unfortunately, very few lories are completely trustworthy in temperament; they are excitable and inclined to nip. Some can be trusted not to bite only when handled by their owner, while others are friendly towards all those of one sex. Many people scoff at the idea that parrots prefer people of the opposite sex to their own, especially as lories do not always appear to be capable of distinguishing the opposite sex in their own species! However, it is a fact that this is so but it is often impossible to prove since there is little opportunity of proving the sex of a pet bird. A Black-capped Lory, which had proved its sex by the production of an egg, (but was, nevertheless referred to as 'he') clearly preferred men: 'Let anyone of the male sex approach him though. What a transformation! Gone was the flashing eye and snapping beak, and with what honeyed words did he spread his burnished quivering wings and bow his dusky head in humble adoration.' (*Avicultural Magazine*, 1938, p. 200).

Some lories learn to talk quite well, usually the larger species, especially *Lorius* and *Eos*. They may even acquire an extensive vocabulary. S. Dillon Ripley described a Black-capped Lory '. . . whose conversational powers were a constant source of wonder. He would rattle along for minutes on end in a mixture of the Biak language and Malay. The tone of his voice was low and so quaintly pitched that one could never fail to drop all work and stop to listen to his endearing chatter.' (*Avicultural Magazine*, 1938, p. 272).

Care of sick birds. Except those which are particularly likely to occur in lories, it is not my intention to discuss the diseases from which these birds could suffer. The subject is too vast for the layman to write on with authority. The reader is therefore referred to M. Petrak's *Diseases of Cage and Aviary Birds*.

One of the main problems of treating a sick bird is that of diagnosis. Since it is rarely possible to correctly diagnose illness in living birds, all cases of disease, rather than injury should, initially, be treated alike, assuming that the cause of the trouble is unknown.

Immediately a sick bird is discovered it should be isolated in a small cage and placed in a temperature of at least 27°C (80°F). I am not in favour of electrically heated hospital cages, partly because occupants have no choice of temperature. Nectar, of course, would quickly sour in a hospital cage and would have to be changed several times daily. Also, the standard hospital cage with a perforated zinc floor, below which is the heating equipment, is not suitable for lories because of their liquid droppings.

In my experience, by far the most satisfactory method of providing heat for a sick bird is by means of an infra-red lamp. I would advise all aviculturists not to wait until a bird becomes sick before obtaining one, but to have one ready for any emergency. A great advantage of the infra-red lamp is that it can be directed to one part of the cage, allowing the patient to move out of the heat if it wishes to do so. The nectar will need to be changed more frequently than normal, even although it is not placed directly in line with the lamp.

The other requirement of a sick bird is a broad spectrum antibiotic, which can be obtained with a veterinary surgeon's prescription. This is normally in powder form and is given for four days or as prescribed. With lories there is no difficulty in administering an antibiotic as it is simply added to the nectar. It is advisable to offer a small amount of nectar when an antibiotic has been added, to ensure that it is all taken. With other parrots it is often difficult to ensure that the antibiotic is taken, because it is added to the drinking water and the bird may refuse to drink, especially if it can quench its thirst with fruit or greenfood. With lories this problem does not arise unless the sick bird refuses to eat or is unable to retain food inside it—indeed, vomiting is a common sign of illness in a lory.

One thing that all experienced parrot keepers dread is a bird's refusal to feed. When this happens it is extremely difficult to persuade it to start eating again.

Fortunately, it is easier to force-feed lories than other parrots because, with the aid of a teaspoon, nectar can be given.

Force-feeding can cause a certain amount of stress to a bird which is not tame—mainly because it is necessary to catch it several times a day—but faced with the alternative of watching a bird die, force-feeding can be tried.

Even a sick lory can inflict a serious bite so, as mentioned previously, the bird should be held in a towel which has been folded into several layers. With the larger species, force-feeding is very much easier if one person holds the towel-wrapped bird and another administers the food. With small species this task can easily be carried out by one person. Although a syringe can be used, it is very much easier to employ a small teaspoon. A small amount of nectar, containing an antibiotic, is poured into the bird's beak and the bird will normally lap or swallow it at once. If it refuses to swallow from the start, there is nothing that one can do, but if it does so after a few spoonfuls, this is an indication that it has had enough.

An extremely important point concerning force-feeding is that only a small amount of food must be given at each feed. Too much will cause the bird to vomit. As its strength returns, a sick bird will begin to feed on its own and force-feeding will no longer be necessary.

Antibiotics, correctly used, are invaluable to the aviculturist. They should never be used as a preventative (as some dealers have been known to do)—only to cure a sick bird. Prolonged or indiscriminate use can cause infertility, damaging the organs of the body and eventually causing death. Correctly used, they can be responsible for complete recovery in apparently dying birds. I have had particularly good results with the antibiotic chloramphenicol, a white powder.

Anaemia is not uncommon in lories. It is easily guarded against by giving vitamin B_{12} in the nectar. Several times weekly I add a few drops of the black-currant flavoured syrup Cytacon (Glaxo Laboratories Ltd, Greenfood, Middlesex) to the nectar of all lories.

Candidiasis can be extremely troublesome and difficult to control. It is caused by the fungus *Candida albicans* which grows in the mouth, even on the tongue, on the outside of the lower mandible and even invades the air sacs of the body. When the latter occurs death soon follows but where candidiasis is confined to the mouth, a bird can, it seems, live indefinitely if treated regularly (in extreme cases, daily treatment is necessary).

A careful watch should be maintained on lories housed indoors, due to the difficulty of keeping their quarters clean. I have only once had candidiasis occur in lories kept in outdoor aviaries; in this case, a Meyer's Lorikeet which was feeding young and was obviously searching for some item of food in the peat on the floor of the aviary, had the lower mandible clogged with peat, an ideal breeding ground for the fungus. A few applications of Nystatin ointment cured this bird.

Lories which have spent some time in indoor premises are the most susceptible. When buying lories it is therefore wise to examine the mouth and tongue for signs of the fungus.

Its appearance can vary from hard, dark matter caked around the outside and the inside of the lower mandible to soft, whitish, almost fluffy matter. The latter is, in my experience, extremely difficult to eradicate and its removal may cause bleeding. The hard matter is easily removed with the quill of a small feather or with a child's soft paint brush. Treating the affected area with Nystatin ointment will often effect a cure.

The soft, whitish matter I have unfortunately found impossible to permanently eradicate in one Fairy Lorikeet in my possession. At the time of writing it has been affected for nearly two years, despite constant treatment and the absence of all signs of the disease for several periods of two or three months.

Infected lories will be seen ceaselessly moving the tongue and the feathers around the beak may appear dirty or damaged.

When consulted on the treatment of *Candida albicans* the Department of Veterinary Microbiology, College of Veterinary Medicine, Washington State University, advised as follows:

'Increase vitamin A many fold over usual levels over a period of six to eight weeks and then give three or four times the usual amount indefinitely. Avoid all antibiotics in the feed and if too much feed (food, fruit, etc) with a high level of sugars is used this can help produce lesions.'

It was stated that experimental Candidiasis for student instruction was produced at will in chickens by feeding 50% cerelose in feed or by 1000 grams of Aureamycin per ton of food.

Tapeworm. Lories seldom seem to be infected with the *Ascaridia* worms which are so common in Australian parrakeets but many newly imported lories are infested with tapeworm, often severely so. Two newly imported Black-winged Lories, for example, were found, after death, to contain 20 and 14 worms each. One aviculturist who purchased six lories, wormed them after a post mortem report on one revealed that death was caused by tapeworms. The result was that the remaining five passed 'an unbelievable number of tapeworms' 30 hours later.

As it is easy to rid lories of these parasites it is a sound precaution to worm all newly imported birds. Yomesan (Bayer, Leverkusen, Germany) tablets (for children) are ideal for this purpose. They are expensive but the cost is negligible when compared with that of a lory and the knowledge that one's birds are free of tapeworms. A tablet should be crushed and added to the nectar—one tablet per 5oz weight or, for a large lory, about ½ per bird. This product is harmless if over-dosed. When Yomesan is added to the nectar, slightly less nectar than the bird would drink in a day should be provided, to ensure that none which might contain the crushed Yomesan remains at the bottom of the nectar container.

Nails. It is most important that lories' nails are not allowed to become over-grown as this can result in all kinds of tragedies. As an example of what can happen, a Yellow-backed Lory died in the nest, after it was trapped by an over-grown nail in the wire ladder below the nest entrance, and a Purple-capped Lory broke its leg after catching an overgrown nail in the wire mesh of its aviary. Nails must therefore be trimmed if they are too long or exceptionally curved. Ordinary nail clippers are more suitable for use on the larger species, whereas sharp scissors or clippers can be used for the small species. The nail should be cut beyond the vein, or bleeding will occur.

Foot defects. On rare occasions, aviary-bred lories leave the nest with all four toes pointing forward, or this defect occurs after fledging. My experience with a

Dusky Lory shows that, if treated immediately, this can be cured. About six weeks after it left the nest, one morning it refused to leave the nest-box where it always roosted with its parents. When I opened the lid, it squawked but made no attempt to leave the box. I saw that its feet were clenched and immediately caught it, took it indoors and caged it.

As this condition could have been caused by a vitamin deficiency, I sprinkled Phillips Yeast Mixture (contains 90% dehydrated brewers' yeast, 6% calcium carbonate, 2% sterilised bone phosphate, 1% sodium, also trace elements), on its nectar and gave Cytacon and Albevite (water soluble premix containing 13 vitamins—Vitamin A being the main ingredient—and six trace minerals, manufactured by Philips Duphar) much in excess of the normal daily addition to the nectar. A week later, the toes on one foot had regained their normal position. After a further week, the toes on the other foot were still bunched forward; there had been no improvement whatsoever.

My husband and I therefore decided to bind the toes up in their proper position. We attempted to use the quills from a cockatoo's flight feathers, but found these were not strong enough; in their place we used a plastic shirt collar stiffener cut to the length of the toes extended into their correct position; this was placed under the toes and the two front and the two back toes were bound together with Elastoplast. At first the young lory was not able to move about very easily but it soon learned to do so. After a week, the binding was removed and it was with great relief that I saw that the toes remained in their proper position.

It has been suggested that paralysis in lories is due to a deficiency of thiamine hydrochloride (vitamin B_1), a plentiful supply of which is found in the embryo and pericarp of seeds. This could be the reason why paralysis has been reported more frequently in lories than in most other captive birds.

2

Accommodation

From the aviculturist's point of view, lories are aviary birds. Keeping them indoors, whether caged or in flights, presents certain almost insurmountable problems, not met with in other parrots. These all occur as a result of the diet consisting principally of nectar. I have heard of single lories kept as pets which are offered nectar perhaps twice daily, the other foods provided being such as to prevent the droppings being too liquid. Modifying the diet to suit the conditions under which lories are kept is, in my opinion, very wrong. One must design the accommodation to suit the lories.

It may be necessary to cage newly imported or sick lories—and the difficulties soon become apparent. Ideally, the floor covering, in a *deep* tray (which is impossible to obtain in ready-made cages) should consist of peat or pet litter; the latter is obtainable from pet shops. Unless the cage is very large, the floor covering will need to be changed daily, thus the expense will be considerable. Alternatively, several layers of newspaper can be used but this will need to be changed every few hours as a pool of 'droppings' will soon accumulate, especially beneath the favourite perch. Caging lories always results in a rather sickly smell, more pronounced in some species and, in most cases, not noticeable when the same birds are kept in an outdoor aviary.

Using an open parrot cage is out of the question as the droppings are squirted some distance and will foul the area surrounding the cage, which will need to be protected—especially the floor. For this reason, keeping caged lories in a room which is carpeted is not practicable, unless a large area around the cage is covered with a plastic mat or some washable substance. If lories have to be kept indoors a metal box cage, such as the type made for Mynahs, is the most suitable but, unless specially made, is large enough only for temporary accommodation.

Like all parrots, lories have periods of inactivity but when they are active they are very lively indeed. Added to the fact that permanently caged lories often become grossly fat, it can be seen that the disadvantages of caging lories are too numerous to consider keeping them in this way.

Even indoor flights, not less than 1.5m (5ft) long (for birds imported during the winter) are not really suitable because of the difficulty of cleaning them. If they are carefully designed, much can be done to facilitate cleaning. Tiling the walls or using formica is expensive but hygienic, and the floor, even although covered with several layers of newspaper, will be easy to clean if a modern kitchen flooring is used, not only in the flight but throughout the birdroom. Nectar and droppings will be found a surprising distance from the birds.

The wire netting is the most difficult part of an indoor lory flight to clean. It quickly becomes sticky and should be washed down with warm, soapy water once a week, together with any woodwork in the flight. For this reason, and because it will provide a greater sense of security, only the front of the flight should be constructed of wire netting.

I have found that small species do quite well in an indoor flight during acclimatisation, the only problem encountered being with Fairy Lorikeets, whose beaks and claws tend to become overgrown. I dislike having to keep large newly imported lories indoors for any length of time and feel that they are usually better off out of doors, even if the weather is not very warm. Obviously one must exercise one's common sense in this matter, much depending on the situation of the aviary and the shelter it provides, and how settled the weather is when the birds are placed outdoors for the first time. Should they show any sign of feeling the cold they will have to be returned indoors.

I am not suggesting that lories imported in January or February should be placed outdoors at once, only that advantage may be taken of a mild spell, often experienced in Britain in March or April, to try the birds outside, with a nest-box for roosting. All birds received from May to October should, if possible, be placed outdoors almost immediately, otherwise they will have to winter indoors.

Lories in aviaries are a joy to watch. They are the most playful and acrobatic of all parrots and use the full length and width of the aviary, unlike many of the larger parrots. For this reason, aviaries should be as large as possible; length is, of course, the most important dimension. For medium-sized lories, ie, 23cm (9in) to 30cm (12in), I would suggest an absolute minimum of 3m (10ft), and 4.3m (14ft) to 4.9m (16ft) is more desirable. Unless the birds are tame it is not a good idea to exceed 4.9m (16ft) as this does not encourage them to become tamer. In any case, few aviculturists now have the means to have aviaries longer than 6m (20ft).

It is normally essential, in the case of medium-sized and large lories, to keep only one pair per aviary, and even certain small species will not tolerate others of their own kind. Few lories will tolerate the presence of other lories or parrots, or they may do so until their young fledge, when they will slaughter the other occupants of the aviary. I have never kept lories with any other birds so cannot speak from experience on this point, but in the early years of this century when large mixed aviaries were the general practice, lories were kept with all kinds of birds. They apparently paid little attention to small seedeaters, for example, but time and time again they killed other parrots in the aviary.

They are often extremely clever at doing this and work in pairs to achieve their aim. This applies particularly to the Chattering and Yellow-backed Lory (*Lorius garrulus*). One instance of this behaviour was recorded by Donald Risdon, director of the Tropical Bird Garden, Rode, Somerset, formerly at Keston Foreign Bird Farm. He described Yellow-backed Lories as 'the most murderous parrots I have ever known.' He once kept a pair in a large planted aviary, 15m (50ft) × 4.6m (15ft), in which they hatched a baby, but failed to rear it. A Mistle Thrush and an Indian Green-winged Dove in the aviary were killed and 'half torn to pieces' before it was realised that the lories were to blame. They were found to be the culprits when the remains of the dove were propped up in a life-like position to test their reaction.

'Presently the Lories approached the corpses one on each side with sideways leaps and much bobbing and tail wagging. Suddenly and without warning they pounced like a couple of hawks. Both birds and the corpse fell to the ground in a heap where they proceeded to re-enact their "crime". The sinister aspect of the whole affair was that the Lories never attempted to chase or bully the other birds so that one might have had warning of their evil intentions. It was all done by stealth.' (*Avicultural Magazine*).

Another British aviculturist almost had a similar experience when one of his pair of Yellow-backed Lories found its way into the adjoining aviary and savagely attacked a hen Derbyan Parrakeet (*Psittacula derbyana*). Fortunately, he was nearby and was able to intervene.

The above instances are two of many which could be related and which will, I hope, emphasise the importance of keeping lories on their own. Visitors to a certain very well-known bird garden in England may wonder at the temerity of the owner in having a display of lories of many species in an enormous aviary. Members of the public see a positive riot of colour but most aviculturists are well aware that not only are the various species inter-breeding, but they are also killing each other's young as they fledge. Colony breeding, except perhaps in a large aviary with certain small lories, all of the same species, is not to be recommended.

The materials used in the construction of lory aviaries should be given careful consideration. Undoubtedly, 1in square welded mesh is the most suitable wire for all but the smallest species. When it is painted black, the birds are more easily viewed and the life of the wire is increased, especially if bitumen paint is used. This is best applied with a roller.

I use 1in square mesh for all lories from the size of the Meyer's and Iris Lorikeets upwards. When my small colony of Meyer's was first placed in the aviary, it worried me to see them putting their heads and shoulders through the wire to reach the honeysuckle (*Lonicera*) growing over the roof of the aviary. I had visions of them pushing their small bodies through the 1in square openings and hastily covered the roof with asbestos. This was removed when the birds were used to the aviary and I realised that their escape was impossible.

In the adjoining aviary, however, the Dusky Lories were doing their utmost to attack their new neighbours but the double wire partitions prevented this. The latter precaution is an absolute necessity for all parrot aviaries; without it serious injury and even death can result, especially to newly fledged young. Lories are particularly quarrelsome to birds in adjoining aviaries, especially when the latter are first placed in the aviary. There should be a space of at least 2.5cm (1in) between the two sections of wire.

With the high cost of welded mesh and wire netting, the fancier erecting a range of aviaries may believe that omitting to double wire the flights will be a way of cutting the cost but it will be false economy, an omission which may prove fatal to some of the occupants. It is also an insurance against birds finding their way into an adjoining enclosure, should there be a weak point in the wire which, as I have already shown, can prove disastrous.

Another detail of the aviary which requires some thought is the feeding hatch. As it is inconvenient to enter the aviary to carry out feeding, especially if the birds are breeding, a feeding hatch is essential. In a range of aviaries backed by a service corridor, the hatch can be of the usual type, ie, merely a small flap opening on to the feeding shelf. The flap should be hinged at the top so that it closes on its own should the catch not be in position. Where there is no corridor and thus no protection against escape, a more elaborate type of feeding hatch may be required, especially if the lories are very tame.

The one I shall describe was designed by my husband after the escape of a tame Yellow-backed Lory at feeding time. Fortunately, as these birds are not strong flyers it was recaptured after a short chase when a coat was thrown over it!

Over the feeding shelf a wire mesh cage is built, slightly higher than the feeding vessel; this is left open at the front so that when the hatch is opened the nectar dish can be placed in position. A hole is cut in the wire above the dish and of about the same size. The lory stands on the wire cage and drinks the nectar from the dish through the hole provided. Escape is impossible.

Many lories become so tame that they fly to the feeding hatch to investigate as soon as it is opened. Some are eager to sample the fresh, warm nectar, while others are so tame and fearless that they may attempt to make their exit or even to nip one's fingers. Birds in the latter category definitely require the safety type of feeding hatch.

The latter is normally placed in the shelter, in which case it will not be necessary to cover the shelf. If, for reasons of access, the feeding shelf is placed at the opposite end of the aviary from the shelter, and the food would have no protection from the elements, the shelf must be covered. As some birds may, at first, be wary of using a covered feeding hatch, or because they have not previously been kept in an aviary, the nectar should be put in a hook-on container at the side of the perch nearest the hatch and moved a few inches daily towards it until, finally, it is in the required position.

As lories almost invariably roost in their nest-box at night, an elaborate shelter is unnecessary. An open-fronted shelter, enclosed on the top and three sides, will provide adequate protection during bad weather and, if the nest-box is placed inside, the birds will have a dry roosting place in the very worst weather. If the aviary is in a very exposed position or a cold climate, a fully enclosed shelter is recommended—but the nest-box must be placed inside or the birds will not sleep in the shelter.

For the few small species which do not prove completely hardy in colder climates, such as *Vini* and *Charmosyna* lorikeets, a heated shelter is a very acceptable alternative to taking them indoors during the winter. Under the latter conditions I feel that they are less likely to breed than birds which remain in the same aviary throughout the year; the disadvantage is that it could be May before they can be returned to their outdoor aviary. Also, there is a likelihood of them becoming overweight when housed indoors.

If electrical heating, usually in the form of tubular heaters, is used in the shelter, provision should also be made for lighting. A single bulb, left on for two, three or four hours to give twelve hours during which small lories can feed, is of almost equal value to a heater. If a bird is not receiving sufficient food during cold weather, its body temperature drops. Increasing the hours during which it can feed, will help to maintain its body temperature.

A dimmer switch should be used so that the light is reduced gradually; lories will then enter the nest-box. If the light is turned off suddenly, plunging the shelter in darkness, the inhabitants will have no alternative other than roosting on the perches. In a heated shelter the protection provided by a nest-box is less important but a perch cannot give the comfort and feeling of security that a box provides.

Beginners with lories and other parrots sometimes visualise housing them in a planted aviary, but this is seldom possible, although the smaller species usually prove less destructive than the larger ones. The latter are usually very destructive to all growing vegetation but sometimes, quite unaccountably, they leave it alone. This is more likely to happen in a heavily planted aviary, a single shrub or tree being too great a focus for their attention. I housed a pair of Fairy Lorikeets in a very small aviary built around a small cupressus; the latter was speedily destroyed. A pair of the same species owned by a friend, and kept in a 6m (20ft) planted aviary containing softbills and no other parrots, did no damage at all to the shrubs, except to remove some leaves for nesting material.

Further experiments in keeping small lories in planted aviaries may show that this is a most satisfactory method of housing them. For example, Australian aviculturists have found that Musk Lorikeets fare best in large, well-planted aviaries. Even larger species may do well under these conditions but as they cannot safely be housed with other birds, few would provide them with a planted enclosure. Sir Leo Chiozzo Money wrote of the Swainson's Lorikeet (*Bird Notes*, 1919 p. 173) that '. . . in an aviary of moderate dimensions (it) does so little damage to shrubs that they remain a beautiful background for one of the gayest of birds. To see a pair of Swainson's Lorikeets with their two young gambolling in an aviary of privet and laurel, furnished with a few tree perches to enable them to display themselves, is a sight not easily to be forgotten.'

If a planted aviary is not practical, the perches should be as natural as possible. I prefer to use branches from fruit trees, especially apple, or from plane, although many other kinds are suitable. Any buds will be immediately eaten by most lories and many will enjoy stripping the bark. With the latter removed the perches eventually become shiny and slippery and lose their spring; they must therefore be renewed regularly.

Assuming that the aviary is not planted, the base should be constructed of concrete. Peat should be sprinkled over it or at least below the perches. If one has a number of lory aviaries the amount of peat used will form a considerable expense, but I know of no suitable alternative.

3
Feeding

Nectar and pollen are the natural foods of all lories and lorikeets; most species also consume fruit, seeds, blossoms, buds or berries in varying quantities. Small insects, which have been ingested on blossoms and buds and in nectar, have been found in the crops of some lories.

The members of the Loriidae are among the most specialised of all parrots in their feeding habits; their tongues are adapted for feeding on nectar or pollen, a fact which has caused the group to be known as the 'brush-tongued' parrots. 'Brush' refers to the cluster of elongated papillae which are normally contained in a protective 'cup' formed by the arms of the horny U-shaped sheath that terminates the underside of a parrot's tongue. These papillae are not easy to observe as they are normally in use only when the bird is feeding on liquid or soft foods, also sometimes when preening another bird. When the bird is at rest or eating hard food the 'cup' is almost closed, and the papillae shortened and compressed. Under these circumstances the tongue looks like that of other parrots, as it does after death.

When the tongue is protruded the papillae increase several times in length and are held out from the cup, giving the tip of the tongue the appearance of an expanded sea anemone. The movements of the long, extremely flexible tongue cause the papillae to expand and contract and wave rather like the tentacles of the sea anemone.

The tongue would appear to be more highly developed in some species. An eminent aviculturist, Sydney Porter, who was familiar with a large number of lories, felt that the maximum development was reached in the Solitary Lory.

Some lories have a habit of moving the tongue around outside the mouth after feeding, perhaps to clean the beak, and it is then that the papillae, usually white, are most easily seen.

Nectar and pollen would appear to be the main items of diet of most species, thus for those birds kept in captivity a substitute must be found. It is probably true to say that almost no two keepers of lories prepare this in the same way. Fortunately, there is no difficulty in persuading wild-caught lories to sample a nectar substitute, for they will consume almost any sweet liquid. However, the aviculturist must offer a diet that not only maintains these birds indefinitely in captivity but is of sufficient quality to enable them to reproduce.

Throughout this book, under the heading of *Breeding records* for the various species, where successful breeders have recorded details of the diet offered, these have been included. That there can be no hard and fast rules regarding diet will be seen from the wide variety of nectar mixtures and other items offered.

The food used today is, on the whole, rather different to that offered by aviculturists in the early years of the 20th century. In 1908, for example, E. J. Brook had 20 lories of ten species, probably the largest private collection of lories at that time. Later he was to build up what was perhaps the finest private collection of these birds to be formed. His Black Lories, the first lory to breed in captivity (as distinct from lorikeets*) reared young on a diet of 'sop made with milk and barley water, thickened with Mr Millsum's "B.C." food and occasionally a little biscuit or bread added for a change.' Fruit was also offered.

Brook wrote (*Avicultural Magazine* 1908, pp. 84–5): 'I have never been satisfied that the feeding these birds have had was quite satisfactory, though prepared carefully and according to the best advice obtainable. The powdered plain biscuit with boiled milk and sweet fruit was fairly good, but now and then I would see a bird blinking its eyes and looking as though it had a sore head, symptoms that more often than not were quickly relieved by a few drops of magnesia, but then there were the cases where relief did not come but death did, and that swiftly.

'. . . We found in the case of a Violet-necked Lory that died that the stomach was full of milk and very acid; this seemed to confirm what I had long supposed to be the case, that indigestion was the cause of most deaths among the lories.'

It was found that the bowel contents were alkali and contained specks of undigested milk which were very acid. Brook wrote: 'It will be easily seen that a very slight derangement would cause the stomach to become dangerously acid and so cause illness or death.'

He therefore sought a food that would not turn acid in the stomach and was, perhaps, the first to use Mellin's Food. For many years this was widely used for lories and for other nectar-feeders such as sunbirds. Brook found that Mellin's Food caused the digestion of ailing lories to return to normal; he did not use it as a staple diet but only as a 'corrective'.

The staple diet consisted of milk sop with powdered plain biscuit and fresh diluted milk (two parts milk to one part water), slightly sweetened. The biscuit and sugar was replaced by Mellin's Food for three days if the bird appeared to be suffering from indigestion. I believe that any bird which appears to be suffering from indigestion, especially if it is vomiting, should be given nectar which has been greatly diluted with water. It may be necessary to give only a weak solution of sugared water or glucose.

John Yealland (*Avicultural Magazine* 1940, p. 310) described losses among rare Tahiti Blue Lories. Post mortem examination failed to reveal any disease, although in one or two birds there was evidence of anaemia. Essence of beef was added to the nectar in an attempt to rectify this but the losses continued. Further post mortem examinations revealed signs of dyspepsia and it was not until the nectar was diluted with its own volume of water that the losses ceased.

Because of the ill effects of possibly over-rich nectar I feel that it is a wise precaution to dilute the nectar offered to all newly imported lories. It is, after all, far removed from their natural foods, pollen and nectar, and can, perhaps, be compared to a human diet of cream cakes and chocolates.

---

*Allegedly, a pair of lorikeets, whose description fits that of *Trichoglossus haematodus*, reared two young in the collection of the Governor of the Cape of Good Hope, probably between 1781 and 1784.

Today, fresh milk is not used in the staple nectar mixture for lories although bread and milk may be offered as a supplementary food for those which are rearing young. Many aviculturists, myself included, use condensed milk; some use evaporated milk.

It is unfortunate that lories, like other parrots, are destructive to growing vegetation; were this not so, natural pollen and nectar could be included in the diet by planting flowering shrubs in the aviary. Possibly the very smallest species could be kept in a large planted aviary without them damaging the growing shrubs; this was the case with a pair of Fairy Lorikeets. Under such circumstances, they would certainly benefit from being able to feed from honeysuckle and such flowers as fuchsias.

Before the requirements of lories were understood, many existed on diets which would horrify present day aviculturists. Undoubtedly, the lives of many were short but if we are to believe Sir Theo G. Cullum, a *Trichoglossus* lorikeet brought from New Holland in 1794 was still alive in 1822. A good age by any standard but as the bird's diet apparently consisted entirely of soaked breadcrumbs squeezed dry, and an occasional almond, its longevity is quite remarkable. This bird is mentioned in John Latham's *General History of Birds* published in 1822.

A passing reference to lories in *Beeton's Book of Birds*, published in the 19th century, suggests that these birds commonly suffered from fits, often a sign of a dietary imbalance but one that is rare today. 'Some parrots (especially the lories) are subject to fits. They will tumble off their perches, and after a few convulsive struggles lie as if dead.'

I do not suggest that the reader follows the advice on how to deal with a bird in this unfortunate condition! 'When this happens, squirt the coldest water you can over its head. If this does not revive the bird, take him by the legs and dip him three or four times into a pan of cold water. If he should still remain insensible, pluck out a tail feather and lay him on the warm stones. If after this he does not recover, you may make up your mind if you will have him buried or stuffed.'

So far in this chapter no mention has been made of honey, which is or was a widely used component of 'nectar.' From 1973 the price of this food rose so steeply, and continued to rise at such a rate, that most aviculturists with more than two or three pairs of lories could no longer afford to use honey. At San Diego Zoo, which exhibits the best and probably the largest collection of lories in the world, the use of honey was discontinued some years ago. One of the reasons given for this was that this food attracts bees. In a warm climate and during the summer months in a temperate climate, anything which discourages bees should be put into practice.

The natural food of lories, pollen, has a very high protein content, and nectar has a high carbohydrate content. The latter is less important in captive birds since they do not have to expend much energy in obtaining food; therefore the carbohydrate content of the 'nectar' should be low and the protein content high.

The diet offered at San Diego consists of various items made into a 'soupy mixture'. The ingredients are varied but the following are included: cane sugar, Super Hydramin powder (a human protein-vitamin mineral concentrate widely used by keepers of Humming Birds, and manufactured by Nion Corporation,

Los Angeles, California) mixed with water, chopped apples, boiled rice, soaked raisins, ground carrots, white bread, evaporated milk and shredded lettuce.

In complete contrast is the nectar which I prepare for my lories. It consists of two heaped dessertspoonfuls of glucose and one each of malt and Farex* or a similar baby cereal in 1 litre (35 fluid oz) of water. The malt and glucose are dissolved in about 15 fluid oz of boiling water; cold water is added, then about ½ dessertspoonful of condensed milk and Farex.

It would appear that they can distinguish the previous day's nectar by taste. In my colony of Meyer's Lorikeets I used a number of small plastic hook-on drinkers for nectar. On numerous occasions, by way of experiment, I left a drinker containing the previous day's nectar among the fresh nectar; this was never consumed. It is therefore disturbing to read of people who feed lories on alternate days. I feel strongly that anyone who is not prepared to go to the bother of providing their lories with fresh nectar daily should keep seedeaters—or preferably not keep birds at all!

I use small plastic hook-on drinkers only for the small species except for those which unhook them; for these birds the drinkers consisting of a clear plastic tube and a coloured plastic lip, which can be bought in any pet shop (sold for Budgerigars and other birds) are ideal. Large hook-on ('jumbo') plastic drinkers are useless for the large lories; because of their playfulness, the drinkers are unhooked and the contents poured on to the ground.

For any lory of or exceeding the size of a Perfect Lorikeet, I would recommend the use of earthenware dog bowls which are too heavy for them to move. Enamel or plastic dishes will be thrown on the ground or used as play things.

The position of the nectar dish is very important for birds in accommodation with which they are not familiar. Lories find their food under these circumstances more quickly than many parrots but, nevertheless, this must be made easy at first by placing the food at the end of a perch or in a situation where it will be quickly found. In small aviaries, nectar dishes should never be placed on the ground; this is a satisfactory arrangement only in very large aviaries where entering to feed will not cause a major disturbance. A feeding shelf, as described on page 12, is, to my mind, the ideal arrangement.

All nectar containers must be kept spotlessly clean; it is essential to clean them daily before they are refilled. 'Topping up', i.e., pouring new nectar on top of old, is the cardinal sin where nectar feeders are concerned. Every nectar dish should be thoroughly washed in warm water and if drinking tubes (of the kind used for pet Budgerigars, for example) are used for nectar, those should be cleaned with a bottle brush.

Alternatively, a duplicate set of drinkers or dishes can be kept and the used ones cleaned at a convenient time.

---

*Farex is a pre-cooked blend of wheat, oats and maize flours; separated milk powder; bone meal, yeast, salt, iron and ammonium citrate, vitamin B_2 (riboflavin), B_1 (thiamine) and D. Analysis per oz: fat, 2.5%; protein, 14.2%; carbohydrate, 72.7%; mineral salts, 3.6%; fibre, 0.5%; moisture, 6.5%; iron, 6mg; calcium, 250mg; phosphorous, 190mg, vitamin D, 200 units; vitamin B_1, 0.4mg and vitamin B_2, 0.5mg.

In a hot climate it may be necessary to renew the nectar more than once daily. The use of condensed milk is not recommended when the temperature rises higher than about 70°F because it will cause the nectar to become sour. It should be discontinued gradually, if possible, because of the difference in the taste when it is omitted completely.

Condensed milk is not an essential component of nectar but it is used by many aviculturists. There are numerous items which can be used and an endless variety of ways in which they can be combined.

One problem with most nectar mixtures is that the ingredients separate, cereal such as Farex settling on the bottom of the container. Many lories, if offered nectar in two dishes, will in my experience, completely empty one before sampling the nectar in the other, if these are placed far apart. This helps to solve this problem as at least one dish will be licked dry, thus all the contents are consumed, including those which are inclined to settle.

Many aviculturists add multi-vitamins in liquid form, such as Abidec (Parke-Davis) to the nectar. This is an excellent precaution against possible deficiencies. Abidec contains 4000 IUs of vitamin A per 10 ml. To ensure that my lories receive adequate vitamin B (this vitamin is not stored by the body) I give occasionally in the nectar a few drops of the blackcurrant flavoured Cytacon* or Befortiss Elixir†.

The curator of birds at Taronga Zoo in Australia, K. Muller, informed me that when milk powder was omitted from the diet of the lories in the collection they developed dry and frayed feathers and became easily overweight. 'This', he wrote (pers. comm.) 'was caused by a deficiency in sulphur-containing amino acids, which was rectified by adding the milk powder. The problem of becoming overweight remains a major factor with all the small lorikeets.'

The latter, such as the Little and Varied Lorikeets, are fed on a variety of fruits, including apple, pear and paw paw. They are also offered a baby cereal, 'Wheatbix', fortified with milk powder, sugar and vitamins and minerals. Nectar made from honey and water, with added vitamins, is provided but limited.

If lories are obtained unexpectedly and no provision has been made for their diet, an emergency nectar can be made by dissolving sugar or even golden syrup in water. Some birds will also take tinned fruit and the juice from cans of fruit.

When feeding lories—or any other birds—a strict routine should be adopted. One should never be tempted, on seeing that some of the previous day's nectar remains, to make a mental note to feed the bird or birds later; it is all too easy to forget. Although there is some variation in the amount of nectar a lory will consume in one day, depending mainly on whether the day is hot or cold, one soon learns the correct amount of nectar to provide to avoid wastage. Lories must never be without nectar, thus the correct amount is a little more than will be consumed in 24 hours assuming, of course, that feeding is carried out at the same time each day.

*(Vitamin B_{12} liquid; Glaxo Laboratories, Greenford, England).
†(Vitamin B_1, B_2 and B_6; Bencard, Brentford, England).

All lories should be encouraged to eat fruit; some are most reluctant to do so and others can never be persuaded. Example is the best teacher. It was 20 months before my Dusky Lories would sample fruit. One day I saw them taking a great interest in the soft pear being eaten by the lories in the adjoining aviary so I gave them a small piece of ripe pear. To my surprise they consumed all the fruit, leaving only the skin. Henceforth they regularly ate soft pear but continued to ignore other fruits.

Some of my lories perversely refuse to sample the apple offered yet enjoy eating the apples that fall on to the roof of their aviary from the tree above. I should add that these are cooking apples! As lories are fond of eating the leaves which fall on to the roof of their aviary, they can be taught to eat other greenfood, such as lettuce, by placing it on the roof.

Newly imported lories often eat fruits such as banana and tinned paw paw yet quickly lose interest in such food, perhaps because the nectar offered is more nutritious than that which they were receiving prior to importation.

Soft pear, grapes, apple and banana are, of the fruits obtainable in Britain, those most favoured by lories. Orange will also be eaten but because of its acid content, I have never been able to overcome my reluctance to offer it to nectar-feeding birds.

Some aviculturists believe that banana is not a suitable food for lories, many of which will not accept it. Those that will often become very fond of it. My two Yellow-backed Lories receive a banana every night and morning. They have consumed over 12,000 bananas between them and, over a period of ten years, have remained in faultless condition with literally, never a day's illness.

The question of feeding seed to lories is a controversial one. I feel strongly that, with the exception of canary seed, it should be fed only to the small species, for which a diet of nectar alone would be totally inadequate. Some small lories I have kept are very fond of spray millet, which is offered daily; some will also eat canary and niger seed and all show a liking for sunflower.

I believe that if the larger lories are correctly fed they will not normally eat sunflower seed. I have offered this, purely for experimental purposes, to *Chalcopsitta*, *Trichoglossus*, *Lorius* and *Charmosyna* lories but it has never been sampled. It is worth recording, however, that a male Edwards's Lorikeet in my possession for over a year, refused sunflower seed. I lent this bird to a friend for breeding purposes and, when its first two youngsters were three weeks old, it suddenly commenced to eat sunflower.

This seed is often offered in ignorance by those who assume that it is eaten by all parrots. This assumption must have caused the untimely death of many lories; their ventriculus or gizzard, is weak and not muscular as it is in seedeating birds, the gizzards of which are designed to grind up seed. It must be admitted, however, that some lories confined to an exclusive diet of sunflower, have lived for years. Louise Washington (*Avicultural Magazine* 1925, p. 207) wrote of an Ornate Lorikeet which had been in her possession for ten years and was still alive, whose 'main diet' had been sunflower seed. It was also offered small quantities of fruit cake, soft dry bread and raw scraped carrot. No mention was made of nectar.

Due to their small size, millet, niger and canary seed must be more easily digested than sunflower. The larger lories are not likely to show much enthusiasm for small seeds, although they probably coincide more nearly with the size of the seeds taken by lories in nature.

The usual wild greenfoods should be offered especially chickweed, and, indeed, the very sight of it causes extreme excitement in many of my lories. Even the Fairies will sample it and only the Duskies leave it untouched. Seeding grasses, especially annual grass (*Poa annua*), dandelion leaves and flowers are, in Britain, the most easily obtainable wild foods but there are many others which can be offered. Because of the danger of toxic sprays contaminating wild foods, it is advisable to collect them only from areas which are known not to have been sprayed. Washing is also recommended but for those who collect sackfuls of wild foods for a large collection of birds, this is rarely practicable.

Flower heads will be considered a special treat by many lories. When attending to their gardens, keepers of these birds should never discard heads of flowering weeds such as dandelion and cultivated flowers such as marigolds, provided that they have not been sprayed with an insecticide. The heads will be torn apart and eaten with much relish. The flowers of shrubs such as honeysuckle and blossom from fruit trees which fall into aviaries will be sucked dry of nectar and pollen by lories and will be the most natural food that most of them receive.

Vegetables may be eaten by some birds. A pair of Ornate Lorikeets owned by an Italian aviculturist were offered chicory, lettuce, spinach, carrot and radish and were particularly fond of the latter. Plantain was favoured among the wild green-foods offered, which included seeding grasses, groundsel, shepherd's purse and green branches. The pair accepted an unusually varied diet which included a little raw meat once or twice weekly. Some of my Iris Lorikeets relish carrots and celery, although others never sample them.

In the autumn berries from hawthorn and elder can be collected but many lories are reluctant to sample them. Again, it is a great advantage if birds nearby are seen to eat them; many lories are so inquisitive that they will at least sample them, even if they show no further interest.

There are a number of kinds of softfood which can be offered, especially when there are young in the nest. These may be simply sweetened bread and milk or bread or sponge cake (trifle sponge is the most suitable) soaked in nectar.

A Papuan Lorikeet was particularly fond of trifle sponge soaked in nectar and consumed a small container full each day while in my care. I do my utmost to encourage birds which live solely on nectar to take other foods and this was the only item it would take in addition to nectar. After leaving my care, it was kept in a large planted aviary with soft-billed birds and, following their example, soon learned to eat mealworms.

Following a 'recipe' found in *Australian Aviculture*, I made up a softfood recommended for lories. The suggested ingredients were crushed plain biscuits ($\frac{3}{4}$lb), oatmeal ($\frac{1}{2}$lb), semolina ($\frac{1}{4}$lb), peameal ($\frac{1}{2}$ tablespoonful), lard (6 oz) and honey (6 oz). The dry ingredients are thoroughly mixed together; the lard is melted and mixed with the honey and poured over the dry ingredients and thoroughly mixed.

I soon adapted the recipe, using equal parts of crushed biscuits and Farex baby cereal in place of the dry ingredients, adding grated stale cheese on occasions. The result is a crumbly, tasty mixture which can be kept in an airtight tin for a long period. Not all the lories will sample it but some of the smaller birds are passionately fond of it, especially the Iris Lorikeets.

A more elaborate softfood, similar to that prepared for insectivorous birds, can be offered. A Belgian aviculturist informed me that his lories relished an insectivorous mixture made in Germany, 90% of which consists of dried insects.

One way of ensuring that lories receive more variety in their diet is to use a liquidiser to crush fruits and other foods which can be added to the nectar. Another way of varying the diet is to give a nectar which is entirely different to that normally offered. Occasionally I make up nectar using only glucose, Horlicks and Cytacon; this is eagerly taken in preference to the usual nectar.

Mention must be made of livefood. Some lories, usually the larger species, consume gentles and/or mealworms with relish. I hesitate to offer gentles to my birds because unless they have been well cleaned they may prove to be diseased. In recent years there have been a number of cases of owners of soft-billed birds losing large numbers of them simultaneously; in each case the cause has been traced back to the maggots. Mealworms are extremely expensive but are the only acceptable alternative to gentles. Breeding them is a long process but it is worth setting up a culture.

Many lories ignore livefood at all times except when they have young in the nest; then they eat them avidly.

Finally, on the subject of drinking water, I am not convinced that this is necessary for lories offered nectar but provide it as a matter of course. Clean water for bathing is absolutely essential, however.

4
Breeding

Breeding birds should be the aviculturist's *raison d'être* and, fortunately, this realisation is increasingly the case. It is not enough to *keep* birds, especially those which have been taken from the wild; to justify his existence the aviculturist must attempt to breed from the birds he keeps.

Man has a lot to answer for; loss of habitat is a major factor in the decline of the populations of innumerable bird species. Lories, many of which inhabit areas which are not easily accessible, especially in New Guinea/Papua, have—except on some Pacific Islands—not yet suffered disastrous loss of habitat through man's interference but this, I fear, is something which is only a matter of time.

In Indonesia, origin of a large number of Lories, the early 1970s saw the most serious exploitation of wildlife which has yet occurred in Asia. Intensive agricultural expansion, involving the destruction of forests, occurred in order to provide for the exploding human population. A large percentage of Lories are found on islands; island populations are particularly vulnerable because when clearance of forests takes place to any degree there is no alternative habitat.

In 1973 several species of Lories which, hitherto, were almost unknown to aviculture, reached Britain and other countries, an indication that new areas of New Guinea were being 'opened up'. This action will endanger the population of many birds in the years to come, especially if the government is not prepared to set aside reserves or leaves their establishment too late.

The aviculturist can play a unique role in conservation but, where lories are concerned, because of the comparatively small scale on which these birds are kept, only very careful breeding programmes can result in any significant contribution. Lories never have been nor ever will be kept and bred on anything other than a small scale. Fortunately, however, they are not unwilling to nest in captivity and many pairs breed readily.

It is understandable that most aviculturists will prefer, for the sake of variety, to keep a single pair of a number of species, rather than several pairs of two or three species. But it is the aviculturist who is prepared to specialise who is most likely to build up aviary-bred strains. It is essential to start with more than one pair when attempting to found a strain of a rarely imported species. In-breeding eventually may bring about such problems as loss of size and fertility. If one can breed from a second line this will not arise because an outcross is readily available.

Another common mistake of aviculturists is to sell the young produced from a seldom-bred species. Eventually one of the adults dies, a replacement is not available and the single bird is denied another opportunity to breed. If aviary space is limited it is, I suppose, natural that the young are sold but a far better idea is to lend the young to another aviculturist so that they or their offspring are available when another bird is required.

When starting with a species, the first difficulty to overcome is that of obtaining a true pair. In almost all lories, the plumage is alike in male and female or sexual dimorphism is so slight that it is an unreliable guide. Slight variation in plumage is not uncommon in birds of the same species and sex, and will only be misleading if used as an indication of sex. To make matters more difficult still, in many lories the difference between one sub-species and another is so subtle that it could be mistaken for one of sex. One aviculturist who bred from a Yellow-backed Lory and one lacking the yellow on the mantle (*Lorius g. garrulus*) believed that the yellow patch on the male's back indicated its sex and that the two young bred, which resembled the father in this respect, were therefore both males. Such mistakes are understandable by those with little experience of lories.

Another not uncommon fallacy on the part of those who are more familiar with Australian parrakeets, for example, is that because two birds behave affectionately towards each other, they must be of the opposite sex. I believe that the pair bond is stronger in lories than in any other parrots but, unfortunately, it can apply equally—or almost so—to two males or two females. Two lories kept together are seldom more than preening distance apart and, unlike many parrots, spend most of the day perched so closely that they are touching one another. Many pairs spend hours preening each other or playfully quarrelling. Such behaviour is a joy to behold but it is no help in sexing them. Equally, two males may be seen behaving exactly like a true pair—although mating may be less prolonged and less regular in occurrence.

In some species, display may be an indication of sex; in the Fairy Lorikeet, for example (which, in any case, is sexually dimorphic), the male's display is most pronounced and I have never seen an action resembling it from the female of this species. It starts with the male puffing out the body feathers and jerking the head rapidly up and down, all the time uttering short, loud cries. Copulation follows, usually within a minute.

In many other species, however, the display of male and female may be identical —or nearly so. This is so in a true pair of Iris Lorikeets in my possession but it is only because they have proved their sex that I can state that the display of the male is slightly more pronounced than that of the female.

It is usually the case that tame lories display very readily in the presence of human beings, while those that are not tame are wary about doing so. I have, for example, very rarely seen my Dusky Lories display because they are most cautious in their behaviour in my presence; however, observing them from a considerable distance, when they have been unaware of my presence, I have seen a good deal of wing flapping and chasing. From behaviour observation only it would be quite impossible to sex these birds but, they too, by the production of chicks, have proved themselves a true pair.

I was fortunate in being able to select them from four newly imported birds and therefore chose the one with the largest beak and head, and that with the correspondingly smallest head. To pick out pairs by this method, when the birds are viewed in profile, is the most nearly infallible method that I know.

Colour and, to a degree, size, is influenced by the bird's origin—but the shape of the head is not. Special attention should be paid to the upper mandible as this is often quite noticeably broader in the male.

If it is possible to obtain more than two birds, this is strongly recommended. Anyone fortunate enough to be able to obtain half a dozen birds of the same species is almost guaranteed success. The accommodation to breed from three pairs may not be available but that should not deter anyone with an aviary of reasonable size. As soon as the birds have formed pairs, those not required can be sold if there is no other alternative. Careful observation will be needed to separate the true pairs. It is one thing to observe them from outside the aviary but another to catch them up! For this reason, a note should be made of any distinguishing marks. Alternatively, split rings of differing colours can be placed on the leg of each bird.

Having obtained what one hopes is a true pair, the next most important consideration is the accommodation. Ideally, of course, this should not be shared with other birds (see page 10) and while I would definitely not recommend housing various species of large lories together, it should be mentioned that successful breedings have occurred in very large aviaries. In 1913, for example, Lord and Lady Poltimore bred Chattering Lories in an aviary 13m (43ft)× 10.8m (36ft)×3.6m (12ft) high. The aviary also contained Yellow-backed and Purple-capped Lories and Red-collared and Swainson's Lorikeets. Anyone today with an aviary of this size would undoubtedly sub-divide it to give each pair a separate compartment.

The problem encountered by most aviculturists is more likely to be lack of space. The most free-breeding of all the loriidae, the Swainson's and Red-collared Lorikeets, have reared young in amazingly small cages. Years ago Miss Rosa Little bred many young Swainson's from a pair in a cage 91cm (3ft) square ×1.8m (6ft) high. A pair of Red Lories (*Eos bornea*) bred successfully in a much smaller cage, 91cm (3ft)×40cm (16in)×30cm (12in); however, the adult birds were allowed to exercise in the room in which they were housed.

These two instances are not intended to serve as an example of the minimum size of accommodation but to show that like certain other parrots, lories intent on nesting will do so in apparently unsuitable conditions. However, it is up to the aviculturist to provide the best possible accommodation to induce his birds to breed. Sometimes, however, the owner's idea of 'suitable' accommodation does not coincide with that of the lories! A pair of Goldie's Lorikeets at Brookfield Zoo, Chicago, made no attempt to breed when housed in a spacious aviary 7.6m (25ft) long×1.8m (6ft) wide and 2m (7ft) high. When taken indoors for the winter and housed in a wall cage with a pair of Little Lorikeets they reared young!

As I believe that it is essential to leave lories' nest-boxes in position throughout the year for roosting, I have no control over the time of year that the birds nest. This can and has meant that chicks have hatched in January, but lories have successfully reared young during the winter months on numerous occasions. One of the main problems with winter breeding is the high incidence of dead-in-shell, due to the fact that cold air contains less moisture. The problem of winter breeding is not solved by removing the nest-box as a hen which is determined to nest may burrow into the ground, or merely lay from the perch. The effects of depriving lories of a nest-box during cold weather are, in my opinion, more harmful than any possible ill effects caused by laying. To prevent lories breeding when they wish to may prevent them from breeding at all!

In some instances, once lories start to breed nothing, short of separating the pair, will stop them. They will rear nest after nest of healthy young. As no more than two chicks will be reared in each nest (with the exception of some *Glossopsitta* species) and many nests contain a single chick, continual breeding does not appear to have a detrimental effect on the parents' stamina, as it does in species which rear a larger number of chicks.

Parrots which accept *any* nest-box, in marked contrast to those which will spend a whole season deciding whether the box is to their liking, possess a great advantage. Fortunately, most lories fall into this category. Many will investigate and enter a box within minutes of it being placed in the aviary and most will enter within two or three days and roost inside by the end of a week. By and large, lories are very easy to please over the choice of a nesting site and any box of reasonable dimensions is accepted.

There are exceptions, of course, as the following shows. A Swainson's Lorikeet belonging to a friend laid an egg in its nectar dish. She had never entered the nest-box so, feeling that a second box might prove more to her liking, he hung another in the aviary. This, too, was ignored. Having read many times that birds prefer boxes which face north, he decided not to discard this 'old wive's tale'. He altered the box to face in the fabled direction and, to his amazement, the hen was inside within three minutes. She laid her second egg inside so the first was hopefully placed beside it. A further surprise was in store. The hen would not accept the second egg and somehow managed to remove it from the box, despite the fact that the box was 61cm (2ft) high.

No hard and fast rules can be laid down regarding the size of nest-boxes; an approximate guide will prove helpful to those with no experience with lories. The sizes given below are all those in which successful breedings have occurred.

Species	base	height
Blue-streaked Lory	20cm (8in) square	51cm (20in)
Red Lory (*Eos bornea*)	30cm (12in) square	61cm (2ft)
Ornate Lorikeet	18cm (7in) × 20cm (8in)	1.5m (5ft)
	20cm (8in) square	30cm (12in)
Mitchell's Lorikeet	18cm (7in) × 15cm (6in)	25cm (10in)
Weber's Lorikeet	17cm (6¾in) square	36cm (14in)
Little Lorikeet	15cm (6in) square	25cm (10in)
Yellow-backed Lory	log 76cm (2ft 6in diameter)	51cm (20in)

As can be seen from the above examples, size of nest-box is not always in proportion to the size of the lory.

The nesting material provided also varies considerably but peat is perhaps the most widely used for its absorbent qualities. Some aviculturists use a mixture of peat and sawdust while others use rotted wood in place of peat. One used a layer of small pebbles to assist drainage, covered with peat moss and rotten wood but the birds removed the peat moss and wood and the eggs were laid on the pebbles! As much as 10cm (4in) of nesting material is used in some cases but 2.5cm (1in) to 5cm (2in) is more usual. I have found that the small lories do not appear to like a lot of nesting material except that which they can provide themselves. For this reason my Iris Lorikeets have a Budgerigar nest-box complete with concave and the Meyer's have a slight indentation made in the base of the nest, on which peat is sprinkled.

The Iris removed the peat from their box and both species provided their own nesting material by gnawing tiny strips of wood from inside the box. In the case of the Iris, the layer of strips was 1.3cm ($\frac{1}{2}$in) in depth. When the box was examined for the first time in a year, it was spotlessly clean and dry with a very deep layer of gnawed wood at the end furthest from the entrance. A discarded egg which had been laid several months previously was found at the entrance end.

Mrs Burgess, the first breeder of the Black-capped Lory in Britain, recorded that the hen carried 'every splinter of wood she could find into the nest.' I was most interested to learn that a pair of Fairy Lorikeets had half-filled their nest-box with pieces of cupressus, which they had nipped from the growing conifer in their planted aviary. Undoubtedly, many instances of lories taking nesting material into their box must go unrecorded.

It is a source of wonder to all those who breed lories how the nest remains so clean. A typical observation on this fact was made by R. W. Phipps in respect of his Blue-streaked Lories (*Avicultural Magazine*, 1972 p. 195): 'After the young bird had left, the nest-box was examined. Although the litter was damp and compacted, it was not sticky, and the bottom of the box was quite dry and clean; surprisingly so in fact as no escape holes or wire tray were provided in the base.' He commented that from the 'appearance, texture and complete lack of odour' of the nest it was fit for another brood.

I have only come across one account of a lory's nest becoming 'filthy and insanitary' while the young were being reared. The Solitary Lory bred at Taronga Park, Sydney, was at times 'actually standing in a liquid slime of excreta.' It was none the worse for this, however, and, surprisingly, left the nest in excellent condition.

Unless lories are very shy and secretive it is obvious when they are getting ready to nest. Displaying and mating will occur frequently; if this is not followed by the hen spending long periods in the nest the 'pair' may consist of two males. For a few days before the hen lays she will spend most of her time in the nest and, for this reason, it will not be possible to know on which days the eggs were laid— unless, of course, the nest is inspected daily.

It is up to each individual to decide whether or not to check the nest regularly. I feel that this depends on several factors, the main one being the disposition of the birds concerned. Some lories are so nervous during the incubation period that any unusual sound in the vicinity of their aviary will cause them to leave the nest. They may carry this behaviour to such an extreme that it is not realised that they are incubating; if the approach to the aviary does not give a view of the nest, the hen will have left it and will appear sitting unconcernedly on the perch by the time the aviary is reached.

Other hens behave quite differently, dashing from the nest and flying nervously about the aviary. Both types may resent nest inspection; little will be gained from the sight of two eggs reposing in the nest and all may be lost if the hen deserts as a result of this interference. If, however, the hen is tame or not nervous and the nest-box is sited in a position which makes nest inspection easy, a brief look into the nest when the hen is *off the eggs* is unlikely to do any harm. It is pointless to look into the nest while the hen is incubating as it will be necessary to disturb her in order to see the eggs.

Some male lories spend long periods in the nest with the hen during incubation but, with the exception of *Phigys*, *Vini* and *Charmosyna* species, they take no part in this process and do not remain inside the box when the hen leaves.

Lories almost invariably lay two eggs, the only notable exception being some members of the genus *Glossopsitta* which lay three or four eggs.

There are a few instances of the clutch consisting of three eggs in other species, such as those of R. Kyme's Weber's and Iris Lorikeets, Mrs E. Jones' and E. Furner's Swainson's. The only instance I know of three young being reared (not including *Glossopsitta* species) is that of K. Russell's Perfect Lorikeets.

Eggs are normally laid on alternate days but an interval of three days between eggs is not unknown and may even be quite common. An Ornate Lorikeet at Topeka Zoo, USA, laid the eggs of the first two clutches at four day intervals (for subsequent clutches the nest-box was not examined daily).

While the hen is incubating her plaintive cry for food—a sound which carries quite a distance—will be heard regularly. She seldom leaves the box, unless disturbed, and the male feeds her inside. Those with good hearing will have no difficulty in detecting, from outside the aviary (if the nest-box is in an accessible position) the squeaking of a newly hatched chick. Those rash enough to inspect the nest will see that the chick is sparsely covered with down, the colour of which depends on the species. It may be white, light grey or yellow. It would appear that the down colour differs in closely related species and even in sub-species. According to Paulo Bertagnolio the down is white in the Yellow-backed Lory and yellow in the Chattering. As the young grow the down becomes thick and grey and by the time most chicks are two to three weeks old this change has taken place.

With most parrots it is advisable to provide a rearing food of some kind, in addition to the normal diet. With lories, however, this is not necessary because of the nutritious nature of the nectar. It is sometimes found, however, that breeding lories will accept a rearing food in addition to the normal diet. Sweetened bread and milk was taken by San Diego Zoo's Black Lories while there were young in the nest. During this period some lories will suddenly start eating a food for which they have previously shown little or no enthusiasm. When the chicks hatched by K. J. Lawrence's Edwards's Lorikeets were three weeks old the male suddenly started eating sunflower seed. This bird had previously been in my possession and had never shown any interest in seed.

Some lories will avidly consume livefood while rearing young, usually meal-worms or maggots. It is emphasised that the latter must be thoroughly cleaned in bran for several days. If the maggots have fed on contaminated food, failure to do this can cause the death of any bird that samples them. Maggot pupae are relished by some lories and were fed to their young by a pair of Blue-streaked which had previously ignored them (see page 53). These birds were also offered wholemeal bread crumbs and baby food mixed with nectar—another excellent food.

Fresh corn-on-the-cob is a rearing food almost without parallel for parrots but it should not be offered unless a continuous supply is assured. This, of course, applies to any additional food given while the chicks are in the nest. It must be given regularly. These foods will be controlled mainly by the time of the year but should chickweed be available, it should be provided as often as possible.

For the first two or three weeks after the chicks hatch the hen will rarely leave the nest but, as the chicks' down becomes more dense, her outings become more frequent. The growth of a lory chick is comparatively slow, for it will spend six to twelve weeks in the nest, according to its species. It would seem that chicks are most likely to succumb soon after hatching and up to the age of about three weeks. If they survive this period, the chances of successful rearing are high. Death at an early stage has been found, on autopsy, to be due to disease of the liver or kidneys in many instances, thus indicating a dietary deficiency.

One problem very common with lories is that of the parents plucking the young in the nest. A large percentage of all chicks which fledge are quite badly plucked. Fortunately, they feather up quickly and seem to be none the worse for the experience, unless they are so badly plucked that they are unable to fly. Should this happen, a young lory could be killed in attempting to leave the nest. It would therefore be advisable, if circumstances allow, to remove it for hand-rearing.

A question frequently asked by newcomers to breeding lories is: at what age should the young birds be removed from their parents? Unlike some parrots, in which the young may be mercilessly attacked by one parent almost as soon as they are independent, most lories are very tolerant towards their young. However, the latter should be removed before their parents show signs of wanting to nest again, whether this occurs in the following spring or fairly soon after the young are independent.

It is worth pointing out, for the benefit of newcomers to aviculture, that although lories come from tropical climates, they do not require these conditions in order to breed in captivity. Indeed, it is sometimes found that breeding results are better in cooler climates or at colder times of the year. An instance of the latter is a pair of Iris Lorikeets in my possession which had six clutches of eggs in a period of 12 months. Three produced chicks; these were during the colder months and in two cases the temperature was very little above freezing when the chicks hatched. The eggs laid during the hot summer months, and one clutch in early autumn, did not hatch.

A pair of Little Lorikeets imported into South Africa spent the first four years there at Rustenberg, where the temperature was very high. During this time they did not breed. Within six months of being in his possession, Dr D. Russell had reared young from them at his home in Bryanston, north of Johannesburg. He attributed his success to the cooler conditions and partially shaded aviaries, protected by large trees and other aviaries.

I believe that most parrots are more likely to breed in secluded aviaries which are set among trees or sheltered by them. This certainly applies to the forest-dwelling lories. There is an extra benefit to the birds housed among fruit trees or ornamental flowering trees as they will eat the blossoms and extract the nectar.

Some recorded incubation periods in captivity

			days
Chalcopsitta atra			25
Eos borneo			23, 24, 24, 24, 24, 25, 26
,, *cyanogenia*			26
,, *reticulata*			26
Trichoglossus ornatus			27, 28
,, *haematodus weberi*			26
,, ,, *capistratus*			26, 27, 28, 28
,, ,, *berauensis*			25, 26
,, ,, *rubritorquis*			24, 27
,, ,, *moluccanus*			23
,, *euteles*			23
,, *johnstoniae*			23
Glossopsitta versicolor			22
,, *iris*			23, 23, 23
,, *concinna*			22
,, *pusilla*			22, 23
Lorius domicellus			23, 24, 25, 26
,, *garrulus flavopalliatus*			28
Phigys solitarius			26, 28, 28
Vini australis			23

Some records of the ages of captive-bred lories on leaving the nest

			days
Eos cyanogenia			87
,, *reticulata*			85, approx 98
,, *squamata*			80
,, *bornea*			56–64 (one pair's young), 61, 68
Pseudeos fuscata			64, 67, 71, 72, 74
Trichoglossus haematodus haematodus			56
,, ,, *weberi*			58, 59
,, ,, *capistratus*			74
,, ,, *berauensis*			67, 71
,, ,, *moluccanus*			57, 58, 58–64 (one pair's young), 59, 63, 85, 87, 87, 88, 89
Glossopsitta versicolor			37, 39, 43
,, *iris*			65, 67
,, *pusilla*			38, 42, 52
Lorius domicellus			95
,, *lory*			60, 64, 74
,, *garrulus flavopalliatus*			68
Phigys solitarius			61

5
Hand-rearing

The aviculturist who is willing and able to undertake hand-rearing can expect to produce far more young lories than would otherwise be possible. Lories must be among the easiest of all birds to hand-rear and many do not prove to be good parents under captive conditions or, in some cases, are not provided with the diet they need to rear their young. Also, they are indeterminate layers and removal of chicks (or a clutch of eggs) will cause them to lay again. Pairs of small lories in my possession have laid four or five clutches in one season and larger species will also lay a number of clutches. Thus anyone prepared to devote some time to hand-rearing could achieve great success with these birds, especially if he or she decided to specialise in this family and a dozen or more pairs were kept. It is possible that the project could become commercially viable (given the luck without which nothing is possible!), especially if the birds could be sexed at the outset, ensuring no wastage of valuable time, something which often occurs when one is uncertain of their sex.

Let us examine the reasons for hand-rearing. First is the obvious reason: consistent failure on the part of a pair of lories to rear their chicks; secondly, serious feather plucking of the chicks in the nest, which may result in them being unable to fly when they fledge; thirdly, illness or death of one or both of the parents; fourthly, the production of tame birds and, lastly, maximum output of young from one pair, something which is destined to become increasingly important to the aviculturist.

The actual process of hand-rearing is not difficult but it can be time consuming, especially where very young chicks are concerned. However, this need not be so. At San Diego Zoo, which undoubtedly has more experience in hand-rearing lories than any other zoo or individual, chicks are fed only three times daily but, where possible, young chicks should be fed every three hours for the first few days; thereafter, three or four hour intervals will suffice, with a seven hour interval during the night.

The only equipment required to hand-rear lories is a heated cage. An incubator can be used if it is of the sophisticated type manufactured for poultry eggs but I have found that an inexpensive type is not safe except for the very youngest chick; others climb into the wiring where they are in danger of strangling or electrocuting themselves.

I therefore use a simple cage, heated by two light bulbs in the roof and thermostatically controlled. It is made of wood with a Perspex front, thus chicks are easily viewed at all times. The cage measures 18in (46cm) × 12in (31cm) × 16in (41cm) high. If four or more chicks were reared at the same time a larger cage would be necessary.

The question of temperature is an important one. At San Diego chicks are first placed in a temperature of 92°F (33°C) and, when hand-rearing I have therefore regulated the cage at this temperature for young chicks or have allowed it to rise to 95°F (35°C) on occasions. On one occasion when the temperature rose to 100°F (38°C), the chicks felt too hot to the touch and showed signs of discomfort. However, some aviculturists with considerable experience in hand-rearing parrots believe that chicks should, at first, be kept at a temperature of about 100°F (38°C). Perhaps much depends on the immediate environment.

The best age at which to remove the chicks from the nest is, I believe, between six and ten days, ie, before their eyes are permanently open. If removed from the nest when they were several weeks old, it could be difficult to persuade chicks to feed because they would have developed a natural fear of Man. However, two young Yellow-backed Lories whose parents had died, were hand-reared from the age of just over five weeks (see page 135).

At least 12 hours before it is intended to remove the chicks from the nest the incubator or heated cage should be plugged in to ensure that it is maintaining the correct temperature. After removal from the nest, very young chicks should be placed in a small cardboard box (or similar container) on a bed of tissues and placed inside the incubator or cage. If there is food in a chick's crop it can be allowed an hour or two hours in which to settle down before feeding is attempted; if not, it is advisable to feed within the first hour.

The first feed is the most difficult part of hand-rearing, especially if the chick is cold or weak. The warmth, however, will quickly improve its condition, thus making it easier to feed. If it is weak, it may refuse to hold its head up or to open its beak and must be handled very gently and with great patience. Eventually, it should open its beak enough for a drop of food to reach its tongue. Only a small amount should be given at the first feed; in fact, in a very young chick of a small species the crop is tiny and in some chicks one can watch the food travel down into the crop which is quickly filled.

After each feed a chick's beak and, if necessary, its plumage, should be wiped clean with a tissue. When more than one chick is reared, chicks may clean each other's beaks after being fed.

There are two possible methods of feeding a lory chick: with a teaspoon and with a syringe. When I visited San Diego Zoo I saw lory chicks being fed with a teaspoon specially adapted for the purpose by having the sides bent inwards. A syringe is never used because of the danger of food entering the windpipe and killing the chick. Most people use a syringe for hand-rearing parrots but I believe this should be avoided when possible, and it is possible with lories; the very youngest feed readily from a teaspoon. This is also a more natural method as right from the outset the chick swallows the food rather than has it squirted down its throat.

The food on which a lory chick is to be reared is most important. Incorrect diet will, of course, lead to losses. Obviously, many different diets have been used. That used at San Diego Zoo consists of:

½ cup wheat heart cereal

1 teaspoonful of Karo corn syrup

32

2 fresh egg yolks
$\frac{1}{8}$ teaspoonful table salt
$\frac{1}{2}$ teaspoonful of cuttlefish bone meal
4 drops Abidec vitamin supplement (Parke, Davis)

The dry ingredients are mixed with the syrup and egg yolks and milk or water is added to make a soup-like mixture. This is boiled over a low heat for three to five minutes, being stirred gently. It is cooled until 'finger-warm' and the Abidec drops are added.

At Naples Zoo, in Italy, hand-reared lories are fed on a milk-based baby food (containing mineral additives and no fat), cereal, Dextropur fruit sugar, finely grated apple and, if considered necessary, a little meat extract. The milk is prepared by adding 75ccs of water to 8g of powder; to this is added 3g of cereal and 3g of Dextropur. One drop of a multivitamin additive (Protovit from Roche) per week is given. The mixture is made up to the consistency of cream. Chicks are fed with an adapted teaspoon and are fed alternately on each side of the bill to prevent deformity of the beak. However, as chicks feed themselves readily from the front of a spoon from a very early age, I feel this is making the task of feeding more difficult than necessary.

Lory chicks at Naples are kept in a box with towelling on the floor. A shaded electric lamp (100 watt) is hung above the box to maintain the temperature at 100°F (38°C) on the floor level. The heat is gradually reduced as the chicks' feathers develop, by moving the lamp further away.

The food I use for hand-rearing consists of dried skimmed milk (reconstituted per pint: fat, 0.6g; protein, 20.4g; carbohydrate, 30g), Casilan milk protein food, Glaxo-Farley (protein, 90%; fat, 1.8%; mineral salts, 3.8%), Gevral (more normally used by aviculturists for feeding Hummingbirds) and a wheat germ cereal such as Bemax. The latter is placed in a grinder to reduce it to a powder and must make up at least 30% of the mixture to achieve the required consistency. Slightly less than this of each kind of milk food is used and a considerably smaller quantity of Gevral. The proportions are not measured exactly. A small amount of cuttlefish bone which has been reduced to powder by scraping is added and enough water to give a creamy but not thick consistency. A small quantity of Vionate (high potency vitamin-mineral supplement, E. R. Squibb & Sons) is added to one feed daily.

Undoubtedly many equally suitable formulas can be made up. This food was used because of the necessity to provide a high protein, low carbohydrate content diet. My first attempt at hand-rearing lories was a failure because of the high carbohydrate content of the baby cereal used. The chicks were Iris Lorikeets, aged about six and eight days, and removed from the nest during a bitterly cold February. Their eyes were closed and there was little food in their crops; their minute beaks would have persuaded me to return them to the nest had I not known (it had been done at San Diego Zoo) that it was possible to hand-rear this small species from this age.

The first feed, with the adapted teaspoon, was attempted a few minutes after the chicks were removed. The food, at this experimental stage, consisted of the nectar fed to the parents thickened with Farex baby cereal. The chicks refused to

33

take it but I realised immediately that this was because the spoon was cold and the food was not hot enough. Subsequently, I used the spoon to stir the food while it was being heated. These mistakes were rectified and the chicks were fed.

The youngest, with egg-tooth still visible, did not feed quite as readily as the older chick and took air into its crop. I soon discovered that the food will be refused as soon as it begins to cool. For this reason it is necessary to reheat the food if there is more than one chick. On the first day feeds were given at approximately two hour intervals until 11 pm. On the following day I gave the first feed at 3 am, then at hourly or two hour intervals. In 24 hours the chicks had become much stronger, pumping against the warm spoon and gulping vigorously. On the following day the eldest chick still had food in its crop at 11 pm, following the 9 pm feed. Its skin was very dark red and its down looked dry. When I got up at 6 am on the following morning the food was still in its crop. It was obviously dying.

Autopsy showed that it had fatty degeneration of the liver, thus explaining the reason for the full crop—the liver had ceased to function. The surviving chick appeared to be doing well so eight days after its removal from the nest I took from their nest two Meyer's Lorikeets, which had hatched at about the same time. Previously I had heard but not seen them and I was surprised by their solid appearance in comparison with the Iris chick. However, they were so cold, hungry and weak that they could not hold their heads up. It seemed that I had almost left their removal too late but they quickly gained strength.

On the following day the second Iris chick died. Post mortem examination showed that it, too, had suffered fatty degeneration of the liver caused by the high carbohydrate content of the diet. It was therefore necessary to change the diet to the food described above.

When the chicks were removed from the nest, the feather development, such as it was, was far more advanced in the elder chick; the other had no down at all. The latter showed a few rows of feather tracts and rows of feathers were appearing on its head five days after it was removed from the nest; in the elder chick, more rows of feathers were apparent. Feather growth continued at a remarkable rate and on the following day green and yellow feathers were emerging on the underparts of both chicks. The younger one still had no down but the contour feathers of both chicks were at the same stage of development.

After 14 days in the incubator the chicks were moved to the heated cage. Two days later their heads were entirely covered in pin feathers, whereas two days previously only the forehead and front part of the crown, like a dark cap, was covered in pin feathers. By the time the youngest was about 30 days old, both were completely covered in feathers and most of the head feathers were free of quills. A single chick will retain the quills on its head for longer because it has no nest-mate to remove these by preening. A chick begins to preen as early as three weeks of age and, soon after, will preen its nest-mate.

At 32 days old, the rectrices of the elder chick were about 6mm ($\frac{1}{4}$in) but no tail feathers were apparent in the younger one. Two weeks later the tails were full length and the chicks' plumage differed from the adults only in the less sharply defined barring on the underparts and slightly duller colours. The beaks and eyes were dark brown.

A month after their removal from the nest the young Meyer's were becoming aware of what was going on outside their cage. If one was left inside while the other was being fed, it would run up and down, impatiently waiting its turn and watching its nest mate. At that age it was easier to feed them separately as a 'free-for-all' developed if the spoon was offered to each bird in turn! When they were eight weeks old they would venture out of the cage when called which, I suppose, was the equivalent to fledging, for at that age comparable small lories fledge.

They suddenly proved very difficult to feed, shaking their heads as though in disgust after taking only a small amount of food. Until then the elder chick had never refused food, even when its crop was bulging. They would no longer take the food on which they had been reared so I offered them some trifle sponge soaked in nectar and slightly heated. Their reaction was surprising: they took it greedily, not pausing for breath until they were removed with bulging crops. On the following day the sponge cake was omitted as they were only taking the nectar.

For several days they had been attempting to feed themselves in an experimental manner, just as they now tested everything with their brush-tipped tongues. A small, shallow dish of nectar was therefore left in the cage and they were occasionally seen to drink at it. They became increasingly difficult to feed yet their crops never seemed to contain much food, the level of the nectar did not become appreciably lower and I rarely saw them drinking, although they occasionally nibbled at spray millet. Thus the weaning period for these particular lories was worrying because of the suddenness with which they decided they were no longer going to allow themselves to be fed. They lost an appreciable amount of weight, as all chicks do on fledging. However, a week after they started to refuse food they were feeding well on their own. They were then aged nine and a half weeks. They quickly learned to eat fruit, especially grapes and apples, and were soon cracking sunflower seed.

The weaning process of the next lorikeet I hand-reared, an Iris, was much more gradual. It started to drink nectar from a tube on the day it was first offered, when it was moved to a small cage, aged seven weeks. It learned to feed itself very quickly indeed and was soon taking millet spray and apple, then sunflower seed, yet it still 'asked' to be fed and was fed from a spoon for the next four weeks, usually twice daily. Young lories are very strong willed and it is quite impossible to feed them unless they wish to be fed! They will show their disapproval by shaking their heads and flicking the food in all directions.

The age at which lories can be weaned is obviously related to that at which they would fledge; thus, in some lories, weaning will not occur until they are nearly three months old.

An aspect of hand-rearing which I at first found worrying was the opening of the eyes. This may happen several times before they remain open permanently. For example, in the Iris Lorikeet chick hand-reared, its eyes opened for the first time when it was about ten days old. They had closed again six days later and did not open permanently until the chick was 19 days old.

If there is any choice in the matter, I believe it is advisable to hand-rear more than one chick at the same time if the birds are to be used for breeding purposes.

Also young lories are exceptionally active and playful birds and it is sad to deprive them of the companionship of their own kind. Two birds reared together are never bored; they will fight, play and preen for hours on end.

If a lory chick is hand-reared in order to produce a delightfully tame pet bird, it does not matter that it has no companion of its own kind, provided that plenty of time is devoted to it. Its relationship with its owner will be a very close one indeed and few birds will make more affectionate and amusing pets. They have a will of their own, however, and cannot be prevented from nipping or biting in excitement.

I would emphasise that hand-rearing lory chicks is not difficult; if the correct food is provided and hand-feeding is not attempted too soon after hatching, a chick's chances of survival are very high. However, there is one point which needs careful attention when hand-rearing any parrot chick. Before it is fed, the condition of the crop should be checked; if, after the usual interval when the crop would normally be empty, food remains in it, it is advisable to withhold the next feed until the crop is empty. In such cases the crop may feel hard, instead of spongy. This occurred on several occasions in a lory chick which I hand-reared and gave me much cause for concern, for I feared that the liver had ceased to function. But on each occasion food was withheld and the condition corrected itself. If a chick's liver has ceased to function, its condition will deteriorate rapidly and death will occur within a few hours.

Hand-rearing a parrot chick is such an enjoyable and rewarding experience that it might be undertaken, for those with unlimited time, for that reason alone.

Lories hand-reared on their own are often extremely aggressive towards other lories. If it is intended to use birds reared singly for breeding, they should, if possible, be introduced to others of their own kind immediately they are independent. At an early age they are far more likely to become compatible with their own kind. It is extremely difficult to introduce tame lories which have been kept as pets to other lories; unfortunately, they are potential killers of other lories.

6
Natural History

Lories and lorikeets are distributed over a large part of the tropics, being found in Australia, New Guinea and Indonesia. There have been few resident ornithologists in the latter two areas, thus relatively little has been recorded concerning the habits of these birds or most others found there. The natural history of many Australian birds has been well documented and more has been recorded about the wild life of the lories found in Australia than those from other areas; nevertheless, this is comparatively little.

Lories are arboreal (tree-dwelling) birds; they feed, roost and breed in trees and rarely descend to the ground. They drink from water trapped in palm fronds; they may climb down a drooping branch overhanging a stream or water hole and this behaviour has been observed in the Varied Lorikeet. This species has also been seen to drink at stock water troughs.

Lories may also bathe in a stream by dashing at the water and after hitting it with their wings and bodies they fly to a nearby tree to preen. I have seen lories in my collection bathe in a similar way but most will, because of the shallowness of the container, thoroughly immerse themselves, even rolling over in the water. Dashing at the water in the manner described above must be fraught with the danger of becoming waterlogged and drowning if the water is deep, but this method of bathing has been observed in a number of groups of birds, such as Bee-eaters (*Merops*).

Apart from the need to drink or bathe, lories have no need to descend to the ground for all their food is found in trees. Pollen, nectar, small insects (probably ingested with the nectar), fruits, buds and even grain, such as maize, form the diet. However, out of the breeding season these birds are nomadic: they congregate in flocks wherever trees are flowering. Having consumed the pollen, nectar and even the blossoms of the flowering trees, they will move on to another area and may not be seen there again until the trees are once more in flower.

Lories and lorikeets play an important ecological role in pollinating the trees on which they feed. In Australia, such species as the Red-collared and the Swainson's (Rainbow), are found in large flocks, perhaps even numbering several hundred birds, while the eucalypts are in flower, but are not normally met with in eucalypt forests at other times. One Australian, Florence M. Irby, commented of Scaly-breasted Lorikeets, that she would awake to find that the birds had arrived in hundreds, although there was not a sign of them on the previous evening.

She wrote (in Cayley, 1938): 'In the early spring of 1926 the Scaly-breasted Lorikeets came in thousands to the flowering gums in the Casino district. They were accompanied by many Rainbow Lorikeets. The noise they made as they scrambled among the blossoms was almost deafening; and the ground was carpeted with the flowers they had pulled to pieces.'

She described a scene which is typical, wherever large groups of lories congregate.

While nectar is an important part of a lory's diet at certain times of the year, Churchill and Christensen (1970) have shown that 'the brush-tongue in lorikeets is an organ for harvesting pollen and pressing it into a form suitable for swallowing, and that the tongue is not primarily a device for gathering nectar as stressed by Gould and his followers.' This is a logical assumption, for many species of parrots whose tongues are not adapted for feeding on nectar, do so.

However, the work carried out by Churchill and Christensen with the Purple-crowned Lorikeet in Australia show that the staple item of its diet is pollen collected in the canopy of karri (*Eucalyptus diversicolor*) forest. Their evidence indicated the difficult, albeit impossible, task, birds of this species would have if they attempted to extract nectar for anything more than supplementary feeding, from karri or jarrah flowers.

The approximate body weight of the Purple-crowned Lorikeet is 50g; a bird of this weight has a calory requirement of 8.0 kcal daily. Churchill and Christensen calculated that the amount of pollen necessary to provide this is 4.8g whereas the amount of nectar necessary to provide 8.0 kcal would be 8.1g or, in terms of volume, 819cm³—approximately 18% of the body weight of the bird. To achieve this intake a Purple-crowned Lorikeet would need to visit 297 flowers daily during a period of maximal nectar flow or 2,970 flowers during a period of average nectar flow. During a 12 hour day a bird would have to visit flowers at the rate of one every 2.4 minutes in conditions of maximal flow or every 14 seconds under normal flow conditions. Even if the flower refilled with nectar every 60 seconds (an improbably high rate) while the bird waited, the flowers are too small for it to gather 8.1g of nectar. Only under exceptional conditions of nectar flow could a Purple-crowned Lorikeet find time enough to gather nectar in sufficient quantity to satisfy its basic daily energy requirement. The amount of pollen necessary to provide 8.0 kcal, however, equals 4.8g or the pollen of 480 flowers (one every 90 seconds).

Churchill and Christensen demonstrated the presence of pollen and the absence of nectar, both in karri flowers and the alimentary canal of the Purple-crowned Lorikeet during a dry summer month—January 1970. By April 6 of that year there was still no nectar in the flowers of the karri; however, by April 28 there was a nectar flow. On that date, an adult bird feeding on karri flowers from which there was a nectar flow, had a crop nearly full of pollen; it also contained 129 anthers (part of the stamen containing pollen), 34 stamens, 20 insects, and fluid with a sugar content of 30.6%, ie, nectar. It was estimated that the lorikeets swallowed fewer than 7–13 in 2,800 anthers grazed, ie, about 0.5%. The papillae on the tip of the tongue are therefore a most efficient adaptation for collecting pollen.

Churchill and Christensen concluded that when the onset of flowering of karri is not accompanied by a flow of nectar, the Purple-crowned Lorikeet spends most of its day in search of karri pollen grains which it removes by the million without detaching more than an insignificant number of anthers or stamens. They believed that the wet brush on the tongue of the lorikeet plays the key role in this process, whereas the dry hemispherical end to the tongue of other parrots would prevent them from harvesting pure pollen.

They found that there was a fourfold enlargement of the volume of the crop at the time of the nectar flow, also that nectar does not reach the stomach, but is held in the crop. Whether sugars from nectar are absorbed in the crop is not known; if so, it may provide the principal substance from which subcutaneous fat is synthesised. Fat was observed in birds caught during a nectar flow—but not in birds caught earlier in the year. The main area of accumulated fat was at the base of the throat (1.2g in one bird); other areas were on the back, sides and legs (1.4g).

The sugars found in the nectar of the karri flowers are sucrose, glucose, fructose and melibiose.

In Australia, lories feed on the pollen, nectar and blossoms of *Erythrina*, *Grevillea* and *Banksia*. They also eat the seeds of *Casuarina* and grass trees (*Xanthorrhoea*). In New Guinea and Polynesia, coconut palms are a major food source, also *Erythrina*. Kuhl's Lory, for example, from the Polynesian islands (Rimitara, Line Group, etc), is confined to the valleys because coconut palms do not grow in the mountainous areas. On some islands, coconut palms are common near the shore, thus in Biak, Black-winged Lories will be found in this habitat and, in Fiji, Collared Lories are common inhabitants of the coastal coconut palms. In the New Guinea islands of Aru and Kei, Black-throated Lorikeets inhabit the *Casuarina* trees along the sea-shore. On Bali, Mitchell's Lorikeet has actually extended its habitat where *Erythrina* has been planted as a shade tree.

Not all lories are lowland birds; especially in New Guinea, many inhabit mountainous areas. In the Philippines, the little Mount Apo Lorikeet is found in the mountains which give it its name, at an altitude of between 4,000 and 8,000ft.

Some lories feed in the lowlands but roost in the nearby mountains, or feed in mountains and roost at a higher altitude. Mayr and Rand (1937) described seeing small flocks of Alpine Lorikeets passing each evening *en route* for their roosting sites among the higher and uninhabited mountains. Birds going to roost may gather in immense flocks, numbering many thousands. One observer described Green-naped Lorikeets 'flying in vast flocks in a west-east direction about an hour before sunset. The flocks, numbering many thousands, flew fast in a cloud without shape or formation but solidly, the way Starlings do. Their altitude must have been at least 2,500ft above sea level, if not more.'

Some lories fly to nearby islands to roost: at the end of the nineteenth century the Red and Blue Lory was observed crossing in large flocks to neighbouring islands and, in smaller numbers, the same behaviour has been noted in the little Blue-crowned Lory from Fiji.

Most small lories are exceptionally fast in flight and can twist and turn with great agility, although the flight is usually swift and direct. This probably applies to all lories with the exception of those with the largest body size—the *Lorius* species. In captive specimens the flight is rather heavy and laboured.

Among the birds which often feed in company with lories are, not surprisingly, the honeyeaters. More than one species of lory may be found feeding together:

in Celebes, mixed flocks of Ornate and Yellow and Green Lorikeets feed in the same tree; in the Solomons, Massena's Lorikeets and Cardinal Lories congregate together, also two *Charmosyna* species, Meek's and Duchess Lorikeets. In Australia, Scaly-breasted and Swainson's not only congregate but have been known to inter-breed.

It is exceptional for a lory to nest in a site other than a hole in a tree; however, very small species, such as the Tahiti Blue Lory, occasionally nest in rotting coconuts still attached to the tree and the Pleasing Lorikeet from the Moluccas and Aru Islands has been known to excavate a tunnel in an arboreal termites' mound.

With the exception of *Vini*, *Charmosyna* and *Phigys* species, incubation is carried out by the female only. Most lories lay two eggs; some *Glossopsitta* species in Australia lay three to five. Why this should be so is uncertain; if it applied only to the species in one area where the food was abundant only at the time of the year in which breeding occurred, this could be readily understood. But this is not so. Found in northern Australia is the Varied Lorikeet (two to four eggs), in southern Australia the Musk (two eggs) and the Purple-crowned (three or four), and along the eastern coast and in southern Australia the Little (three to five eggs). Possibly the species with the large clutch sizes are more primitive than those which lay two eggs.

Incubation and fledging periods for lories are given in Chapter 4.

Lories are very sociable birds, many species being found in large or even immense flocks. Some social parrots are difficult to breed in captivity unless more than one pair is kept, but this does not apply to lories; most will nest readily despite the absence of other birds of their own species.

Because many lories congregate in large flocks and are noisy and colourful, they are easily observed. This is especially true of the Cardinal Lory in the Solomon Islands, the large flocks of which can be seen in 'their shrieking scarlet hundreds, flashing in small parties from one palm to another.'

In Australia, Swainson's Lorikeets, known there as Rainbow Lories, are not only easy to observe but, at one location, they are a well-known tourist attraction: indeed, the lorikeets of Currumbin have achieved world reknown—thanks to Alec Griffiths. When he moved into his house on Queensland's 'Gold Coast' in north-eastern Australia, he found that lorikeets were breaking down his gladiolus flowers in their efforts to reach the nectar. He therefore provided dishes of honey to distract their attention.

Gradually, more and more lorikeets—Swainson's and Scaly-breasted—arrived to sample the bread and honey offered. Now, up to 2,000 lorikeets daily consume 30 loaves and 70lbs of honey! And 200,000 visitors a year arrive to watch them and to hold out dishes of food to the amazingly fearless lorikeets.

During a drought in 1965, householders in coastal New South Wales and southern Queensland found that many more lorikeets and other nectar-feeding birds were present than usual, and believed the drought was driving the birds to the coast. As a result, sugar and water was offered to many of the visiting lorikeets. However, according to Alec Griffiths, eucalypts, such as the spotted gum (*E. maculata*) which grows in large stands over the central eastern Australian coast, produce more blossoms and nectar in dry years than in wet ones.

Large flocks of brightly coloured lories cannot fail to be conspicuous. When that great naturalist Alfred Russel Wallace visited Amboina in 1857, he described the Red Lory as being '. . . very abundant. Large flocks of them came about the plantation, and formed a magnificent object when they settled down upon some flowering tree, on the nectar of which lories feed.' (*Malay Archipelago*).

However, the small species, especially those which are mainly green, may be extremely difficult to observe. The green and yellow plumage of the small Meyer's Lorikeet, for example, is especially effective as a camouflage when the bird is perched in a tree. This also applies to the small *Charmosyna* species which are predominantly green, thus virtually nothing is known of their wild life and they are almost unknown in aviculture, partly because of the difficulty of locating them.

Apparently, even the larger, brightly coloured Papuan Lorikeet with its long tail—a most conspicuous bird in flight—is easily overlooked when feeding among blossoms or flowering epiphytes attached to moss-covered branches. In some parts of its range the melanistic (black) phase predominates which, after a few hundred years of natural selection, could result in the loss of the red phase (see page 164). The surviving black phase birds would, presumably, be less conspicuous and therefore less vulnerable to predators.

Even such a brightly coloured bird as the Red-collared Lorikeet of Australia can be overlooked as it feeds among *Erythrina* blossom, the bright red blossom almost matching the colour of the Lorikeet's breast and collar.

Some brightly coloured lories are persecuted by man due to their habit of feeding on cultivated grain crops and fruit. Probably this has not had any serious effect on the numbers of any species, except locally. In 1881 Otto Finsch described Cherry-red Lorikeets on Ponapé, in the Caroline Islands, 'approaching fearlessly the neighbourhood of houses and plundering the fruit-trees, notwithstanding all the means taken to destroy them.' This is just one example of local persecution which must apply to the majority of the larger lories and lorikeets.

A few species are sought by natives for their feathers. In Fiji, the beautiful little Collared Lory used to be trapped for sale by Samoans and Tongans, who would periodically pluck them and use their feathers for decoration. This species also has to contend with a predator introduced by man—the mongoose. Low level nests in palm trunks are particularly vulnerable for the mongoose relishes eggs and chicks.

Mayr and Rand (1937) recorded seeing the skin of the beautiful little Fairy Lorikeet worn in the ear of a native 'by having the head of the skin thrust through a hole in the lobe of his ear.' They also stated that the tail feathers were prized by a mountain tribe which used them in their headdress.

Another introduced animal which may even have exterminated the endangered Tahiti Blue Lory on one island, is the rat. Forshaw (1973) recorded that he searched for this species for three days on Bora Bora Island in 1971. He did not find a single specimen and feared that rats had caused its extermination there. If so, this is a tragedy for this, one of the most unusually coloured and beautiful of all lories, is probably verging on extinction, the surviving birds now being threatened by habitat destruction. It inhabits small and widely scattered islands and information on its population is almost impossible to obtain.

Two other endangered small lories are another *Vini*, the Ultramarine, an exquisite little bird garbed in skyblue, violet and white and even more beautiful than the Tahiti Lory, and a small *Charmosyna*, the Red-throated (*C. amabilis*), also from Fiji. However, the difficulties of detecting the latter, a small green species, have possibly led to the belief that it is rarer than it actually is, although this is by no means certain.

The Ultramarine Lory, from the Marquesas Islands, to the east of Fiji, is also seriously threatened by habitat destruction and, apparently, by shooting and trapping. Extremely few examples have been kept in captivity so trapping may occur because the beautiful plumage is attractive to the natives.

The three species mentioned are found on small islands, and island species are particularly vulnerable. A large number of lory species are confined to islands, thus deforestation could cause their extinction in a very short period.

As far as is known, none of the larger lories are facing extinction due to habitat destruction but, because of the rate at which deforestation is occurring, particularly in Indonesia, and also in parts of Australia and New Guinea, this could be an immense threat to their future survival.

7
Chalcopsitta

Genus: *Chalcopsitta* (Bonaparte)

The members of this genus are large birds with a naked area of skin surrounding the lower mandible; this is not conspicuous as it is black, the same colour as the beak except in the Cardinal Lory (*C. cardinalis*) in which the beak is red. The naked skin around the eye is also black. The distinctive feathers of the neck and the back of the head are narrow and pointed and peculiar to this genus. The tail is rounded and relatively long, especially in Duivenbode's Lory. It is possible that the colour of the iris of the eye is an indication of sex in these birds, those with an inner ring of yellow or white being females, as in E. J. Brook's breeding pair of Black Lories and in a proved true pair of Yellow-streaked Lories.

Chalcopsitta species are not adept at holding food in one foot, as are many lories. However, two of my Duivenbode's will grasp a grape in one foot; they seem to have difficulty in doing so and soon drop them.

The members of this genus were little known in captivity until the early 1970s, thus very few breeding successes have occurred at the time of writing and little has been recorded of their behaviour. Yellow-streaked and Black Lories are no longer considered very rare and a few Duivenbode's Lories have been imported. The Cardinal Lory remains almost unknown to aviculturists.

Black Lory (*Chalcopsitta atra atra*) (Scopoli)

DESCRIPTION: It is almost entirely glossy black but when seen in good light the deep purplish-vinous tinge is apparent, also the blue tinge on the rump. The underside of the tail is red and yellow. The beak and legs are black. The iris is dark brown with an inner ring of yellow in some birds. The pointed neck feathers, being the same colour as the surrounding plumage, are apparent only on close inspection. Length: 32cm (12½in).

Mrs Johnstone's comments on this species are worth quoting: 'Though by no means brightly coloured, Ater has a decided and most uncommon charm of its own. At first sight he is nothing remarkable, being apparently a funeral black all over, but when in the sunshine or bright light, it can be seen that he is really a deep purple or claret colour'. The immature bird she described as differing from the adults in the 'small splashes of blood-red on the neck and ears', and in having the skin around the eyes and below the lower mandible white.

DISTRIBUTION: Western New Guinea in the Western Vogelkop, West Irian, and nearby islands of Batanta and Salawati.

Observers have stated that the Black Lory prefers trees on the edge of forests, also small clumps or groves of trees on plains. It has been seen in 'large flocks' and groups of from ten to 20 individuals. Eucalypts and coconut palms are among the trees inhabited by this species.

IN AVICULTURE: The Black Lory is one of the oldest known lories; it was described and figured by Sonnerat in his account of his voyage to New Guinea which was commenced in 1771.

The Black Lory imported by Walter Goodfellow about 1904, which went to Mrs Johnstone, was almost certainly the first of its species to reach Britain. In May 1907 he brought back three more which were described as being in good condition and extraordinarily tame and gentle. These birds went to E. J. Brook at Hoddam Castle. Goodfellow collected three more in October 1926. He recorded (*Avicultural Magazine* 1933, p. 183) a most interesting story regarding a Black Lory he collected in north-east New Guinea. It succeeded in opening the door of its cage and flew off to join a flock of the same species in the neighbourhood. 'This was not near a village but on a hillside with virgin jungle all around, and the cages were in a makeshift shed with an open front. One morning four days later when feeding my birds as usual, a noisy flock of Black Lories flew overhead, and one detached itself from the others and without any hesitation flew straight down to its old cage and tried to get in, which of course I helped it to do.'

Another tame Black Lory was described by 'Olive St. A.S.' (*Avicultural Magazine* 1938, p. 201). It followed its owner about like a dog and 'would clamber on to my shoulder and "chuss" around my neck, keeping up a running commentary of soft mutterings. You could give this bird a piece of paper rolled up into a ball, and it would play for hours like a kitten, lying on its side and "back-pedalling" it till quite exhausted.'

London Zoo exhibited this species in 1937 also during the early 1950's; Wassenaar Zoo exhibited it in the 1950's. It remained very rare in private collections and in zoos until 1971 when this species suddenly appeared on lists from dealers in Singapore.

Having long been enchanted by the tame specimen owned by Mrs N. Howard of Wolverhampton, and never having seen another specimen, I jumped at the opportunity of owning a pair. A friend sent for four birds, two of which I obtained. They were adults and extremely shy, thus I was rather disappointed in them. When moved to a larger aviary they became steadier and therefore more interesting.

When first available in 1971 the price asked by dealers was £120 per pair. Within a few weeks Black Lories 'poured' into Britain and at one time the price dropped as low as £50 or £60 per pair. A few years previously a pair obtained by P. H. Hastings, a well-known English importer of *rara avis*, were advertised for £400!

Black Lories did not prove a particularly welcome addition to the avicultural scene—partly because of their coloration. Another factor which did nothing to ensure their popularity was that, regrettably, losses with newly-imported birds were relatively high, which is unusual with Lories.

For several months from autumn 1972 until spring 1973 I looked after four newly imported birds. At one stage I unwisely tried to introduce two into the aviary 4m (14ft) × 91cm (3ft) × 1.8m (6ft) which housed my established pair of Black Lories. They barely tolerated them for two or three weeks, not allowing them to use the higher perches. One day I heard one of the new birds screaming and, rushing to its rescue, found the established pair had cornered it and were about to attack it: needless to say, the two newcomers were instantly removed from the aviary.

The call of the Black Lory is a very harsh shriek, clearly heard above the cries of my Amazons and other parrots. They can be quite noisy in the early morning, during a heavy shower of rain and before feeding, but they are not noisy for prolonged periods. To date, the only display I have seen from the believed male of my pair is wing flapping, occasionally almost in slow motion.

BREEDING RECORDS: The Black Lory was first bred in captivity by E. J. Brook of Hoddam Castle, England, in 1909. The parents were the birds already mentioned, which were collected by Goodfellow in 1907; there was an adult and a young male, and it was with the latter that the female paired. Two eggs were laid in a large nest-box and it was reported that all three birds incubated although, of course, it is more likely that the other birds were merely keeping the incubating hen company.

The first clutch proved to be infertile and two more eggs were laid during the middle of June; this time the old male was not allowed to enter the box. After four weeks the nest was examined and a week old chick was seen. Brook recorded (*Avicultural Magazine*, 1909 p. 29): 'When the young bird is about a fortnight old, the parents would leave it for about an hour every day, when they would wash and take exercise. They, however, did not leave the young bird without attendance, for the old one was sent into the nest and by way of reward, he was again allowed into the nest box at night.' The young lory fledged after exactly two months. The pair bred again in the following year and in 1911 eggs were laid but deserted.

A pair at Chicago Zoo had eggs, reported in 1937, but they were not fertile. The Black Lory was not bred again in captivity until 1969 when a pair nested in San Diego Zoo in an aviary measuring only 1.8m (6ft) × 1.2m (4ft) × 2.1m (7ft). When the birds had been in the zoo 18 months the hen laid two eggs; both hatched and the chicks were hand-reared from the age of six weeks, when their crops were found to be empty.

It was recorded that the eggs were laid on March 16 and 17 and that the chicks hatched on April 10 and 11, thus giving an incubation period of 25 days. It is not normal for parrots to lay on consecutive days so it may be that the first egg was laid on March 15.

The Black Lories were fed on bread and milk sweetened with Karo syrup, diced or stewed apple, finely ground carrots, soaked raisins or currants, chopped grapes, figs, papaya, and pound or sponge cake.

Subsequently, Black Lories were hatched in San Diego Zoo on February 22, 1970, January 21, 1971, April 10, 1972 (lived only one day), February 19 and March 1, 1974; two hatched on May 7, 1974. The chick hatched in March 1974 was almost entirely red in nest feather but moulted out mainly black.

In the April 1977 *Parrot Society Magazine*, B. von Sorgenfrei reported breeding a hybrid between an Edwards's Lorikeet and a Black Lory.

Bernstein's Lory (*C.a. bernsteini*) (von Rosenberg)

DESCRIPTION: It differs from *C. a. atra* in having red feathers on the thighs; in some specimens the forehead is tinged with red. Forshaw (1973) states that the red on the thighs is usually less pronounced in females. Some birds have some red on the primaries.

Unlike birds of the nominate race, which lose the red 'splashes' in the plumage as they mature, in a *bernsteini* in my possession, the red splashes became apparent after I had had it two years; after three years it had one tail feather which was completely red, tipped yellow, and splashes of red on the upper and lower parts, including the under wing coverts.

Mivart (1896) wrote of this race: 'So trifling are the distinctions which separate it from the Black Lory, that there is small wonder it has generally been confused therewith.'

DISTRIBUTION: The island of Misol (Mysol, Misool), West Irian. Mivart (1896) quoted Rosenberg to the effect that it was 'pretty common in Mysol, flying about in small flocks in the forests and, like *Chalcopsitta ater*, frequently approaching human dwellings.'

BREEDING RECORDS: The only recorded breeding attributed to this subspecies to date is that which occurred in San Diego Zoo in 1974. One chick was reared. It seems likely, however, that the birds concerned were of the nominate race. When received they were immature and showing the splashes of red common to young birds, which led to them being identified as *bernsteini*.

Handsome Lory (*C.a. spectabilis*) (van Oort)

DESCRIPTION: Known only from the Type specimen, it differed from *insignis* principally in having the hind-neck and mantle streaked with greenish-yellow, the back and wings dark greenish-brown and the bend of the wing violet. The breast was dark violet marked with red and streaked with yellow and the abdomen and under tail coverts were dark green. Bright blue was the colour of the rump and the upper tail coverts were dark green, the tail being olive green above and olive yellow below, marked with red.

REMARKS: This bird may have been a hybrid. The Type specimen was a male, collected on the Mamberiok Peninsula in north-west New Guinea. It was intermediate in appearance between *insignis* and *sintillata*, although apparently nearer to the former.

Red-quilled Lory (*C.a. insignis*) (Oustalet)

SYNONYM: Rajah Lory

DESCRIPTION: It differs from *C. a. atra* in having the forehead, forepart of cheeks, thighs and under wing coverts red; the feathers of the throat and flanks are margined with red and there are red markings on the area of the vent and lower abdomen. The head is streaked with greyish-blue, the under tail coverts are greyish-blue and the rump is dull blue.

DISTRIBUTION: Amberpon Island in Geelvink Bay; Onin and Bomberai Peninsulas and the eastern part of the Vogelkop, West Irian.

IN AVICULTURE: Almost unknown. W. Frost, the renowned collector, obtained one in 1925 which he described as 'the only one of its species I have ever met with: it talks and acts, and is altogether a wonderful chum.' He collected another in 1927, but it lived only a short time.

The only Red-quilled Lory I have seen is that at Birdland, Bourton-on-the-Water, obtained in 1970 and still exhibited at the time of writing (1976).

Duivenbode's Lory (*C. duivenbodei duivenbodei*) (Dubois)

DESCRIPTION: This most unusual lory is predominantly dark brown. The head is most strikingly marked with a well defined golden yellow ring from the lores, encircling the beak and throat; the forehead is also yellow. The entire under wing coverts are bright yellow, also the thighs. The underside of the tail is a paler, more bronze shade of yellow. The long, narrow feathers of the nape and the sides of the neck are streaked with yellow. The lower back, rump and under tail coverts are deep, violet-tinged blue. The feathers of the breast have the hidden portion yellow; the primaries are black with a large yellow patch on the inner web. The entire plumage has a yellow sheen to it. The beak, cere and legs are black; the iris is dark brown or dark brown with an inner circle of pale yellow. Length: 31cm (12in).

In *Birds of New Guinea*, Iredale places this lory in a separate genus, *Moniapura*. He described it as 'one of the peculiar Lories, which shows confusion with more than one group. It is of peculiar coloration and form and cannot be reconciled with Chalcopsitta, where it has been placed. . . .'

It *is* of 'peculiar coloration' but its form hardly differs from that of *atra*, although the slightly longer tail gives the illusion of a rather more slender body. The streaked nape feathers, typical of the genus, are present. It is not surprising that a taxonomist should reach the opinion that Duivenbode's Lory belonged elsewhere but anyone familiar with it and other *Chalcopsitta* species in life would, I feel sure, agree that it was correctly placed in this genus. In voice and behaviour they hardly differ.

A friend's comments on the colouring of this lory are worth repeating: 'Most parrots seem to have had their designs made in Carnaby Street, but Duivenbode's caramel chocolate, deep navy-blue and melon yellow forms the most exquisite pattern of colour. Its conception may have been a 'Brownie's' uniform but what genius has done with such a simple scheme! I think that it is quite the most tastefully garbed of all the parrots.'

I must agree with those sentiments. To me, this is the most beautiful of the larger lories.

DISTRIBUTION: North-western New Guinea from Geelvink Bay, West Irian, east to the Aitape area in the territory of New Guinea. It is said to inhabit the lowlands up to 200m and is described as being fairly common. Pairs or small groups of six to eight birds have been observed in the tops of forest trees.

IN AVICULTURE: In November 1929 the first live Duivenbode's Lory reached London. It was received by J. Spedan Lewis and presented to London Zoo. A short while after, Mr St Alban Smith obtained a pair in Singapore and later sent a third specimen to H. Whitley's collection at Primley, Devon.

To the best of my knowledge, it was not kept in captivity again until the sum ner of 1973 when three pairs arrived in London. I was very fortunate to obtain one of these pairs. The following April I imported another pair from Singapore and in 1975, I obtained two more. From these half dozen birds it will, I hope, be possible to build up a breeding nucleus.

I can think of no lory which looks more striking in an aviary; visitors never fail to comment on their beauty. The tamest two are easily induced to display the full glory of their plumage. One has only to stand in front of the aviary, preferably with an offering of grapes, and speak to them, to bring them close to the wire. Here they will lunge the head forward, uttering the typical complaining, almost growling sound, shared with the Black Lory. As they lunge forward, the tail is fanned, the shoulders or wings are lifted to reveal the yellow undersides—in fact, all the yellow parts of the plumage are thrown into prominence. I should like to be able to house these birds in really lengthy aviaries in order to see the full magnificence of their plumage when they are in flight. Sometimes they hold their closed wings above the body; at such times they remind me irresistibly of angels.

It was not until I had kept this species for two years that I saw the full courtship display. The male revolves around the perch and then flaps the wings vigorously to reveal their most startling feature—the golden undersides—when hanging below the perch. The display is one which would not disgrace a Bird of Paradise!

Lilac-naped Lory (*C.d. syringanuchalis*) (Neumann)
DESCRIPTION: Doubtfully distinct. The head and back are said to be darker, often with a dark violet sheen.
DISTRIBUTION: North-eastern New Guinea from the Aitape area east to Astrolabe Bay.

Yellow-streaked Lory (*Chalcopsitta sintillata sintillata**) (Temminck)

DESCRIPTION: Adult birds are among the most beautiful of the lories known to aviculture. The dark green plumage is set off by the bright red forehead, lores, thighs, under wing-coverts and underside of tail. The hind part of the crown, the nape and the ear-coverts are black and there is a yellow band across underside of flight feathers. The streaked feathering is exceptionally prominent in this species. In the specimen I saw at West Berlin Zoo the small spiky neck feathers stood out like spikes around the head when the feathers were not sleeked down. On the green parts of the plumage, the lighter green streaks are conspicuous as are the

*previously *scintillata*.

orange-yellow streaks on breast and mantle. Feet and beak black; iris dark brown. Length: 29cm (11½in).

An immature bird in my temporary possession was very much duller throughout, especially on the head, which lacked the clearly defined markings of the adults. The forehead was dull red.

DISTRIBUTION: Southern New Guinea from Triton Bay and the head of Geelvink Bay, West Irian, east to the lower Fly River, Papua. Rand and Gilliard describe this species as being common in lowland savannahs and adjacent forests. It has also been observed in coconut plantations. Flocks of 30 or more birds have been seen; its abundance depends on the presence of the flowering trees on which it feeds.

IN AVICULTURE: This species has a similar history to the members of the genus already described in that it was known to aviculture from the early years of the 20th century and when collected by Frost and Goodfellow in the 1920s. A pair exhibited by O. Millsum in 1909 were, apparently, only the second of their kind to appear on the show bench. In the same year E. J. Brook possessed a single specimen. The Yellow-streaked Lory did not reappear on the avicultural scene until the early 1970s. The first specimen (also the finest, to date) I saw was in 1971 in West Berlin Zoo. In 1972 pairs were offered by dealers in Singapore. As with the Black Lory, the price was high—over £100 per pair—but within a year it had dropped very considerably and one dealer (who quickly became insolvent, incidentally!) was offering pairs at £35.

Green-streaked Lory (*C.s. chloroptera*) (Salvadori)

DESCRIPTION: Differs from *C.s. sintillata* in having the under wing-coverts green or green with red markings. The streaking on the body feathers is said to be narrower and the body colour lighter.

DISTRIBUTION: South-eastern New Guinea from the upper Fly River east to the Kemp Welch River.

Carmine-fronted Lory (*C.s. rubrifrons*) (G. R. Gray)

DESCRIPTION: The streaking of the breast is said to be wider and more orange than in the nominate race, and that on the abdomen yellower and more extended. According to Rothschild and Hartert (1896): 'The majority of the Aru specimens have the breast more washed with brown and have very dark orange stripes along the shafts of the feathers on the breast as well as the hind-neck, but the British Museum possesses specimens from New Guinea that are just like our Aru Skins.'

DISTRIBUTION: Aru Islands.

Cardinal Lory (*Chalcopsitta cardinalis*) (G. R. Gray)

DESCRIPTION: Almost entirely red, darker and more brownish on the back and wings; tail rusty red. The feathers of the underparts are edged with buffish-yellow.

In many birds there is an indication of a yellow patch on the lower ear coverts. the bill is mainly red, the base of the upper mandible being black; the legs are dark grey. The iris is orange-red, red or reddish-brown. Immature birds have the beak brown. Length: 31cm (12in).

At one time this species was placed in the genus *Eos;* one characteristic wh. ch indicates its affinity with *Chalcopsitta* is the area of naked skin surrounding the lower mandible.

DISTRIBUTION: Solomon Islands; Feni, Nissan and Lavongai islands in the Tanga, Lihir, Tabor and Duke of York groups. This species is said to be numerous throughout the Solomon Islands and has been observed in small parties. It frequents mangroves, coastal plantations and lowland forest. According to Mayr (1945), Cardinal Lories often fly from one island to the next. Small berries and vegetable matter, apparently from coconut flowers, have been found in the crops of these birds.

G. W. Stevens recorded (*Cage and Aviary Birds*, July 10, 1969) that before visiting the Solomon Islands he was told that the Cardinal Lory would be the first bird he would see. He wrote: '. . . as we drove through the coconut plantations, owned by the giant, seemingly omnipresent Unilever combine, there were the Cardinals in their shrieking scarlet hundreds, flashing in small parties from one palm to another as they fed, in company with social groups of the Coconut Lory (*Trichoglossus haematodus*).* They made a splendid sight against the tropic blue sky.'

'In July 1967 while walking in the bush in the Shortland Islands, at the Northwestern end of the Solomons, I found a young one being fed in the secondary forest and decided to take it home to rear. Initially it did quite well on a thin mixture of honey and water, with a tiny amount of Abidec, but showed no inclination to go on to more solid food, such as sweet potato. Eventually I lost it.

'This may be the reason why this parrot is so rarely kept in the Solomons as a pet, for I saw one only which was so nervous that it seemed unlikely to settle down well in confinement.'

IN AVICULTURE. It is almost unknown to aviculturists but why this should be so, when it is so common and other parrots from the Solomons are imported, it is difficult to say. In 1974 a London dealer advertised this species; I visited his premises for the express purpose of seeing a 'new' species but was to be disappointed. He had incorrectly identified a *Trichoglossus* lorikeet!

The birds received by Dr Burkard of Switzerland in 1976, two pairs of which went to Walsrode Bird Park in Germany, are the only specimens I know of which have been kept outside their native country.† Dr Burkard informed me that his Cardinal Lories are reminiscent of *Trichoglossus* species in behaviour, being vivacious and playful and rolling on the ground. He described them as easily tamed, noisy and very hardy.

T. h. massena.

†Before this, San Diego Zoo received two specimens in 1944.

8

Eos

Genus: *Eos* (Wagler)

Members of this genus have the plumage predominantly red, set off with black and various shades of mauve and blue. The tail is proportionately slightly shorter than in *Chalcopsitta* species, and the skin at the base of the lower mandible is feathered, not bare. The bill is orange-red, the iris reddish or reddish-brown and the legs grey. Size varies from 23cm (just over 9in) in the smaller races of *squamata* to 28cm (11in) and 31cm (12in) in *histrio* and *reticulata*.

The immature plumage is more distinctive than in *Chalcopsitta*; in most cases the red feathers have dark tips to them, giving a mottled appearance.

Eos species have a musky odour which is particularly strong in the Black-winged Lory. Even skins retain the odour.

The best known species is *bornea* which has long been available at a lower price than most lories. Two of the remaining four, *histrio* and *semilarvata*, are little known to aviculturists.

The courtship display varies slightly among members of this genus. Dr A. J. Wright compared that of two in his collection, *reticulata* and *bornea*. That of the former is more elaborate, with head bobbing, wing spreading, hissing and vocalisation. However, the display of *bornea* is performed at a faster pace. Another South African aviculturist who has kept these species, Dr W. D. Russell, informed me that his male *reticulata* displayed by 'dancing around the hen in a crouched position, with the feathers of the head and nape raised', while the male *bornea* prances up and down along the perch, 'calling out with a low whispering noise.'

Black-winged Lory (*Eos cyanogenia*) (Bonaparte)

SYNONYM: Blue-cheeked Lory
DESCRIPTION: This handsome lory is predominantly red and black above and dark red below. A violet V shaped patch, with the top of the V pointing towards the beak, covers most of the side of the face, the feathers being slightly elongated; the remainder of the face is a brighter shade of red than the rest of the plumage. The mantle is red and the wings are almost entirely black, only part of the primaries and secondaries being red. There is a golden-yellow spot on the fifth primary. The thighs and a spot on the flanks are also black. The under tail coverts are red and the central tail feathers are black, the inner webs of the feathers being red. The bill is orange and the iris dark red with a faint inner ring of white. Length: 28cm (11in).

Immature birds have the feathers of the head, neck and underparts irregularly margined with purple-black.

DISTRIBUTION: Islands in Geelvink Bay, West Irian: Numfoor, Biak, Manim and Mios Num. Mayr and de Schauensee (1939) observed it on the island of Biak and found that it was 'Common only near shore in coconut trees in the village of Korrido. Not seen inland or in the mountains. The birds travel swiftly in small flocks.'

IN AVICULTURE: It is not often available, no doubt due to local distribution and remote habitat. Walter Goodfellow collected a single specimen for Mrs Johnstone in 1907 and O. Millsum, writing in *Bird Notes* (September 1909) of his Black-winged Lory, stated: 'Extremely rare, for a long time I thought it to be the only specimen in England, but our esteemed member, E. J. Brook, Esq., also possesses one and was under the same impression.'

Brook's specimen was housed with a Yellow-streaked Lory (*Bird Notes*, September 1909) '. . . which is rather a morose bird, and when it (*cyanogenys*) gets bored with its companion it wakes it up by biting its legs and catching hold of its tail with a foot and pulling at it till the moroseness of *scintillatus* turns into a rage of good humour.'

During recent years this species has been included in the collections at London Zoo, Kelling Park Aviaries (Norfolk) and Amsterdam Zoo. Since 1971 it has been irregularly offered for sale in England. I know of two tame specimens which are delightful birds.

The musky odour is particularly strong in this species. I recall a two-hour car journey with a Black-winged Lory in a box. At the end of two hours the car was filled with the bird's odour. I looked after it overnight and, by the evening, the room in which it was housed bore the unmistakeable signature of the Black-winged Lory. In an aviary, of course, the odour is much less noticeable.

BREEDING RECORDS: This species was bred by Gilbert Lee in the USA in 1934.

In Britain, it would seem that this species has been bred on only one occasion. The pair owned by Mr and Mrs C. Wright of London reared two young in 1976. Eggs were laid on alternate days but hatched on consecutive days after an incubation period of 26 days. At 13 days old, the chicks' beaks were black and the small feet were blackish. They had white down and their eyes were starting to open. They left the nest when 75 days old, fully feathered except on the shoulders where the parents had plucked them.

The adults were very protective towards their young and would viciously attack anyone who approached the nest-box, working as a pair, flapping their wings and giving a high-pitched scream.

They were fed on nectar made from honey, Ostermilk, Complan and Farex or Farlene. Apple, pear and grapes were also eaten but maggots and mealworms were refused.

During 1972 hybrids between a male Black-winged and a female Red Lory (*Eos bornea*) were bred at San Diego Zoo. In 1973 three young were reared by this pair.

Stella's Lorikeet (*C. p. stellae*) is as hardy as most other lories. Photo by San Diego Zoo.

A 28-day-old Yellow-backed Lory (*L. g. flavopalliatus*). Photo by San Diego Zoo.

Opposite:
Red-collared Lorikeet (*T.h. rubritorquis*).
Photo by San Diego Zoo.

The Red Lory (*Eos bornea bornea*) has hybridised with, among others, *E. histrio* and *T. moluccanus.* Photo by San Diego Zoo.

Opposite: Salvadori's Lory (*Lorius lory salvadorii*) differs from *L.l. erythrothorax* by having a well defined blue band on the hind-neck. Photo by San Diego Zoo.

Mt. Apo Lorikeets (*T. johnstoniae*) will sometimes fight among their own kind when they come into breeding condition.

Opposite: The Blue-faced Lorikeet (*T.h. intermedius*) is a beautiful subspecies of *Trichoglossus haematodus*. Photos by San Diego Zoo.

Mr. Robert Buzikowski
of the San Diego Zoo is
shown hand-feeding
some lories kept there.
Photo by San Diego Zoo.

Ornate Lorikeet (*T. or-natus*). Photo by Horst Mueller.

Opposite: Swainson's Lorikeet (*T.h. moluccanus*) is easily tamed in captivity. Photo by San Diego Zoo.

Two young Yellow-backed Lories (*L.g. flavopalliatus*). Photo by San Diego Zoo.

Ornate Lory (*T. ornatus*). Photo by San Diego Zoo.

A pair of Iris Lorikeets
(*G. iris*). Photo by
Horst Mueller.

A young Scaly-breasted
Lorikeet (*T.
chlorolepidotus*). Photo
by San Diego Zoo.

The Purple-capped Lory (*L. domicella*)

The Black-winged Lory (*Eos cyanogenia*) is not often available to fanciers. Photo by Horst Mueller.

The Rainbow Lory (*Trichoglossus haematodus moluccanus*) is one of the most beautiful of all the lories. It can become firmly established in aviculture. Photo by San Diego Zoo.

Black-capped Lory
(*Lorius lory lory*).
Photo by Horst
Mueller.

Blue-streaked Lory (*Eos
reticulata*). Photo by
Horst Mueller.

Blue-streaked Lory (*Eos reticulata*) (S. Muller)

SYNONYM: Blue-necked Lory.

DESCRIPTION: Another very handsome member of the genus, its distinguishing features are the conspicuous bright blue streaks on the mantle and hind neck. An area including the ear coverts and most of the side of the face—but not the lores or cheeks—is a darker shade of blue. The upper part of the wing is irregularly marked with black, the secondaries being red and black and the primaries mainly black. The bend of the wing and the lesser wing coverts are usually entirely red. The upper side of the tail is black and the thighs may be partly black; some of the feathers with red inner webs. The rest of the plumage, including the upper tail coverts, is red. The beak is orange red. Length: 31cm (12in).

Immature birds have the feathers of the breast edged with blue-black. That bred by Phipps was described, shortly before it fledged, as 'differing from the parents only in the blue head markings and dark grey instead of orange bill'.

DISTRIBUTION: Tenimber Islands, Indonesia; it has been introduced to the Kai Islands and Damar Island in Indonesia.

IN AVICULTURE: This lory was not often represented in collections, until 1971 when it was frequently offered for sale by dealers in Singapore. Quite a number reached England but this number was small compared with the large consignments of Goffin's Cockatoos from the same island. The latter must have been affected by the reported widespread deforestation there but what effect it has had on the population of this lory is not, at present, known.

London Zoo exhibited the Blue-streaked Lory as long ago as 1862 and 1874 and received two more in 1904. E. J. Brook had a pair in his collection in 1911, and Mayer collected some in 1927. It appears that it was rarely imported from that time until 1971.

BREEDING RECORDS: The first recorded breeding took place in California in 1939 when Mrs Bonestell reared one youngster. The first British breeding occurred in 1972. A pair belonging to R. W. Phipps of Maidenhead, which had been obtained during the previous summer, were placed in an aviary measuring 2.4m (8ft) × 1.2m (4ft) × 1.8m (6ft) high during March. They had been housed in unheated indoor accommodation from December.

Mating was observed during March but the birds showed no interest in the nest-box, except as an object for roosting *on*, until late May. Maggots and hemp were offered during the early part of June and proved more popular than when offered previously. The birds were out of the box so much that Mr Phipps doubted whether any eggs had been laid. On inspecting the box on June 23 he was surprised to see a chick, a few days old.

Soon, larger quantities of more solid foods, including fruit, greenfood and boxed dates, also maggot pupae (previously ignored), were being consumed. Wholemeal breadcrumbs and baby food mixed with nectar were then accepted. Fresh corn cob was eaten when hung from the aviary roof, but only partly stripped when placed in a dish.

From mid-July the chick was heard being fed. On August 3 it 'was covered with grey down and some quills showed, mainly on the wings. On August 14th some red feathers were visible on the head and a few days later red was also seen on the back; by this time the bird was about two months old. Early in September, in addition to a general increase in red and black feathers, some light blue ones had appeared on the crown and back of the head, a colouring which is not present in the adult; a fair growth of tail was observed'. (*Avicultural Magazine*, Nov./Dec. 1972 pp. 95–6). It fledged on September 25, an estimated 14 weeks after hatching. That night it roosted on a branch in the shelter, the adult birds sleeping on top of the nest-box.

The adults were observed feeding the young Blue-streaked Lory for the next two weeks and appeared compatible until October 9 when they made a 'mock attack' on the young bird, which was therefore transferred to another aviary. It was independent and feeding on apple and corn cob. On October 12 the adult birds spent a considerable period in the nest and had renewed their interest in cuttlefish bone. The box was removed to prevent a further breeding attempt.

This species was bred by W. Riley of Lancashire in 1973. His pair was obtained in July of that year and placed in an aviary measuring 2.1m (7ft) × 1.5m (5ft) × 1.8m (6ft) high. A nest-box measuring 51cm (20in) × 25cm (10in) × 33cm (13in) with a 7.6cm (3in) entrance hole was provided, mainly for roosting purposes during the winter. On September 10 Mr Riley was surprised to find two eggs in the nest. Inspection was not carried out again until October 1 when one chick was seen, but this was thought to be dead. On October 6 however two chicks were seen in the nest; they 'were covered with greyish white fluff'.

As Mr Riley left home very early in the morning, the food was checked at 5.15 am and it was found that the birds were feeding during the hours of darkness, as nearly all the nectar disappeared during the night. The mixture given consisted of two dessertspoonfuls of Farlene, one of honey, one of condensed milk and two drops of Abidec to nearly a pint of water. When the chicks hatched four drops of Abidec were given, also half a teaspoonful of glucose and a dessertspoonful of malt extract, and a small amount of Readybrek. Canary seed was eaten but sunflower, hemp and apple were ignored.

The weather was very cold at the end of October, with freezing fog at night. On November 5 a frame covered with clear PVC was fitted to the front of the aviary. By November 17 the chicks were almost fully feathered but with fluff on the breast. They appeared to be about two thirds of the size of the adults and slightly duller in colouring. Icicles were hanging from the bottom of the nest-box and the holes in the bottom were enlarged to allow the liquid droppings to escape more quickly. The chicks fledged on December 19 and 21, ie, when they were 12 weeks old.

This species was among those listed by D. S. Edwards (*Parrot Society Magazine* June 1974) which he had bred in 1973 in Rhodesia. Also in 1973, Walsrode Bird Park in Germany reared one Blue-streaked Lory. In 1974, Dr A. J. Wright of Durban reared two; he gave the incubation period as 26 days and the fledging age as 85 days. That year Naples Zoo, Italy, was successful in rearing two young and the zoo in Pietermaritzburg, South Africa, bred one.

Violet-necked Lory (*Eos squamata squamata*) (Boddaert)

SYNONYM: Violet-naped Lory.

DESCRIPTION: The plumage is rather variable, the general effect being more mottled and less clear-cut than in most lories. The dull purple which extends over most of the underparts and the small size, render this species easily distinguished. In adult birds the underparts are almost entirely dull purple in most specimens, except for a broad band of red on the breast. The forehead and the forepart of the crown are red, also the lores, cheeks and ear coverts. The rest of the head and throat, usually also the neck, are dull purple, also the scapulars which are tipped with black. The secondaries and greater wing coverts are red, tipped with black, and the primaries are black with the base of the inner webs black. The upper side of the tail is purplish-red, the underside being yellowish-red, more yellow at the tip. The bill is orange-red. The colour of the iris varies; it may be red, orange or yellow. Length: 27cm (10½in).

Immature birds have the feathers of the underparts edged with purple, thus the underparts appear almost entirely of this colour. The ear coverts are tinged with purple. The iris is brown.

P. Bertagnolio recorded of his Violet-naped from Schildpad (*Avicultural Magazine*, July/August 1974, p. 136): 'The male has red irides and dark blue under tail coverts; the female brown irides with brick-red outer edges, while her under tail coverts are a mixture of purplish-blue, greenish and reddish, all rather pale, but whether these characters represent true sexual dimorphism or only individual variations I cannot say.'

DISTRIBUTION: Schildpad Islands; western Papuan islands: Gebe, Waigeu, Batante and Mysol.*

In 1925 Wilfrid Frost reported that 'immense numbers of Violet-necked Lories' could be purchased from the natives of Halmahera, suggesting that it was plentiful in the wild. Mees (1965) wrote of this race: 'During the morning hours many assembled in the crowns of flowering Erythrina trees in search of nectar. All three evenings shortly before sunset I watched flocks of this bird crossing the channel and returning to Atkeri on the opposite coast, a distance of about 2 miles.'

IN AVICULTURE: It is occasionally offered for sale and is among the less expensive of the lories.

BREEDING RECORDS: The first recorded breeding of this species took place in 1926 by M. P. Soudée of Châtillon. In February the hen laid two eggs; the chicks failed to break the shells. The second clutch was more successful and one youngster fledged on August 15. In 1939 Mrs Bonestell of California was successful in breeding one Violet-naped Lory; it was reared by her pair of Blue-streaked Lories with their own young.

A hybrid between a male Violet-necked and a female *Eos histrio* was bred at San Diego Zoo in 1931. Two eggs were laid in March; one chick hatched but died after about three weeks. In August two more eggs were laid, one of which hatched.

*See p. 61.

In 1972 Paolo Bertagnolio of Rome bred this species. He felt that they belonged to the race *attenua*, a subspecies not recognised by most taxonomists. He described them (*Parrot Society Magazine*, February 1973) as being 'mostly red, except for an irregular dark purplish-blue collar (only indicated or broken in some specimens), dark purplish-blue abdomen and under tail-coverts (divided from the red breast by a precise horizontal border), black outer wing quills with red inner bases, black tips to the inner quills and greater coverts, purple-red tail quills with red and golden surface. Total length a little over 20cm (8in).'

Bertagnolio obtained three birds which were kept with another *squamata* and a female Edwards's Lorikeet; all five slept in the only nest-box, as is usual with lories. On May 1972, two eggs were found in the box, produced by two Violet-necked Lories which had agreed well together from the start. The male roosted with the female but the other three lories were consigned to the space between the top of the box and the ceiling of the shelter. On May 10 inspection of the nest revealed two newly hatched chicks 'covered by a long and rather abundant white (or very, very pale gray) down.' On May 21 both had their eyes open and towards the end of the month the down was 'gradually replaced by a second, very dark grey down, short and thick'.

On June 6 red feathering was apparent on the crown, and two or three days later on the underparts. The other lories were seen leaving the box on occasions and the Edwards's was repeatedly attacked by all the inmates so had to be removed.

The first chick fledged on June 28, 80 days after hatching; the second left the nest a few hours later. Both spent their first night on the perch but soon learned to roost in the box. Within a week they were able to fend for themselves but continued to beg food from their parents.

The plumage of the young birds differed slightly from that of the adults; the nuchal collar was less distinct and a violet-blue ear patch connected the eye and the collar. There were purplish-blue fleckings on the crown and nape, lower back and upper tail coverts. The breast feathers were scalloped with purplish-blue. The beak was black, red at the base, and the cere and skin surrounding the eye were light grey. These became blackish a month later, when the beak was orange-yellow.

In 1973 two chicks were hatched in May; one lived only a short time so the other was fostered to Ornate Lorikeets which were rearing a considerably older chick. In March 1975 Bertagnolio informed me that there were two more chicks in the nest, aged seven days.

In 1973 the zoo in Pietermaritzburg, South Africa, reared three Violet-naped lories.

E.s. riciniata (Bechstein)

DESCRIPTION: Adult birds have a prominent grey collar, usually extending to the hindcrown, although the nape is red in some specimens. The scapulars are red. Immature birds have the head red and extensive black markings on the underparts.

DISTRIBUTION: Weda Islands and the islands of the northern Moluccas.

E.s. atrocaerulea (Jany)

Doubtfully distinct. Allegedly differs from *riciniata* in having the underparts, including the thighs, bluish-black, the mantle washed with blue and the ear coverts blue-black. All these would appear to be juvenile characteristics. Mees (1965) stated: '. . . until adult specimens of *atrocaerulea* become available, the status of this race must remain doubtful.'

DISTRIBUTION: Known only from Majir Island in the Molucca Sea, Indonesia.

Obi Violet-necked Lory (*E. s. obiensis*) (Rothschild)

DESCRIPTION: This race has black scapulars. The violet-grey collar is variable and may be absent; some birds have violet-grey crown and the nape red.

DISTRIBUTION: The island of Obi in the northern Moluccas.

Red and Blue Lory (*Eos histrio histrio*) (P. L. S. Müller)

SYNONYMS: Blue Diademed Lory, Blue-tailed Lory.

DESCRIPTION: Distinguished by the *very* broad band of dark violet-blue which extends across most of the lower parts from the upper breast; the area below the blue band is red. The head is red except for the broad dark violet-blue band across the crown and a streak of the same colour through the eye which meets the violet-blue on the nape and mantle. The scapulars, flight feathers and thighs are black and the wing coverts are red, tipped with black. The tail is reddish-purple above, red below; the under tail coverts are washed with blue. The cere is white, the beak orange, the iris red and the legs pale grey. Length: 31cm (12in).

Immature birds are blue on the crown and nape and below the eyes; the underparts are red variably marked with dusky blue and the thighs are mauvish-blue.

DISTRIBUTION: Great Sangi (Sanghir) and Siao Islands.

Little is known of its present-day status but at the end of the 19th century it was described as not common on Great Sangi where it had retreated into the mountainous interior because of the growth of coconut plantations around the coast. During the same period, however, *talautensis* was very common. Large flocks were observed by Hickson (1889) flying from one island to the next at roosting time. He wrote that it was 'abundant and numerous living specimens were obtained from the natives.'

IN AVICULTURE: Always a rarity in captivity, it was exhibited at London Zoo as long ago as 1871. Shaw Mayer collected a pair in 1929 and brought them to England. It is virtually unknown to present-day aviculturists although Mrs N. Howard of Wolverhampton kept two specimens at different times during the '60s and the early part of the '70s as companion for a Black Lory. When Kelling Park Aviaries (Holt, Norfolk) had an extensive collection of Lories in the 1960s, this species was exhibited there. At the time of writing, one specimen of the race *challengeri* has been exhibited since 1972, at Birdland, Bourton-on-the-Water. San Diego Zoo had two specimens during the 1960s.

BREEDING RECORDS: I know of no published breeding records for this species but have seen a colour transparency of a young *histrio* bred in Denmark. A hybrid between *Eos histrio* and *bornea* was exhibited at San Diego Zoo in 1937.

Talaut Red and Blue Lory (*E.h. talautensis*) (Meyer and Wiglesworth)
DESCRIPTION: It has less black on the wing coverts and flight feathers.
DISTRIBUTION: Talaud Islands.

Challenger Lory (*E.h. challengeri*) (Salvadori)
DESCRIPTION: Differs from the nominate race in having the blue band on the breast less extensive and broken with red. The blue line from the eye does not meet the blue of the mantle. It is considerably smaller, ie, 25cm (10in).
DISTRIBUTION: Nenusa Islands.
IN AVICULTURE: See under *E.h. histrio*.

Red Lory (*Eos bornea bornea*) (Linné)

SYNONYM: Moluccan Lory.
DESCRIPTION: Predominantly red, with some black and blue on the wings and under tail coverts. The primaries are black with a bright red speculum and the secondaries are red, broadly tipped with black. The greater wing coverts are blue, also the scapulars in some specimens. The area surrounding the vent is cobalt blue and the under tail coverts are very dark blue, almost black. The bill is orange, the iris orange-red and the legs light grey.

Four races of *Eos bornea* are recognised by Forshaw (1973), three of which are distinguished mainly by size. Forshaw points out that it is not practical to recognise *bernsteini* and *rothschildi* when there are intermediate populations. The only race which the aviculturist is likely to recognise is *cyanonothus*, with its darker shade of red.

Eos bornea varies in size from about 25cm (10in) to 30cm (12in).

There is considerable variation in the plumage of immature birds. They have been described as having the under tail coverts red and the vent and thighs red, sometimes suffused with dull blue, also as having the feathers of the abdomen edged with blue. This has not been confirmed by those who have bred this species in captivity. D. R. Moore described the young bird he bred as being an exact replica of the adults except for the lighter colour of the beak. Two Red Lories bred at Paignton Zoo were much duller than the parents with black beaks and 'black wing flashes instead of blue.' Another aviculturist recorded that the beaks of the two young he bred had become orange one month after leaving the nest and the dark areas on the wings had disappeared.

On fledging, a chick bred from what were thought to be *E.b. cyanonothus* was described as being slightly darker maroon in colour with much 'more blue on its chest and belly' and some blue on the lores and the side of the neck. The beak was brown but gradually changed to yellow-orange (as in adults).
DISTRIBUTION: Amboina and Saparua, Indonesia. In the wild, flocks have been observed feeding on flowering *Eugenia*, *Erythrina* and other species. On Buru it has been reported as common in most areas, especially in mangroves, but rare in open grassland and hilly country near the coast.

IN AVICULTURE: This is the best known member of the genus and the only one which has been imported consistently over the years. It is perhaps the most freely available of all lories.

BREEDING RECORDS: This species has been bred on quite a number of occasions in Europe and the USA. In 1967 two breedings in Britain were reported. A pair owned by D. R. Moore went to nest in February; two eggs were laid, one of which hatched in March. The young bird was said to be reared entirely on maggots for the first week, after which apple and nectar were fed to it by the adults. It spent nine weeks in the box. On fledging it was described as an exact replica of its parents except for the lighter beak. The previous year the pair had hatched one chick which died at the age of a few days. No livefood was available on that occasion.

At Paignton Zoo in 1967 a pair reared two chicks in a cage which measured only 1.5m (58in) high, 91cm (37in) deep and 1.7m (67in) wide. The nest-box was provided in April but no interest was shown in it until December when two eggs were seen inside. By the end of the first week of January 1968 chicks were heard in the nest-box. The first fledged on February 19 when it was approximately seven weeks old and the second on March 3, about 9 weeks after hatching.

A pair obtained by Dr A. J. Wright in England in June 1970, were exported to South Africa about September 1971. They soon settled down and were provided with a nest-box which measured 23cm (9in) square × 38cm (15in) high. Mating was observed in January of the following year, the first eggs being laid on the 31st of that month and the second on February 3. These disappeared after a few days, perhaps because there was no material in the box to protect the eggs. A dried daisy bush was therefore placed inside, which deterred the birds from entering for a few days. When they overcame their fear, they chewed up the bush leaving about 2½cm (1in) of debris at the bottom of the box.

The two eggs of the second clutch were laid on March 14 and 17 and incubated by the hen. On April 10 (27 days after the first egg was laid) the nest-box contained a chick covered with light grey down and a dented egg which measured 28.3mm × 23mm. On April 27 the chick's eyes were open. On June 7 it looked out of the nest for the first time and it fledged on June 17, 68 days after hatching.

Food available during the rearing period was nectar made from honey, Complan, sunflower seed, grapes, banana, apple, Cape gooseberries, flowering grasses and flower blooms. Immediately after fledging the chick started to sample sunflower, banana and nectar.

This breeding occurred indoors in a cage measuring 90cm (3ft) × 40cm (16in) × 30cm (12in); however, the adult birds were allowed to exercise in the room every morning and evening, readily returning to their cage. Three weeks after it fledged, the chick was plucked between the shoulders by its parents and was therefore removed to a separate cage. All three were allowed to exercise in the room together and then appeared quite compatible. A second clutch was laid (July 20 and July 23) but both eggs were broken.

From the information provided by the owner of this pair it can be seen that the incubation period is 24 days and commenced with the laying of the first egg. Dr Wright recorded in the *Parrot Society Magazine* (October 1973) that the transition to adult plumage is a gradual process which 'takes the best part of a year.' He also found that during the week following the hatching of the chicks, the adult birds consumed less food than usual.

In California, a pair belonging to W. S. Hawkins was housed with two Violet-necked Lories in an aviary 7.6m (25ft) long and 15m (5ft) wide. After three years the Red Lories nested but this was not suspected until a chick was heard calling on January 14, 1973. Investigation revealed a nearly fully feathered chick. The Violet-necked Lories were therefore removed from the aviary. After the chick fledged the hen laid again in another nest-box; the young bird roosted in the box in which it was reared.

Other breeders of this species are Rio de Janeiro Zoo, Brazil, 1967 (one reared), Asson Zoological Park, France, 1967 (six), Wassenaar Zoo, Holland, 1970 (two), 1972 (two) and 1973 (one), the late Lady Baillie, 1973 (four) and 1974 (four), J. Bunker, Stratford-on-Avon, 1973 (one). In 1974 this species was reared at Jurong Bird Park, Singapore (seven) and Naples Zoo, Italy (two). Also in South Africa, Dr W. D. Russell had bred from his pair for four consecutive years up to 1976. The young left the nest when aged between 56 and 64 days.

Eos bornea has hydridised with *E. histrio* and *Trichoglossus moluccanus* (see below), among others.

Buru Red Lory (*E.b. cyanonothus*) (Vieillot)

DESCRIPTION: It differs from the nominate race in its darker shade of red; it is smaller. Immature birds are said to have the ear coverts variably marked with blue.

DISTRIBUTION: Buru.

BREEDING RECORDS: A hybrid between a male of this race and a female Swainson's Lorikeet was bred at San Diego Zoo in 1972. It had the crown red, the rest of the head and the nape being of the same shade of blue as the female parent. The underparts were mainly red with some blue on the lower breast. The wings and part of the thighs were green.

Rothschild's Red Lory (*E.b. rothschildi*) (Stresemann)

DESCRIPTION: Said to differ from the nominate race only in being slightly smaller.

DISTRIBUTION: Ceram, Indonesia. Birds from Goram, Ceramlaut and the Watubela islands are apparently intermediate between this race and *bernsteini*.

BREEDING RECORDS: Bred at San Diego Zoo in 1968, 1969 and 1970.

Bernstein's Red Lory (*E.b. bernsteini*) (Rosenberg)

DESCRIPTION: Said to be slightly larger than the nominate race.

DISTRIBUTION: Kai Islands.

Wallace's Lory (*Eos wallacei*) (Finsch)

DESCRIPTION: Predominantly red, with a collar partly encircling the neck. The abdomen and under tail coverts are purple; the primaries are black with the base of the inner web red and the secondaries and greater wing coverts are red, with the tips black. Some of the inner quills and the scapulars are dull purple. The tail is dull purple-red above, the underside of the feathers being red at the base of the inner web with yellowish-red reflections towards the tip. The bill is orange-red. Length: 27cm (10½in).

Immature birds have the feathers of the head, neck, back, breast and sides edged with purple and the ear coverts tinged with that colour. The back is dusky purple and the under tail coverts are purplish-red.

DISTRIBUTION: Western Papuan Islands: Waigeo, Gebe and Batanta.

NOTE: Wallace's Lory is not recognised by present-day taxonomists and is generally regarded as a synonym of *Eos squamata*. However, I have included it because I am familiar with a live adult specimen which agrees exactly with the description given by Salvadori (1896) except that the nuchal collar is not complete. This bird could not possibly be mistaken for *Eos squamata*, or for any other *Eos* species.

It is of interest to note that the range of *Eos wallacei* given by Salvadori was worded: 'The western Papuan Islands—Waigiou, Guebé, Batanta, and a small island near Misol.' In his *Check-List*, Peters (1961), who states that *Eos squamata squamata* replaces *Eos wallacei*, gives the distribution of *E.s. squamata* as 'Western Papuan Islands: Gebe, Waigeu, Batanta and small island near Misol' and Forshaw (1973) gives the range of *E.s. squamata* as 'the Schildpad Islands and on Gebe, Waigeu, Batanta and Misool.' It would be of interest to know whether there are any skins of *E.s. squamata* in existence labelled Gebe, Batanta or Waigeou or whether this is an error resulting from the assumption that *wallacei* is synonymous with *E.s. squamata*.

IN AVICULTURE: The bird referred to above is in the collection of Raymond Sawyer of Cobham, Surrey. Delightfully tame, it is a cherished pet with the whole household. When obtained it could talk a little but has considerably extended its vocabulary, even repeating phrases in different voices, according to the tone of voice of the teacher—a rare feat in a parrot other than the Grey (*Psittacus erithacus*).

Ceram Lory (*Eos semilarvata*) (Bonaparte)

SYNONYMS: Blue-eared Lory, Half-masked Lory.

DESCRIPTION: Predominantly bright red with the area from the beak to the ear coverts violet-blue, with a line down the side of the neck of the same colour. The abdomen and the under tail coverts are also violet-blue. The underside of the tail is dull red, dusky near the tip. The primaries are black with a red speculum, the secondaries are tipped with black and the wing feathers nearest the rump are strongly suffused with blue. The bill is orange, the iris orange-red and the feet grey. Length: 24cm (9in).

In immature birds only the ear coverts and the area below the eyes are blue; some of the feathers of the abdomen are edged with blue. The red areas are paler and duller and the scapulars are brownish-grey edged with pale blue.

DISTRIBUTION: The mountains of central Ceram, apparently at elevations about 5,000ft. It is said to be very common in certain areas. Two lories collected by Goodfellow on the island of Obi were named *Eos goodfellowi* but are no longer considered sufficiently distinct to warrant separation.

9
Pseudeos

Genus: *Pseudeos* (Peters)

The single species in this genus is closely related to *Trichoglossus* from which it differs in the shorter tail and prominent area of bare skin surrounding the lower mandible. Also, it has a very distinct colour scheme. Photographed in black and white, a Dusky Lory could be mistaken for a *Trichoglossus* species. Its voice is like that of the larger members of the genus and its behaviour is also similar. The hissing, neck-arching and bowing display is typical; at least in captive birds, vigorous wing-flapping is also part of the display. One aviculturist informed me that in his pair 'Treading is preceded by a sideways hop and weave movement along the perch and back again.'

Dusky Lory (*P. fuscata*) (Blyth)

DESCRIPTION: The coloration of this species is extremely variable—more so than in any other Lory with which I am familiar. There are two colour phases—orange and yellow—and stages in between. The vivid, fiery orange of the brightest coloured birds is very, very striking, while the dull yellow birds at the other end of the colour range would not be recognised as the same species by the uninitiated.

I will describe a typical bird of the orange phase. The forehead, part of the crown, throat and ear-coverts are black, also the entire upper parts, except for the rump which is white or yellowish-white. The crown is golden bronze and the feathers below the black nape have orange-brown edges. There is a narrow collar or brilliant fiery orange between the upper breast and the band of orange above the throat. The feathers of the upper breast are black, edged with whitish, below which there is the second orange band and a haphazard band of black and a patch of dark, fiery orange on the abdomen. The under-wing coverts are orange and the upperside of the tail is blue and bronze. The under tail coverts are dark blue and the underside of the tail pale bronze. The inner webs of some of the tail feathers are orange. The wings are almost black, tinged with orange on the secondaries. The prominent area of naked skin at the side of the lower mandible is orange and the eyes are bright orange-red. Length: 24cm (9½in).

Immature birds have the bill brownish-black with the base of the lower mandible yellowish. The iris is brown. The naked skin at the side of the lower mandible is brownish-yellow, gradually becoming more orange as the bird matures. The iris is brown. (See p. 66).

It would appear that the Dusky Lory is sexually dimorphic, a fact I have seen recorded only by Dr O. Finsch (1900). He described the rump colour of eight specimens as follows: male, yellowish-white; female, silvery-white; immature male, yellowish. These descriptions agree with that of my pair and three other breeding pairs of which I know. The rump is probably yellowish in all immature birds, male and female.

The white rump gave rise to the subspecies *incondita* (White-rumped Lory), named by Dr A. B. Meyer in 1896. Only ten years later Ernst Hartert wrote that it should not be maintained because of variation among individuals, apparently without realising the characteristic was a sexual distinction.

DISTRIBUTION: Throughout New Guinea and the island of Salawati (western Papuan Islands) and Japen Island (Geelvink Bay). Rand and Gilliard (1967) described it as inhabiting forest and open savannah, up to 2,000m. Dusky Lories have been observed in flocks of from 20 to a hundred or more individuals and allow a close approach when feeding. Flowering coconut blossoms and *Pittosporum ramiflorum* form part of their diet. Forshaw (1973) stated that the stomach contents of birds collected at Manokwari comprised remains of small black fruit stones, light green pulp and fine vegetable matter, probably flower fragments.

W. R. Ogilvie-Grant (1915) quotes Goodfellow to the effect that this species was very numerous at Wakatimi. 'Long before sunset and until it was quite dusk flocks of many hundreds, coming from all directions, flew over with a deafening noise. Often some weak branch would give way under their weight, causing a panic just as the noise was beginning to subside, and clouds of these birds would again circle around, seeking a fresh roosting place and keeping up a continual din.'

IN AVICULTURE: Until 1972 this species was almost unknown in aviculture. Under the name of White-rumped Lory, it was collected by Goodfellow in 1907 and obtained by Mrs Dalton-Burgess in 1922. A pair was exhibited by London Zoo in 1909 and there was a pair in the collection of E. J. Brook in 1911. Grant collected two in 1915 and, in 1925, Louise Washington reported in the *Avicultural Magazine* that she owned two. One purchased by G. E. Whitmore in 1933 for £7.10s was exhibited with much success. He described it as 'a most delightful bird to keep and playful as a kitten.' It was fed on Nestlés milk, honey, Bovril, apple and grapes.

In 1972 Mrs S. Belford imported a single Dusky Lory—the first seen for many years. It was delightfully tame and I much enjoyed looking after it for a while. An endearing aspect was its extremely gentle nature; some tame lories give their owner a nip now and then but the Dusky was never guilty of such behaviour.

After several months Dusky Lories began to appear, and were regularly imported into Britain from dealers in Singapore for the next two years. I was fortunate in obtaining an exceptionally striking pair of the brightest, fieriest orange imaginable. Keen bathers, they are invariably in immaculate condition and attract the attention of visitors. At first they were extremely reluctant to sample any food other than nectar, except the flowers of a honeysuckle (*Lonicera*) growing near their aviary. Soft pear is the only fruit relished and spray millet the only seed eaten.

BREEDING RECORDS: According to E. Hopkinson (*Avicultural Magazine* 1940, p. 313), the 'White-rumped Lory (*fuscata*)' was bred at Paignton by the well-known aviculturist, H. Whitley, who never recorded his breeding successes. This species became generally available in 1972 and it would appear that, in Britain, Birdland, Bourton-on-the-Water, was subsequently the first to breed it. Apparently two youngsters were reared in 1974, one of which died several weeks after fledging.

In 1974, this species also reared young in Naples Zoo, Italy. Two pairs were received in the summer of 1973 and these were housed in the same aviary until one pair went to nest. Two eggs had been laid by April 7, when the second pair was removed. Both eggs had hatched by May 1 and the youngsters fledged on July 10 and 11 (after at least 71 days in the nest). In her description of the immature birds in *Zoo* (April, 1975), Marie-Louise Wenner mentions the pointed tail feathers* ('Chaque plume de la queue était pointue, alors que la queue des adultes présente des plumes aux extremités arrondies'). The second pair at Naples laid during May and the young birds fledged on August 16 and 17.

In 1976, three of the four pairs at Naples nested successfully. One pair destroyed one youngster when it was fully feathered, but the second chick was reared. A second pair hatched two chicks, one of which died when two or three days old; the other was reared. A third pair, consisting of one normal and one yellow phase bird, reared two chicks, one of each colour phase.

Judging by the number of successes which have occurred since 1974, it would appear that the Dusky Lory is a ready breeder in captivity, and may perhaps prove as prolific as some *Trichoglossus* species. In 1975 there were at least four successes in Britain. My own pair reared one youngster after failing to do so the previous year; on two occasions a chick had been hatched but had died when about two days old. In 1975 the female laid her first clutch near the beginning of April; the nest was not inspected because she is rather nervous while incubating. She is a 'master' at the art of pretending that her eggs do not exist, sitting innocently on the aviary perch yet disappearing silently into the nest-box in less time than it takes to blink. The male spends long periods inside the box during incubation—even for lories they are a most devoted pair. The first clutch was again unsuccessful, the chick being heard on May 10 and living for only two days.

The hen laid again at the beginning of June and a chick was heard on June 28. On July 2 it was still alive and I altered the diet by giving wheat germ cereal in place of Farex in the nectar, also adding Horlicks. When bread and milk was offered the bread was left and the milk taken, so the latter was offered daily while the chick was in the nest. Ripe, soft pear was also eaten. The Dusky Lories seemed anxious to get at the millet sprays provided for the Meyer's in the next aviary and when I offered them some, they ate it eagerly, instead of destroying it as they had done in the past. A spray was therefore given daily.

From the time the chick was two weeks old the parents spent very little time in the nest-box. The weather throughout was very warm until about a week before the chick fledged on September 3. I could make only scanty notes on its development as, without taking the box down, it was impossible to obtain a good view of the chick. On July 20, when it was three weeks old, I saw it preening itself. A week later it had some colour on the head, which was surrounded by a halo of

---

*A feature of newly fledged lories of several species.

fluff. On August 2 the orange feathers of its breast were apparent and four days later it was almost fully feathered on the head and back, with down remaining on the breast and rump. On August 14 it seemed to have been plucked slightly on the wing butts and there was little down apparent. By August 23 it was fully and perfectly feathered.

On fledging, its colours differed markedly from those of the adults. In place of the clear bands of colour on the breast it had almost the entire breast bright orange with a smudge of dark brown across the upper breast where the adult has a clear band. Each feather on the wings had a bronzy, almost iridescent centre, and the orange patch on the outer web of each tail feather was far brighter than that of the adults. The rump was almost golden in colour, brighter than that of the male. The most noticeable feature of its appearance was the dark brown eye and beak which gave it a gentle, appealing look. On fledging, it was smaller than the female but within two weeks it had equalled her size, which is smaller than that of the male. Adult eye colour was acquired in a few weeks and, less than four months after fledging, it was seen to display. The three birds lived in perfect harmony until the youngster was removed from the aviary the following February. It was very steady when it fledged and was far tamer than its parents.

In 1976 the female laid at the end of April and a chick was heard on May 22. The nest was seldom inspected because the parents actively objected to this, screeching loudly and approaching as though to attack. At the first inspection on June 20 the chick was covered with long white down and had orange quills on the top of the head. Eight days later it had the top of the head and the nape of the neck feathered, also part of the wings. It fledged on August 14.

In 1975 the Dusky Lory was also bred by Mr and Mrs Aberdeen of Boston, Lincs, from a pair obtained during the previous year. Two chicks fledged on August 12, when they were described as being mainly dull brown with grey on the upper and lower back. In 1976 four young were reared.

D. Gainey of Deal, Kent, obtained a pair of Dusky Lories in October 1973. The female laid two eggs in July 1974, one of which had hatched by July 30. It died when about four weeks old. In 1975 two eggs were laid and again only one hatched. The parents were nervous and very vocal when the nest was approached. The chick fledged on August 31 when just over three months old. It was described as having a red appearance in the areas where the adults were orange, being otherwise dark brown. In addition to nectar, fruit was given daily, including pomegranates; seeding grasses and dandelion heads were also eaten.

A pair of Dusky Lories was obtained by Mr and Mrs Scholz of Witham, Essex, in December 1973. In September 1974 the hen laid but deserted after being disturbed by the Yellow-backed Lories in the adjoining aviary. In 1975 they were moved to an aviary where the hen laid on June 1 and 3; the eggs were found to be broken on June 25. The hen laid two more eggs during July, one of which hatched on August 5. The other egg was fertile but the chick failed to free itself from the shell. The young bird fledged on October 17 (ie, at 72 days) when it was duller than the adults 'with the bars across the breast being only just visible, the whole of its front being dull red mottled black.'

In 1976 the pair reared one youngster, after the death of the chick at ten days in the first nest. The parents were very aggressive and attacked anyone who entered the aviary. The two young Dusky Lories were housed together and became very tame; they learned to imitate the sound of water being poured from a jug and attempted to talk.

In South Africa, a pair belonging to Dr W. D. Russell hatched two chicks in 1975. However, the parents deserted them after the nesting log was inspected. In 1976 two chicks were hatched; one was reared and left the nest at 64 days.

In the USA the Dusky Lory was bred on several occasions by W. Sheffler who also bred a hybrid 'White-rumped' × Swainson's. At Taronga in Australia, two hybrids between a male Solitary Lory and a female 'White-rumped' were reared in 1957, and another in 1958. K. Muller, Curator of Birds described them (pers. comm.) as follows: 'In appearance they resembled closely the *Domicella* lories, being predominantly red and blue pattern with a short tail, and resembled closely the Black-capped Lory. They were slightly smaller than the White-rumped Lorikeet, but considerably bigger than the Solitary Lory.'

10

Trichoglossus

Genus: *Trichoglossus* (Vigors and Horsefield)

The members of this genus can be distinguished from those described so far by the smaller size, generally more slender build and the absence of the naked area of skin surrounding the lower mandible. Almost every species and subspecies is barred, often prominently or distinctly, on the upper breast.

The many races of *T. haematodus* are perhaps the most complex of the entire Psittacidae. In some cases identification is not possible without knowledge of origin. When the skins from certain islands whose birds form separate subspecies are compared, one can see a slight difference in size and colour but individual variation and the discrepancy in plumage between immature and adult specimens, can be as marked as the difference between close subspecies. Forms which are considered to be subspecies by some systematists should perhaps be considered only as geographical varieties due to isolation.

Jeremy Greenwood's remarks (1969) (*Birds of the World* Encyclopedia) are worth quoting regarding '. . . the sub-species from eastern and South-eastern Australia, *T.h. moluccanus*, it intergrades with the Cape York sub-species *T.h. septentrionalis*, there being a decrease in size from south to north. Such a gradual change, or cline, is characteristic of the type of geographical variation found in a continuously distributed population. In contrast, a break in distribution allows sharp differences to develop between the populations on either side of the gap. Thus, in the rainbow lorikeet, the form of north-western Australia, *T.h. rubritorquis*, separated by unsuitable country from *T.h. septentrionalis*, is quite distinct, with a red collar and a black belly. As in the *moluccanus septentrionalis* population, there is a decrease in size of *T.h. rubritorquis* from south to north. This illustrates Bergmann's Rule; the body size of warm-blooded animals is larger in the cooler parts of the range (to conserve heat). The sub-species occurring on islands to the north of Australia are even smaller than the northern-most Australian ones.

'Apart from *T.h. rubiginosus*, all forms east of Celebes and Timor are fairly uniform. The red of the breast is tinged yellow and the belly varies from purplish-black to grass green. The forms *berauensis*, *intermedius*, *micropteryx*, *massena* and *deplanchii*, form a clinical series, each sub-species slightly distinct from its neighbours. The sharpest changes in coloration occur where the populations are separated by wide stretches of sea. The presence of only one sub-species, *massena*, over the whole range of scattered islands from the Bismarcks to the New Hebrides may indicate that the colonisation of this area is relatively recent. In contrast, the islands to the west have three distinct sub-species.

'In the Lesser Sunda Isles a different sub-species occurs on most of the islands and the normally red parts of the plumage are yellow. To the north-east is a group of sub-species with pure red breasts and black, purple-glossed bellies.

'In the extreme north-west of the super-species' range is the Celebes population.' (Ornate Lorikeet).

Ornate Lorikeet (*Trichoglossus ornatus*) (Linné)

SYNONYM: Ornamental Lorikeet.

DESCRIPTION: The forehead, crown and ear coverts are dark purplish-blue; there is a patch of yellow behind the ear coverts. The cheeks, throat and a patch on the side of the neck are red; the lower part of the face and the breast is barred with red and blue-black, the latter colour being found on the edges of the feathers. The under tail coverts and the area surrounding the vent is yellowish-green. The under wing coverts are yellow, this being the only member of the genus without the coloured band; the underside of the tail is also yellow, the bases of the inner webs of the tail feathers being red. The rest of the plumage is dark green with variable yellow markings on the lower breast. The beak is orange and the iris dark orange. Length: 25cm (10in).

Immature birds have narrower blue-black margins to the breast feathers and an increased amount of yellow on the abdomen. P. Bertagnolio described the beak as dark brown and the thin, bare eye-ring and the cere as light brown instead of black. Three weeks after fledging the beak was pale orange spotted with dark brown in the two chicks he reared in 1970.

Mivart (1896) quotes Meyer who 'shot a specimen near Menado with quite yellow plumage, perhaps a bird escaped from captivity, or an individual variety.'

DISTRIBUTION: Celebes and most of the larger off-shore islands, such as the Togian group, Peling, Banggai and Buton. It is a common bird, inhabiting wooded mountainous areas up to about 1,000m, but tending to avoid dense primary forest. It feeds on pollen, nectar, fruits, blossoms and the seeds of various trees, including those of *Casuarina* and *Tectona*. It has frequently been seen feeding in company with Yellow and Green Lorikeets (*T. flavoviridis*).

IN AVICULTURE: Frequently available during the early part of the 1970s but apparently never common before this period. It has been known since 1734 when it was figured by Seba.

BREEDING RECORDS: The medal of the Avicultural Society was awarded to John Bunker of Stratford-on-Avon in 1970 for the breeding of this species. He obtained a pair in July 1969 which had been imported 12 months previously. They were placed in a small flight before being transferred to winter quarters at the end of November, an all wire flight cage 1.2m (4ft) long, 61cm (2ft) wide and 91cm (3ft) high. In February a nest-box was placed on the floor of the cage so that they became accustomed to it before they were placed outside again. The base was covered to a depth of 7cm (3in) with a mixture of peat, soil and wood chippings, dampened and rammed down tightly. The birds showed an immediate interest and roosted inside.

Three weeks later they were observed mating; the cock regularly fed the hen. During the third week of April the hen remained inside the box, the cock joining her when anyone approached. Examination revealed two eggs. As the atmosphere was very dry, the floor of the cage was moistened daily. The hen regularly left the box during early May, but as the birds were very nervous and suspicious of interference the box was not examined again until May 28. There were two chicks, estimated to be about two weeks old and sparsely covered with white down. The nest-box, which was 'quite dry and sweet', still contained the eggshells.

The chicks were examined again on June 6 when they were covered in dense white down. On June 14, pin feathers were visible on their heads and backs. On July 10 they were fully feathered, with tails as long as adults and 'minimal vestiges of down'. They differed from the adults only in the slightly duller plumage, almost black (instead of orange-yellow) bills and black irises. The youngsters fledged on July 18 and July 21.

After Bunker's report of his success in the *Avicultural Magazine* (November/December 1970), J. W. Hudson (Merley Tropical Bird Gardens) reported (March/April 1971) that he had been successful in rearing a single youngster in 1969 and in 1970, both of which were thriving.

A pair of Ornate Lorikeets obtained by Mr and Mrs P. J. Coulson of Northants in September 1969 were transferred to an outdoor aviary in the spring of the following year. It measured 2.7m (9ft) × 91cm(3ft) × 1.5m (5ft) high. They were extremely shy and retired to a large nest-box, 1.5m (5ft) high, when anyone was in the vicinity. It was thought that they were probably two males so it was with some surprise that two eggs were seen in the box on March 27 1971. On April 21 faint squeaking was heard from inside the nest-box and, when both birds were away from the nest on April 25, it was inspected to reveal two chicks covered with long fluff.

One was found dead on May 2; its crop was empty. The other chick was found in a cold, weak condition on May 16 and was removed, warmed and fed with nectar and cake from a syringe. After an hour it was returned to the nest. It fared well for two days when it was again found cold and hungry. It appeared that the chick was not fed at night for it was found in the same condition for the next two or three mornings.

On May 23 the parents stopped feeding the chick. It was therefore removed and fed four times a day, the last feed being at 10.30pm. It became very tame and made a delightful pet. The adults went to nest again and reared two chicks. Food provided was nectar made from Complan, Nestlés condensed milk, honey with vitamins A and D added. Brown bread, sponge cake, chickweed, fruit and soaked sunflower were also offered.

The first recorded breeding of this species was that which occurred in France in 1883. In the USA it was bred by Mrs A. R. Hood in 1932 (two nests of two). At San Diego Zoo 37 were reared during the period 1968 to 1973. Also in the USA, four were bred at Topeka Zoo Park, Kansas, in 1969 and four more in 1970; at Los Angeles Zoo two were reared in 1969. Cairo Zoo bred this species in 1961 and Rotterdam Zoo in 1960 and 1962.

In Italy, P. Bertagnolio has been successful with this species on several occasions. In 1968 his pair nested in a quiet aviary only 1.2m (4ft) long, with shelter attached.

The nest-box used was 30cm (12in) high and 20cm (8in) square; 7.6cm (3in) of well moistened peat moss was placed on the bottom. On April 12 there were two eggs in the box but on the 28th the hen unfortunately died due to eating contaminated greenfood. The eggs were transferred to the nest of a pair of Swainson's Lorikeets containing eggs laid on about April 9. Two chicks were seen in the nest on May 8, one of which was found to be an Ornate Lorikeet when it began to feather up at the age of three weeks. It fledged on July 3 and the Swainson's on July 6. It had therefore spent 56 or 58 days in the nest.

In 1969 a female Ornate was obtained and later that year two more which later proved to be hens. Each pair was housed in an aviary 4.5m (15ft) long. When the nest-box of the pair including the old male was inspected on April 20 one egg was seen; there was a second two days later. On May 18 two chicks, with white or very light grey down (similar to that of Swainson's Lorikeets) were seen in the nest. On June 12 they had the appearance of 'two fatty balls covered by a short and thick mouse-grey down.' They were close-ringed on June 19. Four days later light and dark green feathering was visible on the scapulars and abdomen and the purplish-blue on the crown and the red on the nape was apparent. They fledged on August 6, after 80 days in the nest. In 1971 two more youngsters fledged on March 6, after only 66 days in the nest.

Also in Italy, the Ornate Lorikeet was bred by N. Fiorentini of Merano in 1974. An aviary-bred pair, hatched in 1971, was obtained and placed in a breeding cage 1.2m (3ft 8in) long × 40cm (16in) × 50cm (20in) high. This was placed outdoors and protected by a transparent plastic folding door. In April 1974 they were provided with a nest-box which was hung outside the cage. A 10cm layer of moist rotten wood and mould was placed on the bottom of the nest-box. To prevent this from drying out, holes were made in the bottom of the nest, into which water was poured by means of wicks.

Much displaying and courtship feeding was seen—but no eggs were laid. As it appeared that the birds were two males, a proved female was obtained from P. Bertagnolio. When put in the cage, one at a time, both birds attempted to pair with it, and when all three birds were together, the males fought each other. Presumably one was removed. Eggs were laid on August 16 and 20 and hatched on September 11 and 15; the youngest chick died on September 23. The surviving chick fledged on November 23 when it was not fully feathered. These birds received an extremely varied diet (see p. 21).

In the USA, a pair of Ornate Lorikeets at Topeka Zoological Park, Kansas, reared three nests of young during 1969. Obtained in July 1968, they were housed in an exhibition unit measuring only 2m (6ft 8in) × 2m × 1.25m (4ft). After the birds were seen to enter their nest-box several months later, the box was inspected daily. The first egg was laid on April 5 and the second four days later. The first chick hatched on May 2 and there were two chicks in the nest on May 10. They were covered with long golden down. The chick was first heard calling on May 18. Ten days later the crushed sugar cane used to absorb moisture in the base of the nest-box had to be changed and it was replaced again on June 24. The chicks left the nest on July 8 and 9. On July 28 the parents began to persecute their young which were removed on the following day.

The eggs of the second clutch were laid on August 7 and 11 and hatched on September 2 and 4. The young birds fledged on November 5 and were removed on November 18, four days after their parents started to attack them. On January 12 1970 a chick hatched from the third nest; the second egg was infertile. The young bird left the nest on March 13. One month later its beak was in the process of changing from black (which colour had been attained at the age of 26 days) to orange. Its plumage was almost identical to that of the adults but the colours were duller. It was removed on March 31, when the adults started to persecute it. This behaviour towards all the young birds may have been due to the small size of the enclosure. By the beginning of April the female was again incubating two eggs, thus four clutches were produced in a 12 month period.

Other zoo breedings include those which have occurred at San Diego, 1973 (six), 1974 (two—at least one parent was reared in the zoo), and Naples, Italy, 1973 (one) and 1974 (seven) and Chester Zoo, 1976 (four).

The Ornate Lorikeet has hybridised with several species, including Swainson's and Scaly-breasted. A male Ornate paired to a female Red-collared produced a hybrid which resembled the male in shape and arrangement of colours and had the orange collar of the female.

Green-naped Lorikeet (*T. haematodus haematodus*) (Linné)

DESCRIPTION: The forehead, forecrown and chin are blue and the ear coverts and throat are purple-black. There is a greenish-yellow band on the nape. The lower throat and upper breast are bright red with purplish-black edges to the feathers which give a barred appearance; the centre of the abdomen is green and the lower abdomen, flanks, thighs and under tail coverts are yellow with most of the feathers edged with green. The under wing coverts and part of the flanks are red and there is a broad yellow band across the underside of the flight feathers. The underside of the tail is olive, the outer feathers with yellowish inner webs. The back, wings and the upper side of the tail are green. The bill is orange-red and the iris is red. Length: 26cm (11in).

DISTRIBUTION: Amboina, Buru, Ceram, Ceramlaut, the islands of Goram, Watubela and Western Papua, islands in Geelvink Bay except Biak; western New Guinea along the north coast, east to Humboldt Bay, and in the south to the Upper Fly River.

An interesting description of the wild life of this species is found in the *Proceedings of the Academy of National Sciences, Philadelphia* (Vol XCI p. 112): 'The only lory found on Sarong Island itself. It seems to prefer coconut palms to any other tree. This species and *Lorius lory* were often seen in the Tamrau in March flying in vast flocks in a west-east direction about an hour before sunset. The flocks, numbering many thousands, flew fast in a cloud without shape or formation, but solidly, the way starlings do. Their altitude must have been at least 2,500ft above sea level if not more.'

IN AVICULTURE: Fairly frequently available.

BREEDING RECORDS: It is difficult to know, with breeding records attributed to this subspecies and, indeed, to any other *haematodus*, whether the race has been correctly identified. As this is the nominate race, those in doubt of identification are more likely to refer to their birds as 'Green-naped'; the following refers to an account under that name, in which no description of plumage was given.

In 1971 a pair belonging to D. G. Bloom of Mildenhall, obtained in the previous February, succeeded in rearing one chick. Previously the hen had laid clear eggs, except for two clutches, in which the chicks had died when about two weeks old. A chick hatched on July 7 1971 fledged on September 2. It was removed from its parents on the following day as it had been plucked almost naked. The diet offered was nectar made from honey, condensed milk, Farlene and Virol, also sunflower seed, fruit (usually apple) and chickweed. The adult birds spent much time on the aviary floor searching among the weeds—possibly for insects, although maggots and mealworms were ignored. In 1973 the pair reared two nests of two youngsters.

Nine Green-naped Lorikeets were bred at Berne Zoo in 1966 and two at Prague Zoo in 1967.

Mitchell's Lorikeet (*T.h. mitchellii*) (G. R. Gray)
SYNONYM: Red-breasted Lorikeet.
DESCRIPTION: Differs from the nominate race in being slightly smaller and in having the head and nape dark chestnut-brown and some dark olive green feathers on the forehead; the cheeks and throat are also dark brown. The breast is scarlet with bluish, green or yellow edges to the feathers. The abdomen is purplish-black. There is a considerable variation among individuals in the colour and markings of the upper breast. Length: 23cm (9in).

Immature birds have the abdomen dark green and the breast paler. Clifford Smith of Yorkshire, who bred this species in 1962, described the young on fledging as having the head green and the bill black, while John Eyre described the newly fledged young of his pair as 'dull editions of their parents with black beaks and nearly black heads.'

According to Hartert (1896b): 'Immature birds have blackish edges to the red feathers of the breast, a more dusky crown and the nape more or less tinged with green.' He noted 'a variety' which showed 'broad yellow subterminal bars to the feathers of the upper breast.'

It is possible that the coloration of the breast feathers is an indication of sex in this subspecies. Of four skins I examined, two had the upper breast entirely scarlet; both were labelled as males. The other two had well defined green or yellow edges to the feathers; both were labelled as females. In his account of the breeding of Mitchell's Lorikeets (*Parrot Society Magazine*, April 1971), L. G. Shaw stated that when his pair came into breeding condition 'the hen's breast feathers were a much brighter yellow than previously and the cock bird's breast was a much deeper red.'

Clifford Smith, the first breeder in Britain, recorded that: 'The cock has a brilliant red breast while the hen is slightly less brilliant with a tinge of yellow.' (*Avicultural Magazine*, 1963, p. 32).

DISTRIBUTION: Bali and Lombok.

In 1930, German ornithologist B. Rensch, found this subspecies to be very common in Bali at 1,200m in *Erythrina* trees around Lake Bratan. He suggested that it might have colonised the island from Lombok after the introduction of coffee after widespread planting of *Erythrina* as shade trees in the plantations. It is absent from montane forests in Lombok where there are no suitable trees for food.

IN AVICULTURE: Mitchell's Lorikeet is fairly frequently imported. In 1903 Seth-Smith described it as 'hardly likely to be met with by aviculturists. Only three specimens were known at the time, two of which were in London Zoo and one in Amsterdam. In 1910, it was no better known; according to W. T. Page (*Bird Notes*, 1910), there were only two in Britain—one at London Zoo and another in the collection of C. T. Maxwell.

BREEDING RECORDS: In Europe, Dr J. P. Derscheid was the first breeder. Two young ones left the nest in September 1936, both of which were alive in September 1938. In 1937 the pair reared another youngster. In Holland, this subspecies was bred at Wassenaar Zoo, two or possibly three being reared. Two more were bred in 1941 and 1943 but all were killed in an air-raid in 1944.

In Ceylon Dr W. C. Osman Hill bred three Mitchell's Lorikeets during 1937–38. The hen laid in a hollow tree stem 46cm (18in) long and 7.6cm (3in) in diameter and apparently spent little time on the eggs during the day. Chicks were heard on November 29. Two weeks later it was necessary to remove the other occupants of the aviary, Swainson's Lorikeets, which were being attacked by the Mitchell's. The chicks fledged on January 14 and 16. The pair nested again in March and a chick fledged on May 18.

The Avicultural Society's medal for the first breeding in Britain was awarded to Clifford Smith. His pair was housed in an aviary 3m (10ft) long, with sleeping quarters in an adjacent birdroom. The nest-box contained a layer of small pebbles covered with peat moss; rotten wood formed the base.

The pair began to show an interest in the box at the beginning of May 1972; on May 14 two eggs were seen on top of the pebbles. All traces of peat moss and wood had been removed. When anyone approached, the hen would leave the nest which, on June 15, was found to contain one clear egg and one containing a fully developed chick dead in the shell.

Two eggs were seen in the nest on July 22. The nest was not inspected again until August 6 when there was one chick and one egg. On August 14 there were two chicks, one much larger than the other. The first fledged on September 30 but the second was found dead in the nest on October 7, although the adult birds were still visiting the box. The food offered to them consisted of nectar, canary seed, millet sprays and gentles.

At Kelling Park Aviaries in Norfolk, two Mitchell's were bred in 1968, two more in 1969 and four in 1971. K. W. Dolton of Hallow, Worcester, bred one in 1968 and P. Farrant bred two in 1969. Birdland, Bourton-on-the-Water has bred this species on several occasions. B. Bertram of Cambridge bred one in 1973 and, in 1974, Birdworld, Farnham, bred two, Los Angeles, two and San Diego, two.

Forsten's Lorikeet (*T.h. forsteni*) (Bonaparte)

DESCRIPTION: It differs from *mitchellii* in lacking the barring on the scarlet breast and in having the crown, forehead and cheeks dark purplish, almost dark purple on the hindneck in some specimens. The abdomen is dark mauve or purple. The forehead and cheeks are streaked with violet-blue and the nuchal collar is light green. Length: 23cm (9in).

Immature birds have been described as being exactly like the nominate race and *fortis*, with the nape and the area behind the collar quite green. The red breast feathers have a yellow tinge and dark green edges; the abdomen is green, not purple.

DISTRIBUTION: Sumbawa. It inhabits open rain forests up to at least 1,000m.

IN AVICULTURE: Frequently available and one of the most often imported lorikeets of recent years. In 1901 Frank Finn described it as 'the most common lory in the Calcutta market' since 1894 when he went to Calcutta. It was first exhibited at the London Zoo in 1896; in that year, according to Seth-Smith, it became 'almost as common in the bird-market as Swainson's Lorikeet.'

BREEDING RECORDS: This subspecies was bred in Calcutta Zoo in the last year of the nineteenth century. The Avicultural Society's medal for the first breeding in Britain was awarded to Mrs Michell of Bedale in 1905; one youngster was reared. In 1906 two clutched of two eggs were laid, the first two chicks being killed by Swainson's Lorikeets when two weeks old. One was reared in the second nest.

Two Forsten's were bred at London Zoo in 1930 and another in 1935. In 1932 Mrs Chichester of Ballymena bred one and the pair bred on several other occasions.

In the USA, Gilbert Lee bred this species in 1931 (four reared), W. J. Sheffler in 1934 (two), Mrs Bonestell in 1938 and San Diego Zoo in 1966, 1969, 1971, 1972, 1973 and 1974. In Australia, at Taronga Park Zoo, seven were bred during the period 1941 to 1943. Other breeders of Forsten's Lorikeet are Wassenaar Zoo, 1959; Moscow Zoo, 1965; Amanzimtoti, 1966; Kelling Park Aviaries 1968 and 1971 (seven); Padstow Bird Gardens, 1971 (two) and 1972 (one), Wassenaar Zoo, 1969 (four) and 1971 (one), Berne Zoo, 1969 and Toledo Zoo, USA, 1974 (four).

Forsten's Lorikeet has hybridised with Swainson's, Red-collared and Scaly-breasted Lorikeets.

Djampea Lorikeet (*T.h. djampeanus*) (Hartert)

DESCRIPTION: The head is dark brown with a violet sheen, streaked with blue on the forehead and, to a lesser extent, on the cheeks. The nuchal collar is light yellowish-green, followed by a patch of violet-black on the mantle, some of the feathers being red at the bases. The upper breast is scarlet, the lower breast mauvish-black. The thighs, ventral area and flanks are yellow and green and the under wing coverts are red and yellow. Length: 25cm (10in).

This is one of the most handsome subspecies. Cain stated of it: 'Within each area of the body the colouring is remarkably uniform and intense; a resemblance to members of the genus Lorius (=Domicella) is noticeable.'

Forshaw believed it to be doubtfully distinct from *forsteni*.

DISTRIBUTION: The island of Djampea in the Flores Sea.

Stresemann's Lorikeet (*T.h. stresemanni*) (Meise)
DESCRIPTION: According to Cain (1955) it is intermediate between the *djampeanus* and *capistratus* subgroups. It resembles *forsteni* in general appearance but has the breast more orange, the feathers being red at the base and often almost yellow at the tip. The bases of the interscapular feathers are also yellow, instead of red. The nuchal collar is a more greenish-yellow, rather intermediate between that of *forsteni* and *mitchellii*. There is a slight tendency to green on the feathers just above the collar.
DISTRIBUTION: The island of Kalao tua in the Flores Sea.

The subspecies *fortis*, *capistratus* and *flavotectus* form another subgroup in which red is replaced by yellow. The yellow and dark green of the underparts makes them immediately recognisable from the *djampeanus* group in which this area is brilliant red and purplish-black.

Sumba Lorikeet (*T.h. fortis*) (Hartert)
DESCRIPTION: This is slightly the larger of the members of the subgroup and apparently has a heavier bill. The green of the nape extends as a superciliary stripe above the eye to the cere. The forehead and cheeks are streaked with violet-blue; the lores and throat are green, sometimes tinged with black. The abdomen is blackish-green. According to Hartert (1896b): 'There is a great deal of variation in the colour of the breast and under wing coverts; these parts being strongly washed with deep orange in some specimens, chiefly old *males*, sulphur-yellow without orange wash in others.'
DISTRIBUTION: Sumba Island.

Edwards's Lorikeet (*T.h. capistratus*) (Bechstein)
DESCRIPTION: The forehead, cheeks and chin are dark blue with shaft streaks of almost the same colour; the throat and ear coverts are dark green, also a wide stripe above the eye which has shaft streaks of a lighter green. The nuchal band is greenish-yellow or yellow. The upper breast is yellow; some of the feathers are narrowly edged with green in the female and red in the male. This sexual distinction is not invariable but it does apply in many instances. The abdomen is dark green; the sides and thighs are dark green and yellow. The under wing coverts are orange and yellow and the inner webs of the lateral tail feathers are yellow. The bill is orange. Length: about 27cm (11in).
DISTRIBUTION: The island of Timor, Indonesia.
IN AVICULTURE: There has been much confusion regarding the names Edwards's and Blue-faced Lorikeets. The former was frequently and erroneously referred to as the Blue-faced instead of *T.h. intermedius*. *Capistratus* did not become well known in aviculture until about 1967, since when it has been regularly available. In 1903 Seth-Smith described this subspecies under the name of 'Blue-faced Lorikeet' and commented that it was very rare in Britain.
BREEDING RECORDS: In the USA it was bred by Mrs Belle Benchley, at San

Diego Zoo in 1921 (two reared) and 1932 (one reared). In Europe, Alfred Ezra's pair laid several clutches between 1928 and 1930 but no chicks were hatched. What may have been the first breeding in Britain occurred in 1966 in the aviaries of W. H. Brown of Tonbridge; he reported that he had two *capistratus* about to leave the nest. Also in 1966, two were reared at Kelling Park Aviaries and in 1967 two were reared by R. H. Grantham of Barnet. At Merley Tropical Bird Gardens two were bred in 1969 and two in 1970. A pair belonging to R. T. Kyme of Kirton, Lincs, reared one in 1972. Received in the spring of that year, the pair was first seen mating on May 11. Eggs were laid on June 29 and July 1; one was infertile and the other is reported to have hatched on July 21. When the chick fledged, aged 74 days, its neck, breast and back were nearly bare where the parents had plucked it. It differed from them only in the beak colour, which was blackish. In addition to nectar, the adult birds ate spinach beet, apple, sowthistle and white sunflower seed. During recent years, this subspecies has been bred in Britain on numerous occasions.

In the USA, Busch Gardens, Tampa, reared 13 between 1966 and 1973; in Mozambique, Beira Zoo reared four in 1969 and, in Rhodesia, D. S. Edwards bred three nests of young from one pair in 1973.

Wetar Lorikeet (*T.h. flavotectus*) (Hellmayr)
DESCRIPTION: According to Forshaw, it differs from *capistratus* in having the breast paler yellow and seldom marked with orange. There is no orange on the under wing coverts.
DISTRIBUTION: The islands of Wetar and Roma, near Timor.
IN AVICULTURE: It is doubtful whether this subspecies would be identified, unless its origin was known. Frost collected this race in 1958; at least one specimen went to Wassenaar Zoo.

Rosenberg's Lorikeet (*T.h. rosenbergii*) (Schlegel)
DESCRIPTION: This distinctive subspecies is recognised and distinguished from *T.h. haematodus* by the very wide nuchal collar, which is yellow and wider than in any other race. It also has extremely heavy blue-black barring on the breast. There is a broad band of orange-red on the underside of the flight feathers. Between the collar and the nape is a narrow dull reddish band. The interscapular feathers are wholly yellow instead of green with red bases. There are no greenish streaks on the occiput but a strong purple gloss on the nape, throat, chin and breast bars. Length: 28cm (11in).
DISTRIBUTION: The island of Biak in Geelvink Bay, West Irian. Mayr and de Schauensee (1939) state: 'This beautiful lorikeet seemed to move about in deep forest more than *Eos*. Small screaming parties of 5 or 6 travelled rapidly back and forth over the jungle from one flowering tree to another. Their shrill, constantly repeated notes in flight, changed to a softer but still continuous conversation while feeding.'
IN AVICULTURE: Rosenberg's Lorikeet is not well known in aviculture. It was

collected by W. Frost on several occasions between 1910 and 1927; one brought back in 1910 was believed to be the first to reach Britain.

BREEDING RECORDS: Three young of this subspecies were reared in Barcelona Zoo in 1974; at least one of the parent birds was bred in the zoo.

Western Green-naped Lorikeet (*T.h. berauensis*)

DESCRIPTION: Not recognised by Peters or Forshaw. Cain describes it as being the largest of the sub-group. He states that '*berauensis* shows heavy black breast bars, and a general all-round dinginess due to an infusion of black throughout the green area. There is much black on the nape and chin. The collar is a clear yellow.'

DISTRIBUTION: Western New Guinea and adjacent islands.

BREEDING RECORDS: Using Cain's description, Paola Bertagnolio of Rome, identified his birds as this sub-species. They were received in 1970 from Naples Zoo, and, at first, shared a flight 5m (16ft) × 1m (3ft 3in) × 2.5m (8ft) high with a pair of Citron-crested Cockatoos. In February 1973 the cockatoos were removed from the aviary and the lorikeets were provided with a nest-box with 7.6cm (3in) of damp peat litter in the bottom. The box was not even inspected until the middle of April. Eggs were laid on May 24 and 26 and hatched on June 19 and 20 (25–26 days). The chicks were ringed at the age of three weeks with 6mm (internal diameter) rings. On July 18 traces of green could be seen on abdomen, back and wings. The thick white down was replaced by short, thick and very dark grey down. On July 22 the blue on the crown and the green and yellow on abdomen and flanks were starting to appear. On August 20 the plumage was complete and differed from the adults only in the 'yellow dotting' on the lower cheeks. The cere and naked eye ring were light grey and the bill blackish-brown.

The chicks fledged on August 26 and August 30 at the age of 67 and 71 days. On September 14, when they were transferred to another flight, the beak was reddish-brown and the cere and eye ring dark grey.

Blue-faced Lorikeet (*T.h. intermedius*) (Rothschild and Hartert)

DESCRIPTION: The crown is cobalt with the usual shaft-streaking; there is an area of brown streaked olive before the yellowish-green nuchal band. The nape is brownish and the throat is brown to blackish-brown. The feathers of the upper breast are red, tipped with black and have dull green bases.

Cain (1955) states: '*T.h. intermedius* varies considerably in size and colour, but in nearly all respects it is intermediate between *berauensis* on the west and *micropteryx* on the east. In comparison with *berauensis* it is less blackened through-out and with the breast bars narrower. The collar is more greenish-yellow, the occiput shows a deep tinge of green, and there is a brownish hue on the nape. To the reduction of black on the head corresponds an increase of blue.' Length: 25cm (10in).

DISTRIBUTION: Northern New Guinea from the Sepik River east to Astrolabe Bay; Manam Island.

BREEDING RECORDS: A short account under the heading 'Breeding the Blue-headed Lorikeet' appeared in the *Avicultural Magazine* (Jan./Feb. 1967, p. 8). J. Rawlings, proprietor of Kelling Park Aviaries, Norfolk, described the birds as *Trichoglossus caeruleiceps* from New Guinea and stated that they were not to be confused with *T.h. nigrogularis* from the Aru Islands. However, the two names are considered synonymous but in view of the common name given and its origin, it would appear that this subspecies was intended. The birds were received in December 1965. Two chicks had hatched by July 1, one of which was reared. A second clutch was laid and two chicks had hatched by November 15. London Zoo reared one Blue-faced Lorikeet in 1959.

Southern Green-naped Lorikeet (*T.h. micropteryx*) (Stresemann)

DESCRIPTION: Cain (1955) describes it as being 'a small *intermedius* with the green areas even more free from black, the breast barring even narrower, the collar and the occiput slightly more greenish and the red of the breast slightly paler.' Length: approx 25cm (10in).

DISTRIBUTION: South-east New Guinea east of the Huon Peninsula, the Waghi Range and Hall Sound; Misima Island in the Louisiade Archipelago.

IN AVICULTURE: The skin of a male collected by W. Goodfellow for E. J. Brook is in the British Museum (Natural History).

BREEDING RECORDS: The subspecies bred by G. Blundell of Birdville, Lancs, in 1972 and subsequent years, was at first described by him as being *micropteryx*, and later as *deplanchii* (q.v.).

Stuttgart Zoo reared two lorikeets of this race in 1971 and four in 1973 from a total of 11 hatched. In 1974 four of the six hatched were reared, in addition to eight of the 12 hatched by *micropteryx* paired with another race of *T. haematodus*.

Massena's Lorikeet (*T.h. massena*) (Bonaparte)

SYNONYM: Coconut Lorikeet.

DESCRIPTION: Differs from *micropteryx* in having the back of the head green, the nape a richer, less blackish, brown; the breast is a paler red with narrower bands (which, according to Cain (1955), are 'almost green in some apparently adult specimens'). Forshaw states that the abdomen is slightly paler and the nuchal collar less yellowish (yellow-green). Length: approx. 25cm (10in).

DISTRIBUTION: Throughout the Bismarck Archipelago and through the Solomon Islands to the New Hebrides. G. W. Stevens recorded (*Cage and Aviary Birds*, July 10 1969) seeing this sub-species feeding in company with Cardinal Lories in coconut plantations. He even found it to be common in the middle of towns.

IN AVICULTURE: Fairly frequently imported.

BREEDING RECORDS: The first recorded breeding was that by W. H. Brown of Tonbridge in 1966. His description (*Avicultural Magazine* November/December 1966, p. 155) could apply to any of the sub-species in this sub-group, except *berauensis*. He received two birds in September 1965; on opening the travelling box two eggs were found inside. The pair wintered in an outdoor aviary which measured 3.6m (12ft) × 91cm (3ft) × 1.8m (6ft) high and were even seen 'rolling around in the snow like puppies'. In March they were provided with a nest-box, the bottom of which was covered with a perforated zinc sheet kept in place by strong wire netting, to allow the liquid droppings to drain away. The bottom of the box was then covered with 2in of activated carbon to help to keep the box clean. A 5cm (2in) layer of peat plus 10cm (4in) of crumbled rotten wood was placed on top of this.

On May 19 there were two eggs in the nest and the hen was 'sitting tight.' However, she stopped incubating during a cold spell of weather. On May 21 two eggs were again seen in the nest, one of which was believed to have hatched on June 10. Various foods were provided but only nectar, made from a teaspoonful each of honey, Horlick's and condensed milk in six ounces of water, and a little canary seed were taken. The young lorikeet left the nest on August 9 when it was not completely feathered. The beak was horn-coloured and the blue on the face was duller than in the adults. Three more youngsters were reared in 1974.

Massena's Lorikeet was bred in 1968 at Kelling Park Aviaries and in 1973 at Berne Zoo.

Deplanche's Lorikeet (*T.h. deplanchii*) (Verreaux and Des Murs)
SYNONYM: New Caledonia Lorikeet.
DESCRIPTION: Differs from *massena* in having 'a rather faint powdering of light blue over the head', according to Cain (1955). Forshaw (1973) states that it has 'more blue on the head; less brown on occiput and nape; less yellow on thighs and under tail coverts.'
DISTRIBUTION: New Caledonia and Loyalty Islands. Delacour (1966) stated that it is abundant in the forests of New Caledonia and is a frequent visitor to coffee plantations where *Erythrina* trees, planted for shade, are in bloom.
IN AVICULTURE: Almost unknown or seldom identified.
BREEDING RECORDS: The race bred by G. Blundell at Birdville, Southport, Lancs, was later identified by him as *deplanchii*. Six birds were purchased in June 1970 and kept together. On May 21 1972 two eggs were seen in one nest-box, although the birds had never been seen to enter it. On May 29 there were two chicks in the nest. During the next 21 days only nectar and maggots were offered. The chicks fledged on July 31; they had been plucked on the breast and back. The cock continued to pluck the young until removed, 12 days later. At some stage during the rearing, the other birds had been removed from the aviary. The parents were identified by smearing lipstick around the nest entrance and removing the four birds without lipstick marks! Two of the youngsters bred in 1973 nested when only 11 months old.

Black-throated Lorikeet (*T.h. nigrogularis*) (G. R. Gray)
SYNONYM: Dark-throated Lorikeet.
DESCRIPTION: According to Cain, in this subgroup the tinge of yellow on the

red breast is most pronounced in this race and in *caeruleiceps** 'which have patches of orange and even yellow occasionally.' He also states that *nigrogularis* agrees with the Australian forms 'in having a strong tendency to the development on the breast feathers of a yellow band just proximal to the dark bars and is further characterised by reduced barring and a larger size. It shows none of the general blackening of *berauensis* but has a purplish or purplish-black belly, in this resembling the nearby *rubritorquis* rather strongly.' Length: 28cm (11in).

DISTRIBUTION: Aru and Kei Islands, to the south-west of New Guinea. Many years ago A. R. Wallace wrote (*Annals and Magazine of Natural History*, New Series, Vol XX, p. 475): 'It frequents in flocks the Casuarina-trees which line the beach, and its crimson under wings and orange breast make it a most conspicuous and brilliant object.'

IN AVICULTURE: Rarely imported or not recognised. This subspecies was introduced to aviculture by Mrs Johnstone in 1904. Goodfellow collected two pairs in 1907.

BREEDING RECORDS: In 1966 Kelling Park Aviaries, Norfolk, reared three Black-throated Lorikeets. San Diego Zoo bred four in 1969, three in 1970 and two in 1974. In 1912 Belgian aviculturist M. Pauvvels bred a hybrid between a male Red-collared and a female of this race.

Brook's Lorikeet (*T.h. brooki*) (Ogilvie-Grant)

DESCRIPTION: It differs from *nigrogularis* in the black patch on the abdomen which is more extensive with little or no trace of green.

This subspecies is known only from the Types, two cage birds, and is no longer recognised by most taxonomists.

DISTRIBUTION: Allegedly Spirit Island, off the south coast of Trangan Island, Aru Islands.

Olive-green Lorikeet (*T.h. flavicans*) (Cabanis and Reichenow)

Louisiade Lorikeet (*T.h. aberrans*) now considered synonymous with *flavicans*.

DESCRIPTION: Cain's remarks (1955) on this subspecies are quoted in full: '*T.h. nesophilus* (Ninigo Islands) and *flavicans* (Admiralties and New Hanover) agree in having a head and collar very much like *micropteryx* but with the addition of a very narrow red-brown pre-torqual band, and a strong purple gloss on the black parts. There is no blackening of the green parts, and very little or no breast-barring. The red of the breast is very brilliant and pure, suggesting that already seen in the *djampeanus* subgroup and *T. ornatus*. In comparison with it *nigrogularis* is orange, *berauensis* and even *haematodus* are definitely salmon-coloured. While *nesophilus* is fairly constant in its character, *flavicans* shows a range of variation unparalleled in the genus *Trichoglossus*. In all parts of the range there are some individuals which have the whole of the green areas changed by yellowing or

---

*From southern New Guinea: 'merely a much smaller version of *nigrogularis* with slightly less barring and slightly more purple-black on the belly'.

almost bronzing to a colour resembling old gold. In these individuals there is a strong tendency to deep brown on the edges of the post-torqual feathers (very like a purplish flush overlaid with yellow), and a distinct reddening of the belly and flanks. The yellow of the coverts is also warmer than usual, and there may be a few red splashes or edges on the collar-feathers. Other individuals can be arranged in a complete series showing these peculiarities in decreasing strength; the extreme form has a colour pattern almost indistinguishable from that of *nesophilus*. In the greenest individuals the post-torqual region is blackish, not brown, but it is least differentiated in these specimens and may be pure green like the rest of the back.' Length: 25cm (10in).

DISTRIBUTION: New Hanover and the Admiralty Islands.

BREEDING RECORDS: This subspecies, listed under the name of *aberrans*, was bred at Chester Zoo in 1969 and 1970.

Ninigo Lorikeet (*T.h. nesophilus*) (Neumann)
DESCRIPTION: Differs from *T.h. flavicans* in having the upper parts, under tail coverts and tail green, not bronzy-yellow. Unlike *flavicans*, it is fairly constant in its colouring.
DISTRIBUTION: Ninigo group of islands, west of Manus Island.

The Australian subspecies form another sub-group in which there is an increase in size and in the amount and intensity of the blue of the head. There is no dark barring on the red and orange breast.

Red-collared Lorikeet (*T.h. rubritorquis*) (Vigors and Horsefield)
SYNONYM: Orange-naped Lorikeet.
DESCRIPTION: The whole of the head is blue with the usual bright blue shaft streaking; the broad nuchal band is orange-red followed by an area of blue on the hind-neck. Cain states '. . . there is a strong violet-purple flush over the inter-scapular and post-torqual feathers very similar to that seen in *djampeanus, forsteni* and *stresemanni*'. The remainder of the upper parts are dark green. The upper breast is orange-red and the abdomen is black. The feathers of the thighs and under tail coverts are yellowish-green, tipped with dark green and the underside of the tail is yellowish. Length: 30cm (12in).
DISTRIBUTION: Northern Australia, from the Kimberley division of Western Australia east to the Gulf of Carpentaria, Queensland. Its habits are similar to those of Swainson's Lorikeet. Found in large flocks while the eucalypts are flowering, it also feeds on the nectar from the flowers of such trees as cajaput and grevilleas.
IN AVICULTURE: During the 50 years or so that this species was available to European aviculturists it was, perhaps, the most popular of all lories and received glowing accolades from the writers of the time. The four which arrived at London Zoo in July 1900 were thought to be the first to reach Europe. In 1907 Berlin Zoo exhibited Red-collared Lorikeets and W. T. Page paid £10 for a pair but at

this period they were described as 'very rare'. In 1916 E. J. Brook stated in *Bird Notes*: 'I obtained, nine or ten years ago, two of these birds, which were great rarities at that time.' In 1921 A. Decoux described it as 'still a rare bird in French aviaries', which probably applied equally in other parts of Europe. It would appear to have been imported with greater frequency in later years and until Australia ceased to export its native fauna.

It would now appear to be almost unknown in Europe. According to the late Dr Lendon, the reverse situation obtains in Australia. He wrote in 1973 (*Australian Parrots in Field and Aviary*): 'Although previously a rare bird in captivity, a number has been brought to South Australia from the Northern Territory since the end of World War II and it is now comparatively common in the State'.

In the USA, it has proved so prolific in San Diego Zoo that young bred there have been sent to a number of zoos in the States. However, outside Australia, it has become a rare bird in aviculture, which is greatly to be regretted.

Several writers have dwelt at length upon the playful and amusing habits of the Red-collared Lorikeet. W. A. Upson wrote of his pair (*Foreign Birds*, April 1947): 'Never have I regretted that purchase; their quaint mannerisms are a joy to watch and they afford untold amusement to my wife and I, and to our visitors. They are the star attraction and every act is of a comic variety. . . .

'Soon after I had them I was pottering about in the garden when, on looking towards the aviary my heart missed a beat; there was the hen, lying on the ground with her toes uppermost and the cock doing a kind of victory dance. I feared the worst but imagine my surprise (and relief) to find she was only carrying out her 'daily dozen', this particular act necessitating the feet up and juggling with a twig. . . .'

W. T. Page's pair were equally amusing and 'played and rolled about together like monkeys.' He stated that: 'When I, or even a stranger, entered the aviary, it was simply as a perch for these two birds; they simply crawled over one, and more than once unknowingly I brought them out on my shoulder, but never lost them. . . .'

BREEDING RECORDS: This subspecies has been bred in captivity on numerous occasions. In Britain it was bred in the Parrot House at London Zoo in 1910, when one youngster was reared. Miss Peddie Waddell bred one in 1915 and thereafter the pair bred regularly.

In 1916 E. J. Brook reported that he had been breeding Red-collared Lorikeets for eight years. He described them as being 'as hardy as Budgerigars and nearly as prolific'. In 1927 Whitley bred them to the second generation at Paignton and at Keston Foreign Bird Farm, in the early 1930's, they bred 'steadily the whole year round'.

In February 1953 Wassenaar Zoo in Holland received six Red-collared Lorikeets which had been imported from Australia. In June they were housed in the Louise Hall and in August three nest-boxes were provided. One pair started entering a box in September, enlarged the entrance and broke up the rotted wood. Eggs were laid on October 18 and 21 and hatched on November 14. During incubation, the male entered the box whenever the hen left. The two chicks fledged on December 30, when they resembled the parents, except for the black bill. As the other lorikeets ignored the nesting birds it was possible to keep the youngsters with the adults as part of the colony.

The food offered was milksop made from milk and water, brown sugar, ground rusk and tomato juice—a rather unusual concoction! Apple, greenfood and seed were also provided. In 1954 it was reported that the six original birds had proved to be three pairs, all of which had reared young. The colony then totalled 14. This lorikeet was still being bred at Wassenaar in the early 1960s.

In 1956 J. Simoes bred this species in Lisbon. Housed in an aviary 8.2m (27ft) long, 2m (6½ft) wide and 2m high, the hen laid two eggs. The first hatched on May 28 and the chick fledged on August 20. A second nest produced two more chicks. In Australia it was bred by S. Harvey in 1934, by Adelaide Zoo on several occasions from 1938 onwards, and by R. Rowlands repeatedly. In San Diego Zoo, 31 Red-collared Lorikeets were reared to maturity between February 1969 (first successful breeding) and April 1974 (including 12 in 1972 and 10 in 1973). A number of these were sent to other zoos (San Antonio, Milwaukee and National zoos).

In Australia, the Red-collared Lorikeet has been bred in zoos on numerous occasions (eg, at Adelaide, Melbourne, Perth and Summertown).

This lorikeet has hybridised with the Ornate, Forsten's, Black-throated, Swainson's and Scaly-breasted also, apparently, with the Purple-capped Lory.

Swainson's Lorikeet (*T.h. moluccanus*) (Gmelin)

SYNONYMS: Blue Mountain Lorikeet, Rainbow Lorikeet.

DESCRIPTION: This is one of the most handsome sub-species, the colours being particularly strong and bright. The head is rich blue, almost violet, with blue shaft-streaking; the abdomen is the same colour. The nuchal collar is yellowish-green. The breast is irregularly marked with red and yellow, with no barring. The feathers of the flanks are red and yellow, edged with green and merging into green on the thighs. The upper parts are rich green and the under tail coverts are yellow and green, also the underside of the tail. The under wing coverts are orange strongly tinged with yellow. The eyes and beak are deep coral red. Length: 30cm (12in).

Immature birds have more yellow than red on the upper breast. The bill is brownish on fledging.

An abnormally coloured Swainson's Lorikeet was bred by W. Osbaldson in 1891. He described it as having the head 'red with lacings of white, and the shoulders were tinted with green. The greater portions of all other parts of the wings, body and tail were a bright chrome yellow, intermixed with green feathers here and there; and the tail feathers were tipped with red.'

DISTRIBUTION: Eastern and south-eastern Australia, including Tasmania, Kangaroo Island and westward to the Eyre Peninsula.

The flowers of various species of eucalyptus trees provide this lorikeet with food, thus in eucalyptus forests it is normally only met with where the trees are flowering. It is also found in heavy rain forest, monsoon forest and mangroves. In addition to nectar and pollen, it eats insects and grasses and will feed on cultivated fruits and raid fields of maize. It is therefore considered as a pest by farmers, although it destroys injurious insects and pollinates trees.

This lorikeet visits suburban gardens and parks, where it is easily tamed. In some areas these birds have become tourist attractions, taking bread soaked in honey from visitors to such places as the Currumbin Sanctuary, near Brisbane. Huge flocks are attracted by the food and the birds become so fearless they will climb all over visitors. Many Australians have little trouble in taming them in their own gardens.

In 1911 one lady in North Queensland recorded (*Avicultural Magazine*, July 1911) that she was feeding over 70 in her garden. They had become so tame that at times 20 or 30 birds would be climbing over her. Photographs testified to the truth of this. Mrs Innes had hand-reared a young Swainson's brought to her as a 'bundle of fluff' and, eventually, it chose a mate from the birds which visited her garden. Often, both birds would sleep together in the tame one's cage. When the pair bred, the family group attracted other lorikeets to the garden, and these soon became equally fearless.

IN AVICULTURE. The only Australian lorikeet available to aviculturists outside its native country—except for the Scaly-breast—the Swainson's has proved prolific enough in captivity to become firmly established. However, it invariably commands a higher price than the imported sub-species of *T. haematodus*, partly because it is the most attractively coloured of the subspecies available. Before Australia imposed a ban on the export of her native fauna, in 1961, it was regularly exported to Britain and other countries. The situation has also changed for aviculturists in its native country. The late Alan Lendon recorded (1973): 'This species used to be brought to South Australia from Queensland in large numbers before World War II; since then relatively few have appeared in local bird-shops and it has become much rarer in captivity.'

Sir Leo Chiozza Money summed up this species' attributes many years ago (*Bird Notes*, August 1919, pp. 174–5): 'The habits of the Lorikeet make it an exceedingly attractive feature in a garden aviary. It is exceedingly playful and intelligent and talks quite plainly in a language of its own, which is really much better, if you come to think of it, than if it talked bits of English which it did not understand. . . . The Swainson has been accused of being noisy but, as a matter of fact, it does not often squawk when kept intelligently, and its chatter is exceedingly amusing. It will become, in most cases, very tame, although individuals vary a great deal in this respect. The young play like puppies, rolling each other over and pretending to bite.'

BREEDING RECORDS: The Swainson's Lorikeet has been bred in captivity more consistently and perhaps in greater numbers than any other member of the Loriidae. The first record was that of the breeding which occurred in Germany in 1873. Some records of the prolificacy of this species are clearly exaggerated. Dr Amsler wrote of a pair which reared 20 young in three years. As the normal clutch is two and the young remain in the nest for between two and three months, this is not possible!

A remarkable record is that of a pair which reared young for 16 years in a cage only 1.2m (4ft) long, 45cm (18in) wide and 45cm high. It is true that some pairs would breed continuously if allowed to do so, even during the winter. However, their breeding activities should be curbed so that they are prevented from breeding for several months in each year. Taking their eggs away will merely cause them to lay more; perhaps the best method is to prick the newly laid eggs two or three times with a needle. This will prevent their development and give the hen a well earned rest from feeding chicks, which taxes her strength far more than egg-laying and incubation.

It is of interest that on several occasions Swainson's have attempted to excavate their own nesting site. A pair belonging to A. S. Roger were housed in a small aviary with a pair of Canaries, with whom they lived quite amicably. When the lorikeets began to excavate among the stones on the floor of their aviary, it was necessary to insert some tiles against the side of the aviary to prevent their escape. This did nothing to daunt their enthusiasm for a ground-level nest and they reared two broods of youngsters, between November and March, on the floor of the shelter, in full view through a large opening. The eggs were laid and the chicks reared on bare boards! After the second brood had fledged the adults started to burrow again and the young used the burrow for roosting. As their breeder pointed out, it was 'remarkable that the young did not suffer more from the cold as they came off the nest quite naked except for flights, tail and head feathers and remained like that, only feathering up slowly over several weeks.' (*Parrot Society Magazine*, August 1971).

When Mr Roger moved to Scotland in 1971, he built an aviary measuring 2.4m (8ft) × 5.5m (18ft) × 2.7m (9ft) high for the colony. A 1.2m (4ft) high bank of stacked turf was included to allow them to burrow. The adults made a burrow near the top 'working very rapidly and kicking out the earth behind them like a rabbit does.' The young birds made their own holes which were not as deep.

In June 1971 the adults went to nest, using an orthodox nest-box. Later, however, they 'changed their minds and used the earth burrows after all; on the 12 October a well feathered chick emerged therefrom. That is to say it was almost completely feathered, apart from grey down on the breast and neck.' (*Parrot Society Magazine*, December 1971).

Nearly 90 years previously a pair of Swainson's Lorikeets at Blackpool Aquarium also reared young on the ground. In a small aviary, about 1.5m (5ft) square, the hen laid two eggs on the turf floor. Both hatched and the chicks were reared, despite the crowds which visited the Aquarium while the birds were nesting at the height of the holiday season. This was recorded in 1882.

In *Bird Notes* (November 1920), Wesley T. Page wrote that his pair 'burrowed like rats, and frequently I have looked for them in vain in the aviary, only to see their heads peeping out of a burrow. . . . To such an extent did they carry their burrowing propensities that I had to put slate and netting into the ground to prevent their burrowing from one enclosure to another.'

B. R. Hutchins and R. H. Lovell (*Parrot Society Magazine*, August 1974) described a colony of inter-breeding Swainson's and Scaly-breasted Lorikeets belonging to L. Nelson of Gawler, South Australia. Some of these were digging tunnels in the earth for nesting purposes. The resulting hybrids were fertile and 'breeding among themselves.'

I have not seen it recorded elsewhere that captive Swainson's Lorikeets will nest on the ground when the opportunity arises so it is of interest that collation of much published material on the species should draw attention to this fact.

Although there are numerous breeding accounts for this lorikeet, few include dates of chicks hatching and fledging, presumably because it is so frequently bred. In the accounts (judged reliable) where these details have been included, the number of days the young spent in the nest before fledging were as follows: 57, 59, 63, 85, 87, 88 and 89, which shows a variation in the fledging period of over four weeks.

Incubation periods varying from 23 to 26 days have been recorded. A rare instance of three eggs being laid is given by Mrs E. Jones (*Avicultural Magazine*, 1938, p.16).

This species has been bred in many countries throughout the world. In Sweden, Inge Forsberg bred five young in three nests (one was hand-reared) during 1968. J. L. Runkel of Somerset West, South Africa, informed me (April 1975) that he had two pairs, each of which reared an average of three pairs of young each year. Also in South Africa, Dr W. D. Russell's pair reared a number of young which fledged after 58 to 64 days. The incubation period was 25 to 26 days. He found this species the noisiest in his collection of lories. They reared their young in a hollow log with internal measurements of 11½in (30cm) and a height of 28in (70cm).

An Australian aviculturist reported breeding from a remarkably prolific pair which hatched 20 youngsters between 1970 and 1975, 17 of which were reared to maturity.

Swainson's Lorikeets have hybridised with Ornate, Violet-naped, Forsten's, Edwards's, Red-collared, Rosenberg's and Scaly-breasted Lorikeets, also apparently with the Musk Lorikeet and Red and Dusky Lories. A bird shot in the wild was judged to be a hybrid between a Swainson's and a Scaly-breasted. As these two species often flock together this is quite plausible. An Australian aviculturist who paired a male Swainson's with a female Scaly-breast produced a 'most attractive' hybrid. When it matured, at two years old, it was paired to a Swainson's. The resulting young were 'hardly distinguishable' from Swainson's, except in their slightly smaller size.

Northern Blue-bellied Lorikeet (*T.h. septentrionalis*) (Robinson)
Formerly separated from *T.h. moluccanus* by its smaller size and brighter and purer blue of the head and abdomen.
DISTRIBUTION: North-eastern Australia.

Weber's Lorikeet (*T.h. weberi*) (Büttikofer)
DESCRIPTION: Immediately recognisable in that the plumage is of various shades of green with no markings on the upper breast. It could, however, be confused with the Perfect Lorikeet (*T. euteles*) which has the forehead olive yellow. The head, sides of the neck and throat are dark green with brighter green shaft-streaks; the feathers of the forehead are tipped with blue. The nuchal collar is greenish-yellow, also the upper breast, some feathers of which are tipped with dark green. The abdomen and under tail coverts are dark green with some light yellowish-green,

especially on the thighs and abdomen. The remainder of the plumage is dark green, except the under wing coverts which are greenish-yellow and the primaries are blackish with a long yellow patch on the inner webs. The underside of the tail is olive green. The bill and iris are most conspicuously red. This is one of the smallest of the genus, measuring only 23cm (9in).

DISTRIBUTION: The island of Flores. Hartert (1898) mentioned that Everett had collected specimens from the lowlands up to 4,000ft. It is found in rain forests and *Casuarina* stands.

IN AVICULTURE: When a Weber's Lorikeet was received by Mrs Johnstone in the early years of the twentieth century its identification remained a mystery until its death, a few months later. It was sent to David Seth-Smith who was able to identify it on reference to recent literature. Previous to 1898, it was known by one skin only. Mivart (1896) had considered it as a variety of the Perfect Lorikeet. It has never been common in aviculture and appears to have been imported on isolated occasions only.

BREEDING RECORDS: R. Kyme of Kirton, Lincs, was the first breeder in Britain. In July 1969 he obtained four which he had seen in a dealer's establishment and placed them in an aviary 2.4m (8ft) long with a 61cm (2ft) shelter attached. A nest-box measuring 36cm (14in) high and 17cm (6¾in) square (with 9cm (4in) of peat and sawdust on the bottom) was provided.

One of the four died during the winter but two of the others nested, despite the cold, frosty conditions. In late January 1970 two of the birds were spending long periods in the box. It is of interest that three eggs were laid. When the nest was inspected on February 25 there were two chicks with blackish beaks and white down. They lived only three days.

The third bird was then removed and the pair soon nested again. There were two more clutches before the eggs of the third nest were laid on May 20 and 22. Chicks hatched on June 15 and 17. The white down later turned greyish. When the chicks fledged on August 13 and 14 they had been badly plucked on the back and breast by the parents. Apart from this fact they resembled the adult birds except for the beak which was a reddish-brown in one and blackish-red in the other; their size was slightly smaller. They were removed to another aviary on September 25 when they were noticed behaving aggressively towards their parents.

The following food was used for rearing the young: nectar made with 6oz of hot water, one heaped tablespoonful of Horlicks, three teaspoonfuls of baby rice, one of condensed milk and one of honey. Mealworms and maggots were ignored. Spinach beet and sowthistle were eaten and apple was consumed after the chicks fledged.

In 1971 two chicks fledged in September and two more were hatched in December. The pair and young were sold in 1973.

Cherry-red Lorikeet (*T. rubiginosus*) (Bonaparte)

SYNONYMS: Caroline Lorikeet, Ponapé Lorikeet.

DESCRIPTION: This is the most distinctive member of the genus, being almost entirely dark red, except for the flight and tail feathers, which are olive-brown. The feathers of the back and underparts are indistinctly barred with black and the undersides of the wings are black. Length: 24cm (9in).

Cain (1955) believed that its semi-cryptic coloration was due to the fact that there were no bird-eating hawks in its range. 'This suggestion is further strengthened by the lax and downy texture of the contour feathers, which will prevent the bird from flying as fast (in times of crisis) as the other forms.'

DISTRIBUTION: Ponapé, eastern Caroline Islands.

Little is known about the wild life of this species although as long ago as 1881, Dr Finsch wrote about it in *Ibis*. He described it as 'approaching fearlessly the neighbourhood of houses and plundering the fruit-trees, notwithstanding all the means taken to destroy them. They keep mostly in pairs or in small companies of from three to five. . . .'

Forshaw (1973) quotes Coultas: '. . . the nest is in a hollow in the top of a coconut palm or in a large forest tree and only one egg is laid.' It is improbable that one egg forms the usual clutch which, in other *Trichoglossus* species, is normally two.

IN AVICULTURE: Extremely rare. This species was exhibited at Kelling Park Aviaries (Holt, Norfolk) in the 1960s. J. Wilson of Norwich imported one in 1967 or 1968, an abnormally nervous bird.

BREEDING RECORDS: This species was, according to the *International Zoo Year Book*, bred at Kelling Park Aviaries in 1967. In the USA, Los Angeles Zoo reared one in 1970 and another in 1971.

Varying shades of yellow and green predominate in the following members of the genus, which are easily distinguished from the *haematodus* sub-species.

Scaly-breasted Lorikeet (*T. chlorolepidotus*) (Kuhl)

SYNONYM: Gold and Green Lorikeet.

DESCRIPTION: Predominantly a rich, dark green, tinged with blue on the crown, the Scaly-breast is easily recognised by the feathers of the neck and underparts which are yellow, broadly edged with green. The hidden part of some of the feathers of the mantle are also yellow. Close examination reveals bright green shaft-streaking on the head. The hidden part of some of the feathers below the throat is tinged with red. The most striking features—the red under wing coverts and the broad band across the underside of the flights—are seen only when the birds are in flight. The under tail coverts, thighs and lower flanks are light and dark green and the underside of the tail is yellowish. The beak is orange, also the iris which has an inner ring of white. The feet are greyish. Length: 24cm (9½in).

Immature birds have less yellow on the mantle, hind neck and underparts. The bill is brownish.

A blue mutation is being bred in Australia but, I believe, cannot yet be considered established. A coloured slide in my possession shows this mutation to be predominantly dark blue with white markings on the breast.

DISTRIBUTION: North-eastern Australia, as far north as Cooktown, and southwards, following the coastal belt, to Sydney or the Illawarra district of New South Wales. According to Lendon (1973) it also extends westwards from Duaringa and Chinchilla. He commented: 'On the bird watchers' tour of May and June 1970 this species was found to be widely distributed throughout eastern Queensland but did not appear to penetrate as far inland into the drier areas as did the Rainbow Lorikeet.'

Cayley (1938) quoted Miss Florence M. Irby, whose observations are worth repeating: 'In their swiftness and direct manner of flight they remind one of the beautiful Swift Parrakeet. They often fly very high when going to their feeding trees. I have seen large flocks looking no larger than mosquitoes as they speed across the sky, their gladsome screech making them easily recognisable. Often too they may be heard passing at night. How do they know when the trees are flowering? Waking one morning you find they have arrived in hundreds where there was not even a sign of one the evening before.'

The Scaly-breast is a nomad and found wherever there are flowering or fruiting trees or shrubs. Forshaw (1973) lists the blossoms of the following trees as food sources: *Erythrina*, rain trees (*Pithecolobium saman*), silky oats (*Grevillea robusta*), *Banksia serrata* and *Eucalyptus pilularis*. The seeds of *Casuarina* and grass trees (*Xanthorrhoea*) are also eaten. This species is reported to be very fond of sorghum heads and makes itself unpopular by attacking the ripening crops. Together with Swainson's Lorikeets, it is fed at such places as Currumbin (see p. 40) on bread soaked in honey, in much the same way as visitors to London feed the pigeons in Trafalgar Square; the birds are quite fearless and perch on the heads of their human admirers.

This species often nests at a considerable height. Breeding takes place in any month, except March and April, and is dependent upon the rainfall, especially in the northern part of its range.

IN AVICULTURE: It is not known when this species was first imported but it is known that a dealer received a large consignment in 1883. Seth-Smith (1903) stated that it was 'fairly well known among English aviculturists' even although it was not very commonly imported. Like most Australian lories, it is now rare in aviculture, all those available being aviary-bred.

BREEDING RECORDS: An early success was reported in *Notes on Cage Birds* published in 1899. According to 'H. J.', the hen of his pair started to incubate 'about 21st December' (year not given) and the young fledged on February 26 and March 4. If these dates were accurate, the eldest youngster fledged when just over 40 days old—thus there must be some doubt regarding the authenticity of this report. There is little doubt, however, that the Scaly-breast was bred at Berlin Zoo in 1890. The pair was housed in a glass cage, 1m square and 1m (3ft 4in) high, and the hen laid two eggs. Both hatched and the chicks fledged when two months old. In France, P. Soudée bred Scaly-breasts on several occasions, the first being in 1916. In 1926, Decoux reported that his pair had bred five youngsters during the course of a year and had two more in the nest.

The first certain success in Britain occurred at London Zoo in 1943. Two chicks hatched; one died at an early age but the survivor fledged on October 24.

Other breeders are as follows: Dr Osman Hill in Ceylon (in 1944 he recorded that his pair bred twice a year, rearing two young in each brood); W. K. Penney in Plympton, South Australia in 1935—two chicks reared (gaining the medal of the Avicultural Society of South Australia); Adelaide Zoo, 1946, 1973 and 1974, Melbourne and Sydney zoos, 1973 and 1974 and Perth and Summertown zoos in 1973; San Diego Zoo (17 bred up to 1974), Lady Baillie of Leeds Castle, Kent, four in 1972, five in 1973 and three in 1974; Chester Zoo, one in 1966, two in 1967 and two in 1974.

The Scaly-breast has hybridised with a number of *Trichoglossus* species, including the Ornate and Swainson's. At Natal Zoological Gardens, South Africa, a male Forsten's mated with a hybrid Scaly-breast × Forsten's; the latter resembled a Scaly-breast 'except for some orange flecks on the breast and a slight resemblance of the Forsten's collar.' The two youngsters which resulted were green 'with much brighter breasts than their female parent, and light blue heads, very similar to an Edwards's Lorikeet.'

At San Diego Zoo, four hybrids between a male Scaly-breast and a Meyer's were bred between 1971 and 1973. They were described as closely resembling the male but 'somewhat smaller, more plump and, unlike the father, have yellow rather than red under-wing coverts.'

Perfect Lorikeet (*T. euteles*) (Temminck)

SYNONYMS: Plain Lorikeet, Yellow-headed Lorikeet.

DESCRIPTION: This is the only yellow and green lorikeet without any well-defined barring in its plumage. The head is yellow (olive yellow rather than a pure shade) and there is a light green nuchal band. The upper parts are entirely green, although the greenish-yellow of the upper breast extends on to the mantle in some specimens. The abdomen is also greenish-yellow and the under tail coverts are yellow-tinged green. There is a yellow band on the underside of the flight feathers and the underside of the tail is dull yellow. The bill is orange-red and the iris is red. Length: 25cm (10½in). Immature birds are said to have the head more greenish.

DISTRIBUTION: Timor and the Lesser Sunda Islands (from Lomblem east to Nila and Babar). It is said to be common yet there is an almost complete lack of information regarding its habits in the wild.

IN AVICULTURE: The pair deposited at London Zoo in 1896 was probably the first seen alive in Britain. In 1927 the Duke of Bedford described those belonging to J. Spedan Lewis as 'practically new to aviculture' so it would appear that few were imported in the intervening years. Today it is neither common nor rare; a few specimens are occasionally imported. Probably because it lacks the bright colours of other lorikeets, it has never attained any degree of popularity.

BREEDING RECORDS: It would appear that this species was not bred in Britain until 1970. In that year Kenneth Russell of Wisbech was successful so, apparently, was Penscynor Bird Garden in Wales, but, in the latter case, no report was published. Mr Russell purchased two Perfect Lorikeets in about 1965. Four years later he was still uncertain of their sex but the following year eggs were laid, probably by both birds. Mr Russell therefore exchanged one lorikeet with a Perfect belonging to R. Kyme of Boston. At first the hen would not tolerate the newcomer, attacking it persistently. After she was caged in the flight containing the cock, the two birds were compatible.

K. Russell recorded (*Avicultural Magazine* July/August 1971, p. 115): 'Both birds indulge in a display of rolling the body, neck and head in a circular motion, whilst the long tongue is projected from the mouth accompanied by hissing sounds. The cock's display before the hen is characterized by stretching his body in an upright position with bill pressed into the throat feathers, whilst beating his wings rapidly in the manner of a covert pheasant. It is then that the yellow underwing bar is seen.'

The cock was seen feeding the hen but mating was not observed. March 31 was the date on which the first egg was laid; the box was not inspected again during incubation. Young were heard on April 23 but the nest was not inspected until May 27. Much to Mr Russell's surprise, there were *three* well-grown young. They were badly plucked and 'in a wet condition' so a further layer of sawdust was added to the nest. One youngster was removed to give it a chance to feather more quickly and in 24 hours it was taking nectar on its own. The other two young were devoid of feathers on the back and breast when they fledged but were strong on the wing. Their plumage was duller than that of the adults' and the bill was dark. Mr Russell told me that when the young Perfect Lorikeets were nine months old he was surprised to hear the sound of chicks from their nest-box. At this early age, they hatched and reared two healthy youngsters.

This species has been bred with much success at San Diego Zoo. During the period 1972-1973, 17 young were reared. When I visited the zoo in September 1974 and entered the aviary containing young lories of several species, all of them alighted on me to take apple from my hands and the Perfects were the most fearless and persistent of all the youngsters! They had obviously been handreared.

In Sweden, this species was bred by Inge Forsberg in 1968; three young were produced in a total of three nests; one was hand-reared. Birdland, Bourton-on-the-Water, bred the Perfect Lorikeet in 1974. In the USA, Busch Gardens, Tampa, reared two in 1965.

Yellow and Green Lorikeet (*T. flavoviridis flavoviridis*) (Wallace)

SYNONYM: Sula Lorikeet.

DESCRIPTION: The feathers of the head and upper breast are olive yellow, those of the breast being tipped with dark green. The dark green tips become gradually more pronounced, being very prominent on the light green feathers of the abdomen. The ear-coverts, lores, chin and part of the cheeks are dusky green and the nuchal collar is brownish. The upper parts are dark green, the under wing coverts yellowish-green; the feathers of the under tail coverts and the vent are yellowish-green with darker margins. The underside of the tail is yellow. The bill and iris are orange and the legs are grey. Length: 21cm (8½in).

Immature birds are said to have the yellow markings more greenish.

DISTRIBUTION: Sula Islands, Indonesia.

IN AVICULTURE: The first importation of this species into Britain was probably made in 1931 by W. Frost. It is an extremely rare bird in aviculture, virtually unknown. In September 1974, W. Vandevijer, sent me an excellent photograph of two of these birds which belonged to an aviculturist in France. They were sent to him by a friend who was staying in Borneo.

Meyer's Lorikeet (*T. f. meyeri*) (Walden)

SYNONYM: Lory of Bonthain.*

DESCRIPTION: The crown is olive brown, tinged with golden on the forehead in males; the cheeks, lores and throat are brownish-green, each feather bordered with yellow to give a narrowly scalloped effect. There is a bright yellow patch on the ear coverts which is brighter in the males in my breeding pairs. The upper parts, including the nape, are dark green, with some greenish-yellow feathers on the mantle in some individuals. The nuchal band is absent. The under surface of the body is green and greenish-yellow, each feather bordered with dark green; the abdomen and under tail coverts are more greenish than yellowish. The flights are dark grey on the underside. The tail is green, the lateral feathers having the inner webs and the underside yellowish. The bill is orange-red and the iris cherry red. Length: 17cm (6¾in).

Immature birds have the head more yellow and the yellow and green on the breast less well defined.

DISTRIBUTION: Celebes, Indonesia. It inhabits dense mountain forest between 500m and 2,000m. Along the forest edges it associates with the Ornate Lorikeet which replaces it in the lowlands. A shy species, the Meyer's Lorikeet keeps to thick foliage where it is difficult to detect when quiet. It has been observed in flocks of between 30 and 40 birds.

IN AVICULTURE: This lorikeet appears to have been unknown in England until the early 1960s when a pair was exhibited at Kelling Park Aviaries in Norfolk under the name of 'Lory of Bonthain.' It did not appear on the English avicultural scene again until July 1973 when Mrs S. Belford informed me that she had received some small lories from Singapore which she was unable to identify. On seeing them I realised that they were *meyeri* and, visualising how attractive they would look in a small colony, bought all nine. At the same time at least two more pairs were received by dealers, one of whom was optimistically offering his pair at £150! Since that time a few more pairs have been imported into England.

---

*Originally named as a separate species, *P. bonthainensis*, from southern Celebes, it supposedly differed from *meyeri* in the following respects: (1) The yellow on the ear coverts was less apparent and not so sharply separated from the green of the neck; (2) the green on the back of the neck was brighter, forming a collar; (3) throat, cheeks and side of the neck not undulated with reddish-yellow but more bluish-green, the undersides of these feathers being blue not yellow; (4) broad green bands on the underparts; (5) wings more blackish beneath; (6) yellow on lower back less apparent.

It is seldom that one can keep a truly amicable colony of parrots of any kind but the Meyer's agreed well together and looked most attractive. When they started to breed, there was a certain amount of squabbling. After two and a half years the fighting was, at times, so fierce, that rather than risk losing the surplus males, the colony was split up. Every night the Meyer's had retired to a row of six nest-boxes made from one length of wood. Any disturbance would cause a little head to appear at each hole. Despite the thick wood used in the construction of the 'terraced' boxes, the Meyer's gnawed to such an extent that most of them could be reached from the adjoining box. I was rather puzzled by the comings and goings from the various holes until I discovered this!

BREEDING RECORDS: San Diego Zoo was the first to breed this species.* From a female received in 1969 and a male received in 1972, two chicks were hatched in April 1973; one died at 17 days and the other was reared. Four more were bred that year; hatching dates were August 22 and 23 and December 9 and 10. In 1974 two were reared; one hatched on April 11 and two on August 16. One of the latter died; I saw the other, aged 20 days, in the Zoo's incubator; it was reared by hand. In less than two years, two pairs at San Diego hatched 14 chicks, 12 of which were reared. Four of these went to Busch Gardens, Tampa, Florida.

My own colony of Meyer's disappointed me in the summer of 1974, when they had been in my possession for a year, by making no attempt to breed. It would appear that they were not sufficiently mature for, in December, breeding activities started. By Boxing Day, one hen had been missing for several days. Investigation revealed that she was incubating two eggs. She seemed rather nervous after I had looked into the nest so I resolved not to do so again. Any unusual activity near the aviary, which was the end one of a row and bordered by a narrow path, would bring the male—who spent much time in the nest—or the male and female from the box.

While she was incubating the weather was very mild and there was much displaying and nest investigation by the other members of the colony. It was not unusual to hear them squabbling and on one occasion, two or three fell to the ground locked together like a bunch of sparrows!

On January 18 I heard the cheeping of a chick from the Meyer's nest and heard it almost daily for the next three weeks. On February 9 I noticed that both parents spent a lot of time away from the nest, which was very unusual. By the next day it was obvious that they had deserted. Inspection revealed one dead chick, sparsely covered in longish white down.

On March 1 there was one egg in the nest. Presumably two were laid; the nest was not inspected again. On March 29 I noticed half of the shell of a hatched egg on the aviary floor but did not hear a chick until a couple of days later. The weather at the time was very wintery, with daily showers of snow, sleet, rain *and* hail. The chick lived until April 27. Meanwhile, a second pair had been incubating and chicks were heard on May 23; both died on May 31. Examinations carried out on the three chicks revealed no discernible cause of death in two and fatty degeneration of the liver in one from the second nest. Both the latter had food in their crops at the time of death.

*I have been informed this species was bred in Denmark in 1959.

The next two chicks had hatched by June 10. Unlike the others, they were seldom heard calling for food. One died on June 21 and autopsy revealed fatty degeneration again. There was food in its crop but none in the crop of the second chick which died from no discernible cause on June 23. Both these chicks seemed poorly developed in comparison with those from previous nests.

After the death of the first three chicks I had used a less rich nectar, in case the nectar was causing fatty degeneration of the liver. The birds also received soaked millet sprays, apple and sunflower seed but it had become obvious that no chicks would be reared on this diet and the Meyer's could not be persuaded to take any other foods.

In 1976 the birds again started to breed early in the year—this time in separate but very small enclosures. While still in the original aviary, one hen had laid two eggs by January 11 which were later found to be infertile. The pair was moved to a small aviary about 60cm (2ft) from the original enclosure and had laid a second clutch by March 17—but the eggs did not hatch. There was a third clutch in April which was also unsuccessful. At the beginning of June a fourth clutch was laid and a chick was removed for hand-rearing but died soon after.

The first pair to be moved to a separate enclosure (at the end of December) had laid by the middle of January. A chick was heard on February 7 and on the 15 the nest-box was raided to remove the two chicks for hand-rearing. This was success-fully carried out and a full account is given in the chapter on hand-rearing.

The pair laid again in March and a chick was heard in the nest on April 12. Because my husband and I were going away for 18 days, removal of the two chicks for hand-rearing was not possible and they died when a little over two weeks old. In the third nest, which hatched during May, the chicks died at a very early age, before they were one week old. Several more clutches were laid during 1976 but no more chicks were hatched. One pair laid as late as October, after moulting.

Mount Apo Lorikeet (*T. johnstoniae*) (Hartert)

SYNONYM: Mrs Johnstone's Lorikeet.

DESCRIPTION: This species is easily recognised by the delicate deep pink of the forehead, throat and the forepart of the cheeks. There is a broad stripe of brownish-maroon from the lores, extending behind the eye (said to be more pronounced in the male). The ear coverts are greenish-yellow; the feathers of the underparts are yellow, bordered with green, the green edges being broader on the upper breast and decreasing gradually so that the abdomen is more yellow than green. The under tail coverts are greenish-yellow, also the underside of the tail. The underwing coverts are yellowish-green, greener towards the edge of the wing; the first primary feather is black and all but the first three have a large yellow patch on the middle of the inner webs. All the upper parts are green. The beak is orange and the feet and the skin around the eye are bluish. Length: 16cm (6½in).

In the account of the successful breeding which occurred at San Diego Zoo (*Zoonooz*, September 1972) it states: 'Scattered over the breast are small, rusty orange spots, much more pronounced in juvenile males. This difference in colouring between the sexes also is noted in the adults, but to a lesser degree. In lories and lorikeets, the male usually has a larger head and they can be sexed in that manner before they have fledged.'

Mrs Johnstone described the immature birds she bred as having the beak black and the narrow periorbital ring white. The maroon eye stripe was less clearly defined at the back of the head.

DISTRIBUTION: Mount Apo, south-east Mindanao, Philippines. Walter Goodfellow, who found and collected this species, stated that it inhabited altitudes between 4,000ft and 8,000ft, descending to lower areas to roost. He discovered it in 1903 on the Apo Volcano which falls away in forest-covered slopes to the sea. His first sighting was of a flock of 30 birds. The Bagobo natives called them 'lish-lish' after their call note.

Goodfellow acquired several of these attractive little birds, which quickly became tame. They fought among themselves when they came into breeding condition. He wrote: 'At this time they added a sweet warbling love song to their usual calls, and their love dance was really amusing if somewhat absurd. At these times the males swayed backwards and forwards on the perches with all feathers ruffled, and uttered a blowing noise.' Several eggs were laid by these birds.

IN AVICULTURE: Very rare; the only specimens seen in Britain in recent years were two at Kelling Pines Aviaries, Norfolk, from 1966. In November 1905, three of Goodfellow's birds reached Mrs Johnstone. The following February a female had to be removed when it was chased by the pair which were in breeding condition; later, however, the male preferred the female which had been housed in an adjoining aviary and these birds took possession of a nest-box which measured 18cm (7in)×25cm (10in) high, with a coconut husk at the bottom. Both birds spent much time in the nest which was eventually found to contain two 'bare red bodies with large beaks.' The birds fed mainly on spray millet and sweetened bread and milk with half an orange daily. After the young fledged the nest was found to contain twigs of fir with needles attached and chewed up coconut fibres.

It would appear that this species was not bred again until 1941, in which year two were hatched at San Diego Zoo. The Mount Apo did not breed there again until 1971. Between December 1 and July 7 1972 ten chicks were hatched. Most or all of these were hand-reared by keeper Roby Hewitt. He had reared 35–40 species of Parrots in this way yet remarked: 'When they are small, Mount Apo Lorikeets eat more than any of the other hatchling parrots we have had in the brooder this season.' (*Zoonooz*, September 1972). They were fed only three times daily: at 6.30am, 11.30am and 3pm. At one month of age they were offered the standard lory diet—a mixture of chopped fruits, raisins, lettuce, Karo corn syrup, condensed milk and water. At that age grey down still remained on the rump, tops of the wings and back of the neck.

The incubation period was recorded as being 23 days. From the information supplied by Kenton Lint, Curator of Birds, it is apparent that hatchability was very high. In eight clutches, laid between November 1971 and March 1973, all eggs hatched, in seven cases on consecutive days. (I am not aware whether there were unsuccessful clutches which were not recorded). Of 18 chicks hatched between December 1971 and October 1973, eight lived for six months or more and four died when under three weeks old. In 1974 two more were reared.

T. j. pistra (Rand and Rabor)
Doubtfully distinct from *T.j. johnstoniae*.
Said to have the forehead and face a deeper, duller red and the stripe from the lores to behind the eyes dark blue-brown. The upper parts are said to be slightly darker and the yellow of the underparts slightly more vivid.
DISTRIBUTION: Mount Malindang, western Mindanao.

A guide to the identification of the subspecies of *Trichoglossus haematodus*

Subspecies	Head	Nuchal band	Upper breast	Abdomen	Remarks
T.h. haematodus	Blue with lighter shaft-streaking; throat blackish-blue	Greenish-yellow	Bright red with purplish-black edges to the feathers	Green in centre; feathers of lower abdomen edged green	
T.h. mitchellii	Dark chestnut-brown with grey-green shaft-streaking on crown and cheeks	Greenish-yellow	♂ almost pure red ♀ yellow edges to most of the feathers	Purplish-black	
T.h. forsteni	Dark purplish streaked with violet-blue	Greenish-yellow with dark purple on hind-neck	Scarlet	Dark mauve or purple	
T.h. stresemanni	Dark purplish streaked with violet-blue	Greenish-yellow with dark purple on hind-neck	More orange than *forsteni* —feathers red at base and often almost yellow at tip	Mauvish-black	Yellow bases to the feathers of the mantle. Yellow of plumage more greenish, with less purple gloss than *djampeanus*
T.h. djampeanus	Dark brown with violet sheen, streaked with blue on forehead and to lesser extent on cheeks	Light greenish-yellow with violet-black on hind-neck	Scarlet	Mauvish-black	
T.h. capistratus	Dark blue with shaft-	Yellow or	Yellow—red-tipped feathers	Dark green	
T.h. flavotectus	,, ,,	,, ,,	Paler yellow than in *capistratus*	Dark green	No orange on under wing coverts
T.h. fortis	Violet-blue shaft-streaking on forehead and to lesser extent on cheeks	Green	Yellow, washed with deep orange in some specimens	Blackish-green	
T.h. weberi	Dark green with brighter green shaft streaks. Feathers of forehead tipped with blue	Greenish-yellow	Greenish-yellow feathers tipped with dark green	Dark green	

Subspecies	Head	Nuchal band	Upper breast	Abdomen	Remarks
T.h. capistratus	Dark blue with shaft-streaks of almost the same colour	Yellow or greenish-yellow	Yellow—red-tipped feathers probably denote male and green-tipped female	Dark green	
T.h. flavotectus	" " "	" "	Paler yellow than in capistratus;	Dark green	No orange on under wing coverts
T.h. rosenbergii	" " "	Widest of entire genus—yellow followed by dull reddish band	Brilliant red feathers—broadly tipped with blue-black	Dark purplish-blue	Strong purplish gloss on nape*, throat, chin and breast bars
T.h. intermedius	As for capistratus but with cheeks blackish and ear coverts dark blue	Yellowish-green following area of brown-streaked olive	Red feathers tipped with black	Dark green	Nape* brownish
T.h. micropteryx	" " "	Slightly more greenish than intermedius	As above but black bars narrower and red slightly paler	Dark green	General plumage more free from black and paler than in intermedius; nape* brownish
T.h. berauensis	" " "	Clear yellow	Salmon-red with heavy black barring	Dark green	Nape* black; more black throughout than intermedius
T.h. massena	As for micropteryx but with the back of the head green	Yellowish-green	Slightly paler than in micropteryx	Dark green, lower abdomen greenish-yellow	Nape *rich brown
T.h. deplanchii	Bluer than massena; less brown on back of head and nape	Yellowish-green	" " "	" "	Less brown on nape than in massena
T.h. nigrogularis	Blue on the forehead and cheeks; green on the back of the head; throat purple	Yellowish-green	The red feathers have an orange tinge near the black edges	Blackish or purple-black	

Subspecies	Head	Nuchal band	Upper breast	Abdomen	Remarks
T.h. flavicans	Forehead, lores and area around eyes violet-blue; rest of head black with purple gloss; shaft streaking greyish-green	Yellow; narrow red-brown pre-torqual band	Pure, brilliant red with very narrow black edges to the feathers or none at all	Green tinged with dark purple	Differs from *flavicans* in having upper parts, under tail coverts and tail green, not olive or bronzy yellow
T.h. nesophilus	,, ,,	,, ,,	,, ,, ,,	,, ,,	
T.h. rubritorquis	Head and throat blue	Orange-red	Orange-red—no barring	Very dark green	
T.h. moluccanus	Violet-blue with shaft-streaking of the same colour	Greenish-yellow	Red and yellow—no black barring	Deep violet	*The area of the nape following the nuchal band

I I

Glossopsitta

Genus: *Glossopsitta* (Bonaparte)

See Note on Classification (p. xi).
The members of this genus are small, 15–22cm (6–9in) with the beak black, red and black, or orange. The crown and forehead is red, with the exception of the Purple-crowned Lorikeet, in which only the forehead is red. The central feathers of the wedge-shaped tail are pointed. Sexual dimorphism is slight (*concinna, iris* and *versicolor*) or absent.

A characteristic of the display which has not been observed in any other genus is that both birds sway away from each other in a circular fashion as though their feet were anchored to the spot. They also bob up and down rapidly.

Varied Lorikeet (*G. versicolor*) (Lear)

SYNONYMS: Red-capped Lorikeet, Red-crowned Lorikeet.
DESCRIPTION: The forehead, crown and lores are scarlet; the throat, cheeks and the back of the head are greyish-blue streaked with yellow and the ear coverts are yellow. The entire underparts are longitudinally streaked with yellow, the upper breast being vinous and the lower breast and abdomen light green. The upper parts are green streaked with greenish-yellow. The tail is green, the lateral feathers margined with yellow on the inner webs. There is a conspicuous area of *white* skin surrounding the eye. The beak is ochre-red and the iris is yellow. Length: 19cm (7in).

According to Forshaw (1973), the red of the head is 'duller and less extensive in females' which have the vinous upper breast 'duller and less pronounced.' Boosey (the first breeder of this species) had a number and found them 'very difficult indeed to sex.'

South African aviculturist Peter Oderkerken, who spent some time in Australia, informed me of the Varied Lorikeets he kept there: 'The cock had a black pupil with a thin brown ring and then an orange yellow ring; the hen had a black pupil, the rest of the eye being brown. The cock was overall darker in colour than the hen; he had a larger and darker red cap. His ear patch was more prominent as were his yellow streaks. The dull dark grey-blue throat and cheek patch were a lot lighter in the hen; the mauve upper breast was much darker in the cock.'

DISTRIBUTION: Tropical northern Australia from the Kimberley division of Western Australia, Northern Territory to the coast of north-east Queensland.

Well over 100 years ago this species was seen in immense flocks. Gould quoted

Gilbert to the effect that 'When a flock is on the wing their movements are so regular and simultaneous that they might easily be mistaken for a cloud passing along, were it not for the utterance of their usual piercing scream, which is frequently so loud as to be deafening.'

Forshaw (1973) states: 'They are common in most types of wooded country wherever there are flowering or fruiting trees and shrubs, but are especially attracted to paperbarks (*Melaleuca* spp) and eucalypts lining streams or surrounding waterholes. Along the east coast of Cape York Peninsula, the north-eastern extremity of the range, they are uncommon visitors and may not arrive even although there is a wide-spread flowering of trees. Elsewhere they are nomadic, the movements being governed by the availability of blossom.'

They are found in small parties or immense flocks, often associating with Red-collared Lorikeets. Forshaw states that they are aggressive when feeding, driving away other nectar-feeders such as honeyeaters.

IN AVICULTURE: The first record of this species in captivity refers to the eight or nine pairs received by the London dealer Hamlyn in 1902. W. T. Page obtained a pair in 1904; the hen died in 1910 and the cock was sold in 1912 and lived for at least another two years. Page described these birds as being 'as hardy and accommodating as the Cockatiel.' From the early years of the century until Australia prohibited the export of its native fauna, it was fairly often imported. In 1948, A. Martin commented (*Foreign Birds*, May 1948): '... although imported in small numbers fairly frequently before the war, it was never very common.' He found that, unlike other lorikeets, they disliked cold and 'had to be brought inside for the winter months.' There are conflicting views on this aspect of the Varied Lorikeet. E. J. Boosey described them as hardier than the Swainson's Lorikeet—a species noted for its hardiness. However, the Australian Cayley (1938) believed that they were 'By no means easy to keep in captivity, being very susceptible to cold.'

Today the Varied Lorikeet would appear to be unknown in aviculture outside Australia and New Zealand with the exception of the pair sent to Chester Zoo in 1975. Taronga Zoo listed this species in its inventory for June 30 1973 but has yet to breed it. Peter Oderkerken supplied me with some notes on the unusual behaviour of his pair. 'They liked to lie along a branch, stretched out with one wing on one side of the branch and their head on the other; once I noticed them like this for ten minutes. From this stretched-out position they propelled themselves along the branch with their feet, keeping their breast on the perch and moving the head from side to side.

'They were quieter than the Musks and were quite aggressive. I saw the cock court once or twice; this took place after a heavy rainfall, which I believe stimulated him. It consisted of the usual lorikeet performance. In the north of Australia they breed after the monsoons and I believe the rain was the stimulus in captivity.'

BREEDING RECORDS: The first recorded breeding took place in 1936 at Keston Foreign Bird Farm in England. A chick or chicks were heard in the nest in December 1935—then the sound ceased. The hen laid again and in March a chick was hatched; it fledged in the middle of May. The rearing food consisted of 'ordinary lorikeet nectar and sweetened stewed apple.'

In Australia the Varied Lorikeet was not bred until 1949. A pair which had been in the possession of C. J. Lambert of Horsley, Sydney, nested in September. The eggs were laid on the 16th and 18th; they were incubated by the hen for 22 days. The chicks fledged on November 16 (ie, at 37 and 39 days old) and were independent three weeks later. The foods offered were Weetbix, milk, sugar, honey, apple and thistle. Both parents fed the young. One had a black beak, the other a pinkish beak; they proved to be a male and female respectively.

J. L. Mitchell of the Adelaide suburb of Marion bred this species in 1965. Three years previously he had obtained twelve, with the intention of keeping them in a colony. The aviary in which they were housed measured 4.9m (16ft) × 3m (10ft) × 2.1m (7ft), with a shelter 1.8m (6ft) long. Although a dozen logs were provided, the birds made no attempt to nest until the third year, when two hens produced clutches of four eggs. All the eggs were fertile but the only chick to hatch died after a few hours in the bleak July winter. All the other chicks died in the shell.

In *Birdkeeping in Australia* (Vol. 9, No. 2, February 1966) Mitchell recorded that there were numerous instances of interference and fighting. 'On one occasion an inquisitive bird entered the log of one of the breeding pairs and was promptly torn to pieces. The male bird of another pair seemed to be just as interested in another hen, in fact, more so whilst his mate was sitting and soon afterwards it was noticed that his other hen friend was trying to get into the same log. He did not try to stop her and she often succeeded in getting inside, whereupon the sitting hen would leave her eggs and push her out immediately.'

Because of this behaviour, all birds but the breeding pair were removed from the aviary. Four eggs were laid and one chick hatched on September 29. It left the log on November 10, at the age of 43 days and was completely independent one week later. It was a male, as bright—if not brighter—in colour as the hen—'the only real difference being much less red on the head.'

The nesting log used was 91cm (3ft) in length and approximately 23cm (9in) in diameter. It was hung at an angle of approximately 45° and at about 1.5m (5ft) from the ground. The food offered consisted of apples, bread and milk sweetened with sugar, occasionally with honey, and pears and flowering gum branches, when available. The apples were relished but little interest was shown in the pears.

In display both birds made a 'Zrr-zrr' sound and bobbed up and down on the perch, continually swaying away from each other in a circular fashion 'as if their feet were anchored to the spot.'

Also in Australia, Adelaide Zoo reared two Varied Lorikeets in 1972 and one in 1973. D. Coles, familiar with the birds there, stated (*Cage and Aviary Birds*, December 9 1976): 'Sexual dimorphism was well marked in the breeding pair and remaining individuals were easily sexed by the amount of mauve on the chest.'

Iris Lorikeet (*G. iris iris*) (Temminck)

DESCRIPTION: Immediately recognisable by the scarlet forehead and crown and violet ear coverts and the salmon-pink feathers of the throat and at the side of the lower mandible. The underparts are yellowish-green, the tips of the feathers distinctly edged with dark green. The under tail coverts are green and the underside of the tail is yellow and green. There is a light yellowish-green nuchal band, the rest of the upper parts being dark green.

The beak is yellowish-orange and the iris is orange or brown with an inner ring of white. Length: 20cm (8in).

Immature birds have the beak black in the nest and brownish on fledging. The barred markings on the breast are less well defined.

The sexes are generally described as being alike. In the male of the four breeding pairs with which I am familiar the breast barring is much more prominent than in the female and the mauve ear coverts are larger. Also, the head is much bolder. The crown colouring differs in individuals and the evidence so far suggested by taxonomists for separating three races appears to be confusing. From my own observations it would seem that there are two phases of *G. iris*, one in which there is sexual dimorphism of the crown colour and one in which the crown colour is identical in male and female. The birds which suggest this theory are fully adult, thus there is no possibility that immature plumage is confusing the issue.

Forshaw (1973) states of the nominate race: 'forehead, forecrown and behind eye orange-red: in female forecrown is green variably marked with red . . . occiput grey-blue; cheek patches green, more yellowish in female . . .'. However, when describing *rubripileum* he states: 'hindcrown red, sometimes slightly tinged with green . . . sides of head light yellowish-green'—but is this description to apply to male and female. Does Forshaw imply there is no sexual dimorphism in this race?

In one breeding pair in my possession and in the pair at San Diego Zoo, the forehead of the male is scarlet, also part of the crown, which merges into green (the feathers having red bases); this area is followed by the yellow-green nuchal band.

It is of interest that the male bred by the pair in my possession in which the crown colouring is identical, had the crown mauve in nest feather. At a partial moult, which occurred when it was four months old, the only area in which the feathers were renewed, the mauve feathers were replaced by green ones. From this evidence one might be led to believe that the mauve crown is a feature of immature plumage in this species but this is not so.

In my original pair, the first youngster reared, lacked the mauve crown of its father in nest feather, when the crown markings were similar to that of the female parent, but not as bright. After the first moult, I noted that it had a mauve tinge to the crown. It is likely, but not certain, that its parents were hand-reared birds from the same nest, or at least from the same area, ie, they are of the same subspecies.

In view of the above I am doubtful of the validity of the races *rubripileum* and *wetterensis*.

DISTRIBUTION: Western Timor, Indonesia.

IN AVICULTURE: West Berlin Zoo apparently exhibited this species as long ago as 1932. It was first imported into Britain in 1939, in a collection made by Frost and Shaw Mayer and may not have been imported again until the latter part of

1971 when Mrs S. Belford imported a pair from a Singapore dealer. Soon after, I looked after them while she visited Singapore—and have them still! They are among the most popular birds in my collection with visitors. So delightfully tame are they that it is difficult to pass their aviary without stopping; and so jealous is each bird of any attention bestowed on the other, that this invariably leads to them fighting. The cock will jump on to the hen and the two birds will roll over and over, chattering excitedly.

Two advantages of these little lories is that they are not noisy and they do not require a large aviary. A second pair are quite destructive, considering their small size, and their beaks are extremely strong. Three weeks after being placed in an aviary containing a very hard log, they had gnawed at least an inch deep, working systematically at one point. The first pair, however, have gnawed only at the inside of their nest-box.

The first pair are embarrassingly tame, so their aviary is very seldom entered. On one occasion when I ventured inside, the hen flew on to my head and the cock on to my shoulder. My husband was more amused than I when the hen bit my ear until the blood ran! She can be relied upon to nip fingers offered by un-suspecting visitors.

One has to be very quick indeed on opening the feeding hatch because of the speed with which she can reach it; once she was speedier than I imagined possible and before I realised it, she was out of the hatch. Fortunately, she was far more interested in sampling my finger than in tasting liberty! When one realises that this little bird is badly crippled, her speed is amazing. She was unfortunately bitten by another parrot before coming into my possession; one foot is badly twisted and there is a toe missing on each foot. This causes her much discomfort in damp weather, when she appears to have arthritis in the badly crippled foot. Despite this, she is the keenest bather I have ever encountered and will plunge into a dish of fresh water quite regardless of the temperature and, perhaps, of the presence of snow outside the aviary.

During the middle part of 1972, a dealer in England received from Singapore a consignment of Iris Lorikeets, probably numbering as many as 40. A chance visit in October revealed that the tail end of the consignment, consisting of three birds, remained. He was anxious to sell them as they had been caged and were in very poor condition. Partly because of their sad plight, also because I was keen to obtain more Iris Lorikeets, to have a better opportunity to breed from them, I bought the three, although one was obviously dying. It lived only four days, and it was many months before the remaining two were really fit and had replaced their missing tail and flight feathers.

A greater contrast—not only in feather but also in temperament—with my tame pair could not be imagined. It was not until three years later, when the second pair was placed in a very small aviary close to the house, that they became tame enough to allow a close approach. After I had had them nine months they were in fit condition to house in an outdoor aviary and they then had to share an en-closure with the colony of Meyer's Lorikeets. As they were inclined to bully the latter, they were moved at the onset of the next breeding season, to a very mixed aviary. Here they ignored and were ignored by their larger companions—an ancient pair of Cockatiels (*Nymphicus hollandicus*), a very old Ringneck Parrakeet (*Psittacula krameri manillensis*), a Purple-bellied Parrot (*Triclaria malachitacea*) and a male Red-capped Parrot (*Pionopsitta pileata*). They occupied a nest-box for roosting and for long periods during the day—but no eggs were laid. The male was observed from a distance displaying, on several occasions; it was too shy to do so while obviously under observation.

The display of this species is similar to that described by Mitchell for the Varied Lorikeet (see p. 105).

BREEDING RECORDS: This species was first bred in San Diego Zoo. A male was received from Singapore in November 1968 and a female in June 1970. They nested almost immediately and two chicks were hatched on August 11. One died on September 2 and the other was reared. The pair bred again in 1972; two chicks hatched on March 26, one of which was successfully reared. The other died on May 31.

In Britain, the first breeder was R. Kyme of Boston. His pair was housed in an aviary measuring 2.4m (8ft)×91cm (3ft)×1.8m (6ft) high. A natural log was immediately accepted and was inspected daily by their owner when they were seen to mate. Eggs were laid on June 28 and July 1 1973 and one hatched on July 23. The chick died on August 21. No further nesting attempt was made that year.

In 1974, eggs were laid on May 4 and 6; chicks hatched on May 27 and 29, giving a certain incubation period of 23 days. In addition to the normal diet (nectar made from Farex, condensed milk, honey, B_{12} yeast mixture and water, also sunflower seed, apple and spinach beet) the parents consumed huge amounts of raspberries while the chicks were in the nest. They fledged on August 2, when 65 and 67 days old. They had been plucked by their parents but soon feathered up and were then described as 'smaller, duller editions of their parents, with black beaks.' Unfortunately, the female parent died during the winter.

In 1973, 1974 and 1975 my first pair nested—but without success. On April 25 1973 I noticed that the hen was limping and looked unwell. As the weather was damp, apparently causing the hen's crippled foot to bother her, I caught her up and took her into the house. At 10.40pm I entered the birdroom to dim the light, and had a good look at the hen Iris. As I did so, I was surprised to see her lay an egg. In a few days, during which no more eggs were laid, I was able to return her to the aviary. At the end of June she laid in a small Budgerigar nest-box but ceased to incubate just before the eggs were due to hatch. Several clutches were laid during 1974 and, on one occasion, I picked up a fertile egg from the aviary floor.

In 1975 the hen laid her first egg on about May 20 and on June 11 something about the behaviour of the pair made me suspect that a chick had hatched; this was not confirmed until three days later when a chick was heard. I was fairly confident that the chick would be reared because, as is common with very tame birds, these Iris Lorikeets will sample all foods offered and habitually take a wide variety of items. I was particularly interested to note that there was a steep *decline* in nectar consumption from the time the chick hatched.

The pair consumed mainly seed while the chick was in the nest, also fruit and soft foods. The seeds taken included sunflower, canary, white millet, niger and spray millet. The latter was soaked for at least 48 hours, until it had begun to sprout, and was then washed. However, it was discontinued when the chick was four weeks old and the male unfortunately became ill. He was removed from the aviary on July 8 and ate nothing at all that day despite attempts to tempt him with favourite tit-bits. At 11 pm I force-fed him with nectar and Horlick's; as this bird is so tame, it caused him no stress. The following day his condition had deteriorated; I noted with a sinking heart that he was vomiting, something which is far from easy to cure in lories. I therefore added the antibiotic powder chloramphenicol to the nectar with which I force-fed him. This was continued for the next two days until he was strong enough to object to force-feeding.

Three days later, before the male was returned to the aviary, I failed to hear the usual loud cries of the chick. Examination of the nest-box showed that it had died and autopsy revealed that there had been haemorrhage of the head so I could only conclude that the female had caused this injury. At the time of its death, at approximately five weeks old, its crop was full and it weighed as much as an adult. Its beak was black. The green feathers of the back and wings had been chewed by the hen; I had examined the chick for the first time when the male was removed from the aviary and it then had more feathers than at the time of its death. Greenish-yellow feathers were appearing on the underparts and orange feathers on the crown. The male was returned when the dead chick was removed but the pair made no further attempt to nest that year.

In 1976 the female laid at the end of May and I heard the sounds of a chick being fed on June 26. At last this pair's endeavours met with success. The young bird fledged on August 21 when it was considerably smaller than its parents and had been plucked on the nape of the neck.

In 1975 I obtained two Iris Lorikeets from separate sources during June. What soon proved to be a female had previously been kept for about three years with a bird which, on autopsy, was found to be a male, yet the pair had never attempted to breed. I had once watched them displaying on the floor of their aviary, alternately jumping into the air. When this female was introduced to the male which I managed to obtain, I was gratified to see that the two birds were more than just compatible: it was definitely a case of avian love at first sight.

They were placed in a small outdoor aviary at the end of August and mating was observed four weeks later. Eggs were laid during October and on November 13 I heard a chick. That night there was freezing fog and the temperature fell to 29°F. (−2°C.). Next day two chicks could be heard. The young were being fed on a variety of foods: sponge cake soaked in nectar, apple, grapes, spray millet, sunflower seed and a biscuit-based softfood.

On November 23 both adults were sitting in the aviary preening during the early morning—an indication that the chicks had died. On taking down the nest-box, I was surprised at the size of the dead chicks. That and the development of the feather tracts indicated that they were about 20 days old. With a known incubation period of 23 days, this perfectly agreed with the date I believed incubation commenced, thus the eldest chick was ten days old before I was aware of its existence. (The aviculturist who must work for his or her living is at a disadvantage during the winter months because of the very limited amount of time which can be spent with the birds.)

An autopsy on one chick revealed that it had a chill on the liver and kidneys; it would appear that at three weeks old, with a body weight half that of an adult, the chicks were too large for the hen to brood properly and they therefore became chilled.

The female laid again during January and two chicks were hatched during very cold weather in February. When aged six and eight days they were removed from the nest for hand-rearing (see p. 33). The next clutch was laid during April. A chick hatched during the early part of May and was successfully hand-reared. Three more clutches were laid that year, the last during November.

Unlike the tame pair of Iris, the female of which has laid only between May and September, this pair nest continuously at intervals of between two and three months.

In South Africa Dr W. D. Russell's pair hatched two chicks in their first nest in 1976, which died between three and ten days after hatching. In the second nest one chick died on the third day; the other was reared and left the nest when 65 days old.

Ruby-capped Lorikeet (*G.i. rubripileum*) (Salvadori)

DESCRIPTION: According to Salvadori, it differs from the nominate race in having the 'hindcrown red, sometimes slightly tinged with green; band on hindneck violet-blue; sides of head light yellowish-green.'
DISTRIBUTION: Eastern Timor, Indonesia.

Wetar Lorikeet (*G.i. wetterensis*) (Hellmayr)

DESCRIPTION: According to Hellmayr (1912), it differs from the nominate race in having the cheeks pale grass-green, instead of yellowish-green, also in the bill which was said to be 'more robust'. In his description of the type bird, Hartert (1924) stated: 'The alleged more powerful bill can be of no importance as the bills are not larger in our single specimen of *N.* *iris iris*. The type is not well selected, as its crown and nape are exceptionally almost without the purplish blue wash which is usual in *N.i. wetterensis* as well as in *N.i. iris*.'
DISTRIBUTION: Wetar Island.

Goldie's Lorikeet (*G. goldiei*) (Sharpe)

DESCRIPTION: The forehead and the crown are scarlet and the cheeks and ear coverts are vinous-purple with dark blue and black streaks. The upper parts are dark green, the neck being streaked with light green and the mantle tinged with brown. The underparts are greenish-yellow, streaked longitudinally with dark green. There is a dull olive-yellow spot on the inner web of the flight feathers

*Then classified as *Neopsittacus*.

and the under wing coverts are yellowish-green. The beak is black, distinguishing this species at a glance from the Varied Lorikeet. Length: 19cm (7in).

Sexual dimorphism, if it exists, must be very slight. The red of the forehead has been described as duller and less extensive in the female. Rand and Gilliard (1967) gave a single description for the adult and Salvadori (1891) described the male, also the 'female or immature bird.' Of the three birds at Chicago Zoo in the 1950s, two of which reared young, Karl Plath, Curator of Birds, stated: 'The difference, if any, is too slight to distinguish them apart.'

Rothschild and Hartert (1901) stated: 'The female does not differ from the male except in being slightly smaller—wing about 5mm shorter. The birds in which the crown is purplish-brown and the red confined to the forehead are immature. The purplish striped occipital band is more or less developed in the series before us, irrespective of sex.'

According to Gyldenstolphe (1955), the immature male differs from the adult in having the rosy-red of the chin and the sides of the face paler and less extensive. The red patch on the forehead and anterior part of the crown is well developed but less extended backwards. In the female only the forehead is pinkish-red, the crown and occiput being dark purplish-brown.

DISTRIBUTION: New Guinea from the Weyland Mountains near Geelvink Bay, West Irian, to south-eastern Papua. Rand and Gilliard (1967) suggest it: 'seems to be an uncommon, if not rare bird', also stating that it might be a 'non-flocking species.' However, it has been observed in flocks large and small, from a few pairs to a hundred birds. Forshaw (1973) noted: 'In May 1970, on the southern slopes of the Hagen Range, also in the Western Highlands, I found pairs and small parties in disturbed Nothofagus-Podocarpus forest at 2,800m. They frequented the upper storeys of trees. While light rain was falling they perched on the leafless, topmost branches and, with feathers fluffed, vigorously preened themselves. When leaving they dropped down sharply towards the ground and then levelled out in flight. The flight is swift and direct.

'Food consists of pollen, nectar, flowers, fruits and berries.'

IN AVICULTURE: A very rare bird in captivity, it has been exhibited in Chicago Zoo and in Stuttgart Zoo, Germany. I know of only one private aviculturist who has kept this species–P. Sperber of Ballarat, Australia. His pair nested and one of the two eggs was fertile.

BREEDING RECORDS: Chicago' birds were received from Australia in October 1949. In May 1950 they were placed in an aviary 7.6m (25ft) long, 1.8m (6ft) wide and 2.1m (7ft) high. They made no attempt to breed and were taken indoors during September, where they occupied a wall cage with a pair of Little Lorikeets. In December two of the Goldie's spent much time in one of the three nest-boxes provided and early in February chicks were heard inside. During the middle of the month the bird believed to be the male was seen to feed the female and he often fed the third bird. While the parents were feeding, the Little Lorikeets would peer into the nest hole, obviously interested in what was going on inside. They were removed just before the two young Goldie's Lorikeets fledged, on March 13. On that day the unmated Goldie's was seen to annoy the young birds, so it was removed from the aviary. The newly fledged birds were described as being smaller and duller in colour than the adults 'with some fuzz on the nape.'

The only other breeding success of which I know occurred at Taronga Zoo, Australia, in the 'early 1950s' according to Kerry Muller, curator (personal comm.). A hybrid between this species and a Forsten's Lorikeet was b·ed at Natal Zoo in 1969 (*Encyclopaedia of Aviculture*, Volume II).

Musk Lorikeet (*G. concinna*) (Shaw)

SYNONYMS: Green Keet, Musky Lorikeet, Red-eared Lorikeet.

DESCRIPTION: The distinguishing features are the bright red forehead, lores and ear coverts and the blue crown; the feathers below the ear coverts have blue shaft streaks. The hind-neck and the inter-scapular area are olive-brown, the rest of the upper parts being green and the underparts lighter green. There is an irregularly shaped patch of bright yellow on the sides of the breast. The primaries and secondaries are blackish-brown with green outer webs and tips and the inner surface of the tail is yellowish, the inner webs red on the two outer pairs of feathers. The beak is blackish-brown, tipped with orange-red. The iris has an inner ring of grey-brown and an outer ring of brown. Length: 23cm (9in).

The female has less blue on the head. Immature birds are duller overall with the red of the crown duller and less extensive. According to Lendon (1973) there is less yellow on the sides of the breast. The bill is dark, without the orange-red tip. The bird bred in the Moscicki Collection was described as having the red ear patches shorter than in the adults and the forehead brick red and broken with small green feathers. There was an orange band from the cere, under the eyes, to the point of the red ear patches, and some yellow-green patches in the centre of the breast. The top of the head was green instead of slate-blue.

Peter Oderkerken described the young aviary-bred birds he obtained as having lighter plumage with a greener tinge to the blue-green on the crown. The red forehead and ear patch were replaced by dusky orange. There was a thin black line through the lores to the eye. The beak was black with the merest indication of red on the upper mandible. The brown on the lower nape and mantle was of a lighter shade. The pupil was black with a grey-brown ring and an outer ring of orange-brown.

DISTRIBUTION: Eastern and south-eastern Australia: throughout Victoria, in New South Wales, in and to the east of the Great Dividing Range and in South Australia, as far north as Orrorro; widely distributed and plentiful in Tasmania; also recorded on King Island and Kangaroo Island.

This is a very common species, found throughout south-eastern Australia, except in the alpine region. Lendon described it as 'an extremely common bird in the vicinity of Adelaide at most seasons of the year and is nearly always to be found whenever there are eucalypts in flower in the suburban streets and parklands. At most times of the year, but especially in the summer, odd birds and small parties can be heard and seen coming and going from the large Moreton Bay fig trees at the northern end of the Adelaide Oval, where they presumably feed on the fruit.'

Lendon also remarks that this species' liking for fruit has given it a bad reputation and mentions 'numbers becoming intoxicated through feasting on fermenting grapes.' In *Australian Aviculture* (February 1975) B. R. Hutchings and R. H. Lovell refer to its fondness for pears. They kept under observation an orchard 13 miles north-east of Adelaide and found that the Musk Lorikeet arrived as soon as the pears began to ripen: 'Their arrival each morning was at approximately 7am and they would continue feeding on the fruit until about 10.30am, when small groups would begin to retire until about midday, when all would be gone.' About 3pm small flocks of about 12 birds returned until about 5.45pm. The extreme speed of the flight of this species was commented on.

Musk Lorikeets were known to feed in vast numbers on wheat crops and in orchards. In January 1896 there was a 'plague' of these birds and many were killed in fruit trees with the crude weapons of the time—sticks and stones. They were also very troublesome during the summer of 1889.

In *Handbook to the Birds of Australia*, Gould described it as a very noisy species which kept up a 'perpetual din around the trees in which it is located. During its search for honey it creeps among the leaves and smaller branches in the most extraordinary manner, hanging and clinging about them in every possible variety of position. It is so excessively tame that it is very difficult to drive it from the trees or even from any particular branch.'

IN AVICULTURE: Never a common bird in captivity, it is now almost unknown outside Australia with the exception of those kept and bred in San Diego Zoo and a pair in a private collection in South Africa. It has seldom been kept in England; three were exhibited at London Zoo in 1937.

Early aviculturists found this species more susceptible to death from fits than any other lorikeet. Cayley (1938) stated: 'Does not live very long in captivity' and Lendon described it as 'undoubtedly one of the lorikeets which will not often survive long on a diet of seed alone.'

However, in 1969, while in Australia, Peter Oderkerken obtained a pair of Musks which had bred on several occasions, together with a youngster they had reared that season. He informed me: 'They had been fed on seed with no other additions to their diet. The pair was extremely fit, also the youngster. In Australia I knew quite a few people who had kept Musks on a seed diet in perfect health. But since I was against feeding seed, I started giving them nectar consisting of Farex, wheat germ, honey and vitamin drops mixed with water. They accepted this immediately but I think the transition was a little fast for the youngster and he started to vomit. This was very hard to remedy but I finally cured this condition with the use of sulphamezathine.

'I bought a mate for the youngster in Sydney from a dealer and out of the many unhappy Musks, I chose a strong-looking bird. The dealer was feeding them seed and I could see many were struggling and would no doubt die within a few days. My youngster readily accepted his new friend in an aviary which they had to themselves.

'I saved the dealer's bird by feeding my honey mixture. When it tasted the sweet nectar it kept its beak fully immersed for five minutes, licking the mixture with its brush tongue.

'A supplement which my Musks naturally liked was eucalyptus blossoms, in which they would hang upside down licking the nectar. Incidentally, the eucalypt has been introduced into many countries, including South Africa, and I find that my Moluccans and other lories enjoy this treat as much as the *Glossopsitta* species.

'Musks are very powerful flyers and, I feel, need a long flight. They did well in a small aviary but when I transferred them to an enclosure 3.6m (12ft) long, 91cm (3ft) wide and 2.1m (7ft) high, they seemed to prefer it.'

Before a fourth bird was obtained, the adult hen laid two eggs. Both hatched and the chicks could be heard in the nesting log, which was hung at an angle of 45° under the shelter. Unfortunately, both chicks died during a cold spell. The parents ignored seed while feeding the chicks; they took only nectar, apple, pear, sponge cake soaked in sugared water, carrot and lettuce.

A Musk Lorikeet presented to London Zoo by Alfred Ezra in 1937 was still alive in 1943, despite the war-time restrictions which did not allow such foods as honey and condensed milk to be fed to birds.

A pair rearing young in the Moscicki collection in Belgium in 1958, had un-limited access to raisins, also muscat grapes, mealworms and grated, sweetened carrot. The Musks in the Moscicki collection were said to dislike sun, rain and bathing. They were thus inclined to become loose-feathered and soiled, which caused them to become less active and inclined to mope, according to Miss Diekmann. She wrote: (*Foreign Birds*, May/June 1959) of this species: 'It lacks, furthermore, some of the endearing characteristics of the Lori (sic) family, in so far as it has little of their playfulness, and is not so readily tamed. Those Musks in the Moscicki collection are shy and even retiring little birds, who, in spite of their five years in our midst, have remained outstandingly aloof to our advances.'

'. . . Far less noisy than most Lories, the Musk nevertheless can give a good account of himself considering his size, and the pairs keep up a continuous conversation even if the whole length of the flight separates them. This chatter is carried on inside the nest-box—a hollow log, some three feet deep—and can be heard from time to time, though somewhat more softly, throughout the night.'

Dr J. Dolan informed me that this species rain bathes and bathes in a dish, adding: 'They are very fond of rolling in wet foliage as are the *Vini australis*'. Commenting on Miss Diekmann's observation that this species lacks some of the endearing characteristics of other lories, Dr Dolan wrote (pers comm): 'I cannot agree with Miss Diekmann as far as my two birds are concerned. I see very little difference from the other lories in regard to their behaviour. They spend a great deal of time hanging and playing from the roof of their aviary and the perches. Granted, my two birds are hand-raised, so they show little fear of humans and will sit on your finger if you put it through the wire and will sit very close to you if you enter the aviary. They are extremely affectionate with one another, but make no bones about threatening the Black-caps and Yellow-backs who are on either side. I do, however, agree that they are less noisy. They seem to use their voices less often and when they do, the call is not as piercing as in the other species. Unlike my other lories, they do not roost in a box, but prefer to spend the night in the uncovered portion of the aviary.'

BREEDING RECORDS: The first recorded breeding took place in Germany in 1903. According to Neunzig, a pair belonging to Herr Nagel which were kept in a birdroom, occupied a nest-box hung high in thick brushwood during January. Young were heard during the middle of March. The hen died and the cock reared the youngsters unaided; they fledged on May 10. Another hen was obtained and another nest of young was reared.

In Australia the Musk Lorikeet was bred by Dr W. Hamilton for which he received the medal of the Avicultural Society of South Australia in 1930. At Taronga Park it was bred in 1940; chicks fledged on February 6 and 8. More recently, one was reared at Taronga during the period 1973-4. From 1941 onwards, this species was bred at Adelaide Zoo on several occasions and two were reared there in 1972. Hutchins and Lovell (*Australian Aviculture*, February 1975) give the incubation period as 21 days, the clutch size as two and the fledging period as about six weeks. They found that the nest became very wet while it contained chicks and recommended the addition of charcoal to the nest.

At San Diego Zoo, 11 Musk Lorikeets were bred during the period from November 1971 to June 1972; two more were reared in 1974. Seven received from Sydney, Melbourne and Adelaide Zoos between 1966 and March 1969 died without breeding but two which had come from Melbourne Zoo in July 1969 hatched a chick on February 10 1971. This bird—the first bred in the USA—lived for nearly two years. Two chicks hatched in May 1971 died when three and five weeks old. One hatched in August 1971 lived only 14 days and another, hatched in January 1972, died when 35 days old. Chicks hatched on February 20 and 21 were successfully reared, also one hatched on June 8 1972. Two hatched in April 1972 did not survive long. The keeper recorded an incubation period of 22 days.

The only European breeding that I can trace is that which took place in the Moscicki Collection. Kept in pairs this species was found to be devoted and affectionate but when more than one pair were housed together fighting broke out. The aviary shelters were 91cm (3ft) square and the flights were 5.5m (18ft) long, half turf, half cement. The nest-boxes were left in position throughout the year, in the flights but under cover, and the Musks slept inside every night. Miss Diekmann recorded that the incubation period was between 28 and 30 days, which is far longer than the period recorded by others who have bred this species, and that the hen started sitting when the second egg was laid. According to the aviary attendant, Mr Shutt, the first was laid on June 2 1958, in a hollowed-out silver birch log, with peat on the bottom. He first saw the young bird when it was a few days old and 'completely covered in a blue-white down.' On August 13, when the nest was inspected for the second time, the chick was fully feathered; it fledged on August 23, according to Mr Shutt. Even if the incubation period was 28 days, contrary to San Diego Zoo's experiences with this species (which seems most unlikely in view of the fact that in other small lories it is 22 or 23 days) and if incubation commenced when the second egg was laid, the chick would have hatched on July 2, thus it would have been 52 days old on fledging, an age which one would accept as being correct. Miss Diekmann stated, however, obviously in error (*Foreign Birds*, May/June 1959): '. . . I note that the first youngster to leave the nest was exactly thirty two days old. He is duller in appearance than his parents, and a good deal smaller, but surprisingly clever in flight. There is little of the ungainliness of the average youngster in the way he lands or takes off, and although his introduction to the outside world was followed within half an hour by one of the worst storms of the season, he very promptly followed his mother to shelter.

'... The storm broke with sudden violence as he landed for the second time at the furthest point of the open flight. His parents had bolted into their shelter, and were already calling to him, when the rain came down in bucketfuls. Our Curator, Mr Shutt, his assistant, Mr Noon and myself, were discussing in the shelter of the verandah the advisability of going to the rescue, when the cock, flying heavily against the storm, landed beside his offspring, and started pecking him roughly to one side. Obviously taken aback the youngster retreated to the netting followed by his parent. There the cock jostled and pushed and pecked him in the direction of the shelter, covering the youngster by the spread of his wings. It was not long before they joined the hen, safely out of the rain.'

During recent years Musk Lorikeets have been bred regularly in Australian zoos: Adelaide, 1965 (two), 1966 (four), 1967 (two), 1968 (two), 1969 (four), 1972 (five) and 1974 (five); Healesville, 1967 (three); Melbourne, 1965 (five), 1969 (four), 1970 (one), 1972 (two), 1973 (three) and 1974 (five); Sydney (Taronga), 1970 (two), 1971 (three), 1973 (two) and 1974 (one); Westbury, 1971 (two), 1973 (six) and 1974 (five). Five hybrids between a male Musk and a female Scaly-breasted Lorikeet were reared at Perth Zoo in 1970 and one in 1974.

Purple-crowned Lorikeet (*G. porphyrocephala*) (Dietrichsen)

SYNONYMS: Dietrichsen's Lory, Porphyry-crowned Lorikeet, Zip Parrot.

DESCRIPTION: The forehead and ear coverts are yellow and orange, the lores are orange and the crown is deep purple; the throat, breast and abdomen are bright powder blue. The mantle is olive, the wings being a darker green with the bend of the wing rich blue; the crimson under wing coverts and the yellow patches on the sides of the breast are revealed only when the bird is in flight. The thighs and under tail coverts are yellowish-green and the tail is green with orange-red markings near the base of the lateral feathers. The small beak is black and the iris is brown. Length: 15cm (6¾in).

Immature birds are duller and are said to lack the purple on the crown or show very little. This was not the experience of one aviculturist who bred this species; the young had the crown purple.

It is generally stated that the sexes are alike; Dr W. Hamilton believed that the ear coverts of the male are more orange than yellow and Dr A. Lendon found that in two true pairs, the male had a lighter coloured eye. Peter Oderkerken informed me that in his pair, which had bred before he obtained them: 'The supposed hen had less purple on the crown than the cock and a slightly smaller orange ear patch.'

DISTRIBUTION: South-western and south-eastern Australia, not including Tasmania. It is the only lorikeet found in the southern part of Western Australia;

it inhabits most of Victoria but is less common further north in New South Wales. It is also found on Kangaroo Island.

This is the commonest lorikeet in most parts of South Australia and is an inhabitant of lightly timbered country, also woodland near the coasts. Usually found in small flocks, large numbers may congregate where there are many flowering eucalypts, in order to feed on the nectar. Berries and cultivated fruits are also eaten. Mixed flocks of this species and the Musk Lorikeet are quite common.

It nests from August to December; the clutch comprises three or four eggs. Chris Mead wrote of this species (*Birds of the World* encyclopedia, part 7, vol. 4): 'It is not surprising that a gregarious species such as this, seeking food in parties of tens or even hundreds, is a colonial breeder. Since it nests in holes in trees the density of breeding pairs is determined by available nest-sites. About ten nests per acre have been found and such colonies are the scene of continual activity as birds arrive from and leave for the feeding grounds.'

He also stated that 'Availability of food is the limiting factor to such an extent that the species is sometimes absent for considerable periods from areas where it has been common. In some areas the arrival of flocks coincides with the flowering of a single species of *Eucalyptus*. This dependence on flowers and the species' great efficiency in finding the flowering areas led to an unusual request from the bee-keepers of Western Australia to the Australian Ornithologists' Union. The apiarists, whose bees also feed on the eucalypt's flowers, had lost much of their stock because of a poor flowering season. The lorikeets were absent from the area and the bee-keepers hoped that the ornithologists would be able to tell them where the lorikeets had gone so that they could move their bees in. Unfortunately, even the ornithologists did not know where the purple-crowned lorikeets were, so the experiment could not be concluded.'

John Warham made some interesting observations on this species in *Cage Birds* (July 3, 1958): 'It is most likely to be seen when a flock, breaking cover, dashes across a clearing or a road, a tight-knit body of birds which rips through the air and calls with sharp 'tsit, tsit' cries. Country children often refer to the birds as 'Zit Parrots' because of their voice.

'But they are birds of the tree tops, of the upper canopy of the forest and once the flock settles on to the leafy crown of a tree its members seem to vanish. The green body feathers and the bird's small size make it melt imperceptibly into the maze of shining gum leaves amid which it feeds. . . .

'Purple-crowned Lorikeets are nomads. They follow the flowers of the forest trees on which they depend for food. Seldom, if ever, do they feed on bushes or come down to the ground.

'. . . Fortunately, unlike certain other Australian Parrots, they seem to show no interest in man's crops and I have never heard of them attempting to eat grapes or other soft fruits which might conceivably please their palates. The birds benefit the trees which they visit, for they are believed to play an important role as pollinators of many varieties of eucalypts.

'They are fast flyers, little mobs dashing through the forests seem to sweep along like charges of shot and it is a perpetual wonder how they avoid crashing to their deaths. Sometimes they do come to grief. A flock speeding across the road may strike the telephone wires and only the colourful corpses scattered on the roadside herbage and green feathers fluttering in the wind remain to tell of their passing.

'. . . Four to six eggs are laid. These are white, rounded and without gloss. Their incubation is undertaken by the female and lasts for 18 days.*

'. . . I was shown a pair nesting 40 feet up in the heart of the white gum forest. A small hole in the trunk was their front door and the brood inside was already well grown when I first began to watch them.

'My vivacious sitters were very confiding. They would bounce back into the tree while I was still outside and would hardly wait for me to get out of sight before they were back at the hole: sometimes they came to the nest while I was still plainly visible. . . .

'Feeding was by now infrequent and sometimes other Lorikeets would alight in the tree. My birds were quite tolerant of these visitors: indeed, the pair once preened each other while a third perched only two feet from them. On the last day of my watching the chicks were fed only three times—shortly after dark, about 2pm and presumably at dusk, when the pair retired to the nest to roost. This was the last day in the nest: the following morning they were gone and I saw them no more.'

IN AVICULTURE: Now almost completely unknown outside Australia, this lorikeet has never been very familiar to aviculturists except in its native country. A Purple-crowned Lorikeet exhibited at the 1912 Horticultural Hall show was described as 'a species only recently imported'; it may have been one of the four birds received by the dealer, Jamrach. It would appear that 1910 was the year in which it was first imported. A Mr Wallace collected four and took them to England with a consignment of finches and parrakeets. Always rare in European collections, it is now entirely unknown.

BREEDING RECORDS: The Duke of Bedford was almost successful in breeding this species in 1932. A pair wintered in an outdoor aviary with a heated shelter came into breeding condition in March. Three eggs were laid; all hatched but two chicks lived only a short time and the third died when three weeks old. Evidently the food was not suitable for rearing the young as the adults were seen searching in the grass for food, although they were provided with many kinds of fruit and greenfood. Both the parents unfortunately died a few days after the chicks; the post mortem finding in both cases was septicaemia.

According to J. Delacour (*L.Oiseau et la Revue Francaise Ornithologie*, 1931, p. 302), it nested at San Diego Zoo in 1930. K. C. Lint informed me that two Purple-crowned Lorikeets were received from I. D. Putnam but records were not kept at that time so he was not able to provide details of the breeding which occurred at San Diego.

Also in 1930, Dr W. Hamilton left Australia with two chicks taken from the nest of his pair. They were hand-reared by him on board ship. The male parent

*It is unlikely that this species differs from other *Glossopsitta*, therefore the incubation period would be 22 or 23 days.

had been sent to him from south-east South Australia. A wild-caught bird, it had been unable to fly when it left the nest and appeared to be suffering from French moult. Even at the age of two and a half years it had not grown flight and tail feathers. To Dr Hamilton's surprise it learned to talk, copying an Amazon and repeating 'Hello, cocky boy', 'How are you?', etc, in a clear but gruff voice. The male remained very tame and allowed its owner to carry it about.

In Australia two young were reared by J. Gregg of Croydon in 1936. The next successful breeder would appear to have been C. Lambert of Horsley, Sydney, in 1952. The pair had been in his possession since 1949. They nested in a log with a side entrance. The first of four eggs was laid on July 1; all hatched successfully. Disaster struck when the chicks were five weeks old. They had been seen at the entrance to the log but Mr Lambert had not realised that one of the youngsters was caught in the entrance hole; the parents were unable to enter the log and the other three nestlings died. When the breeding was reported by R. Johnson, there were three well-developed young in the second nest. The hen commenced to lay the second clutch before the first youngster was independent. A nest-box with a larger entrance hole had been provided for the second nest. The rearing food consisted of 'sop' made with honey, milk, Farex, sugar, crushed biscuit, plain cake and chopped apple. Mealworms were offered occasionally.

Other Australian breeders of this species are J. G. Hamilton of Walkerville (1963 or 1964) and E. Bruton of Hawthorndene, Brisbane (1963); two pairs belonging to Mr Bruton nested, one of which laid three eggs which failed to hatch. The other pair hatched two young; one died, due to an accident and the other was reared.

Little Lorikeet (*G. pusilla*) (Shaw)

SYNONYMS: Tiny Lorikeet, Red-faced Lorikeet.
DESCRIPTION: Almost uniformly green, it has the forehead, lores and throat red. The shaft-streaking on the ear coverts is pale green and the nape and mantle are bronze-brown. The underparts are a lighter, more yellowish-green than the upper parts, and the under wing coverts are yellowish-green. Orange-red markings at the base of the tail complete the colour scheme which is less elaborate than that of the other *Glossopsitta* species. The beak is dark brown and the iris orange-yellow. Length: 15cm (6in).

The female may be distinguished by the duller colour and reduced extent of red on the face. Two breeders of this species, R. Rowlands, and Dr W. D. Russell, noted that the male had a more pronounced golden-brown shade on the back of the neck.

Immature birds have a duller shade of red on the face. The edge of the wing and the nape are a yellower shade of green, also the breast. The iris is brown. One of the two Little Lorikeets reared by Dr Russell was paler in colour, which was thought to be indicative of its sex.
DISTRIBUTION: Eastern and south-eastern Australia, including Tasmania, comparatively rare in South Australia. The Little Lorikeet is a common inhabitant of wooded country containing fruit-bearing trees.

In 1938, Neville Cayley wrote that in some seasons it was abundant in the neighbourhood of Sydney, often being found in company with Musk and Rainbow Lorikeets. He stated that it usually occurred 'in flocks frequenting chiefly the tall-timbered areas of flowering eucalypts, and is remarkably fearless and noisy, both while feeding and when in flight. From April until the end of June, one often sees large flocks of these birds twisting and turning as they fly swiftly over the tree tops in search of flowering trees. A voracious feeder, and difficult to disturb when feeding on the nectar—its chief food.

'The nesting-site is in a hollow limb or hole in a tree, usually about twenty feet from the ground.' Cayley stated that the breeding season was from August to December and that the clutch usually consisted of four eggs, occasionally five.

IN AVICULTURE: Even in its native country the Little Lorikeet is a very rare avicultural subject. Outside Australia it would appear to be almost unknown now, although it was apparently imported into Europe as early as 1877. Importations must have been very rare as nothing has been recorded about it. In the USA, San Diego Zoo obtained a single specimen in 1966. In Australia, Adelaide Zoo exhibited the Little Lorikeet during the second world war and, more recently, Peter Oderkerken kept them while in Australia. He provided me with the following details.

'They fed well on nectar made from honey, Farex, wheat germ and vitamin drops; they loved apple, pear, carrot and soaked sponge cake. All my *Glossopsitta* enjoyed being sprayed lightly with a hose and hung on the wire spreading their wings, ruffling their feathers and soaking up the spray. When I placed eucalyptus blossom in the aviary the birds used to hang on the branches in preference to the wire, while being sprayed, and rubbed themselves against the branches and leaves.

'They seemed to be more timid than the Musks, except for one young specimen which used to start what looked like a courtship act near me, meanwhile running his brush tongue along his black beak.

'One bird had a darker shade of brown on the nape and mantle as well as more red on the face. Whether it was an old bird or this was a sexual distinction I do not know. They seemed to agree well with the Purple-crowned Lorikeets and with finches, something I would not attempt with the Musks.'

BREEDING RECORDS: The first successful breeding was recorded by N. K. Bush of Peakhurst, Sydney, in 1948. His pair was housed in a planted aviary 15ft long, 7ft wide and 6ft high, with various finches. The male was hand-reared and the female had been caught as a young bird two years previously. The nest-box was situated 1.5m (5ft) from the ground, under cover; it had a small hollow log fixed on the front as an entrance; 5.8cm (2in) of rotted wood covered the bottom. Four eggs were laid in September 1948 and incubated by the hen. The chicks hatched on October 19 and apparently fledged about the middle of November; they were independent after two weeks.

The parents became very spiteful while rearing the chicks. They were fed on Weetabix, to which was added two teaspoonfuls of condensed milk for one and a half biscuits, then boiled water to form a thin paste. A little canary seed was also eaten. In 1949 three more young were reared. The first two went to America.

More recently, in 1973, the Little Lorikeet was bred by Russ Rowlands in

Australia. It was four years before his pair made any attempt to breed. The first nest was unsuccessful as the diet of 'fruit cake, bread and milk' was inadequate. The pair shared the planted enclosure with various pigeons, ground doves and rails. From a variety of logs and boxes they chose a small nest-box, inside which peat moss was placed.

The first of four eggs was laid on August 18 and incubation commenced on August 20. The first chick hatched after 23 days and three days later there were four chicks in the box. One was weak and survived only a week. When hatched the chicks had very little down but they soon grew white down. The diet was changed to nectar consisting of malted milk, condensed milk, honey and Benger's Food or Complan, mixed with water. Cake, apple and pears were also provided.

As the inside of the nest-box became very wet after a few weeks, the box was cleaned out and commercial cat litter was placed on the bottom. This was carried out every week until the young fledged, at the age of 52 days. At first they could fly only short distances and they were returned to the nest at night because the weather was cold. After a week the chicks began to feed themselves on nectar and by the end of the second week they were independent and showing a preference for the nectar and soft pears. They were never seen to eat seed. The chicks were described as 'a dull example of the parent birds', the green on the body and the red on the face were not as bright and they were smaller than the adults.

Between July 1972 and June 1973 two Little Lorikeets were reared at Taronga Zoo, Sydney, and two more in October 1973 (one hand-reared) and one in 1974. The parents were members of a colony of six birds kept in a planted aviary 6.1m (20ft) long, 1.5m (5ft) wide and 2.1m (7ft) high. They nested in natural logs.

The pair already referred to, belonging to Peter Oderkerken, accompanied him to South Africa when he emigrated in 1970. In March 1975 they were acquired by Dr W. D. Russell, a veterinary surgeon of Bryanston, owner of probably the best collection of lories in South Africa. The Little Lorikeets were provided with a natural log and a small nest-box of the type used for Australian finches; they chose to nest in the latter, which faced north and contained a 3in (8cm) layer of wood shavings.

Laying commenced in August, the fourth and last egg being laid on August 19. An egg-shell was seen on the ground on September 10. Three chicks hatched, one of which died when about two days old. The two surviving young left the nest on October 22, when aged between 38 and 42 days. They were poor flyers and were therefore replaced in the nest for the first ten nights.

Two chicks were reared in a second nest. In 1976 the single chick reared developed cataracts and had to be put down. Each clutch consisted of three or four eggs which were incubated for 22 days. Dr Russell informed me that the male displayed by running up and down the perch, 'holding his head low and whistling and on reaching the hen he bobs up and down.'

The birds were fed on nectar made from three teaspoonfuls of Complan and one each of honey and condensed milk with a vitamin additive, mixed with $\frac{1}{2}$ litre of warm water. At lunch time this mixture was replaced with Pro Nutro breakfast cereal mixed with honey and a little water. Apple was also eaten.

12

Lorius

Genus: *Lorius* (formerly *Domicella*)

The members of this genus are easily recognised; they are large, thick-set lories, with short, rather wide, rounded tails. The beak, which is coral-red in all species, is broad, and the iris is orange-red. All species have the green wings contrasting strongly with the red body; there is purple on the head, abdomen or thighs in most species. Plumage is alike in male and female.

These birds are heavy, rather weak flyers. On one occasion when a Yellow-backed Lory escaped from its aviary, my husband had little difficulty in catching it by pursuing it and throwing a coat over it.

Lorius species love to bathe, not merely throwing the water over their body as some parrots do, but rolling over and over in the water. For this reason, a concrete bath incorporated in the floor of the aviary—well away from perches—is more satisfactory than a dish which will be treated as a plaything unless it is very heavy. These birds often become very tame and some learn to talk quite clearly. They are exceptionally intelligent.

Aviculturists with close neighbours should remember that although these birds do not scream in the same way as some parrots, their voices can carry a long way and may cause some annoyance.

Louisiade Lory (*L. hypoinochrous hypoinochrous*) (G. R. Gray)

SYNONYMS: Purple-bellied Lory, Sudest Lory.

DESCRIPTION: The forehead, crown and nape are black, glossed with purple; the abdomen, thighs and under tail coverts are dark purple. The wings are green, and the rest of the body is crimson, paler on the breast; the under wing coverts are also crimson, the outermost feathers being edged with black. The base of the upper side of the tail is red, the remainder being dark blue-green; the underside of the tail is olive-yellow. The cere is conspicuously white (unlike that of *L. lory* which is dark grey). Length: 26cm (11in).

This species can best be described as looking like a small Black-capped Lory but without the purple on the nape and breast and with the back red.

DISTRIBUTION: Misima and Tagula in the Louisiade Archipelago (eastern Papua). It is common throughout most of its range.

IN AVICULTURE: Not well known, although it is imported from time to time. Undoubtedly, it is not correctly identified on occasions. I can find only two references to this species in the literature. In *BirdNotes* (March 1922, p. 70) the editor reported: 'Mrs Burgess informs us that she has lately acquired a true pair of Purple-breasted Lories (*Lorius hypoenochrous*) (sic), which she believes is new to aviculture, and we think that such is the case.' In 1933 H. Whitley had a pair in his collection in Devon, according to Dr Hopkinson (*Avicultural Magazine* 1940, p. 313).

BREEDING RECORDS: Chester Zoo bred two Louisiade Lories in 1973.

Rossel Island Lory (*L.h. rosselianus*)

DESCRIPTION: Differs from the nominate race only in having the red on the breast of the same shade as the upper abdomen, ie, deep crimson.

DISTRIBUTION: Rossel Island in the Louisiade Archipelago.

Fergusson Island Lory (*L.h. devittatus*)

DESCRIPTION: Differs from the nominate race in lacking the black margins on the greater under wing coverts.

DISTRIBUTION: South-eastern New Guinea, west to the Angabunga River and the Huon Gulf, D'Entrecasteaux and Bismarck Archipelagos, Trobriand and Woodlark islands.

New Britain Lory (*L. amabilis*)

SYNONYM: Stresemann's Lory.

DESCRIPTION: Known only from the type specimen, a female obtained by P. Otto Meyer in Nakanai, New Britain. It was mainly red, with green wings and red under wing coverts; there was a yellow band across the underside of the secondaries. The lower underparts, including the abdomen and the thighs, were dull purple-blue; the under tail coverts were the same colour and were marked with green and pale red. The tail was dark greenish-blue above, olive yellow below, with red at the base. The legs were said to be yellowish-brown, not black. Length: 26cm.

Forshaw (1973), who examined the type, believed that it could be a mutant *hypoinochrous*, as interruption of the genetic factor controlling black pigmentation could have brought about all the distinguishing features.

The type bird was almost certainly a captive specimen as the primaries had been removed.

Black-capped Lory (*L. lory lory*) (Linné)

SYNONYM: Tri-coloured Lory.

DESCRIPTION: It can be briefly described as having the head and part of the upper breast red, except for the black cap (forehead, crown and nape) which has a purple gloss; the underparts and the mantle dark blue, and the wings green with a bronze patch. There is a broad yellow band across the underside of the flight feathers. The rump, upper tail coverts and under wing coverts are also red. The tail is dark blue above, olive-yellow below. The abdomen is brilliant blue and the under tail coverts are a pale shade of blue; there is a blue band on the hindneck. Length: 31cm (12in).

Descriptions of immature birds vary. Mrs Dalton Burgess described the Black-capped Lory bred in her aviaries as having the under tail coverts greenish instead of violet-blue. It had a dark iris and a horn-coloured beak after fledging, a black beak while in the nest. Forshaw (1973) described immature birds as having the under wing coverts blue with the outermost feathers tipped with black. Sub-adult birds have been described as having the under wing coverts a mixture of red, blue and yellow.

L.l. major (from Waigeu), formerly separated by its slightly larger size, is now considered synonymous with *L.l. lory* (Mees, 1965).

DISTRIBUTION: Vogelkop, West Irian, and Waigeu, Batanta, Salawati and Misol in the western Papuan Islands.

This species inhabits lowland forest and is occasionally found as high as 5,000ft. Forshaw (1973) states that pairs or groups of up to ten birds are observed flying above the tree tops and that large numbers come together to feed on trees bearing blossom or fruit. He described them as shy birds which did not allow a close approach. He observed that the rapid, shallow wing beats gave a fluttering appearance to their direct flight and that the yellow under wing coverts were most conspicuous.

According to A. L. Rand, a common food of the Black-capped Lory is the flower of the climbing *Freycinetia*. Pollen and small insects were found in the stomachs of birds collected in the Weyland Mountains. This lory also feeds on nectar and fruits, and possibly small seeds.

IN AVICULTURE: This species is popular in aviculture; the only member of the genus which is better known is *L. garrulus*. Of recent years it has been imported more frequently than the Purple-capped Lory but, in 1888, Bechstein recorded that the reverse was true.

Its colour and pleasing personality ensure that it will always be among the best loved of the lories. In common with other *Lorius* species, it can be very noisy. One aviculturist had a pair which could 'imitate chickens, seagulls, irate blackbirds, steam whistles and ravens, also yelp like little dogs . . .'. The same pair, belonging to A. J. Goddard, showed great intelligence in the way they lured cats to be bitten. Working as a pair, one bird danced along the perch in such a way that the cat was almost mesmerised and sometimes put its nose on the netting—and was immediately bitten. At other times the cock ceased his dancing to suddenly make for the far perch, thus bringing the cat across the wire and over the hen, who bit the cat's feet as it passed and caused it to jump two feet into the air!

BREEDING RECORDS: The first recorded breeding of this species took place in 1921 when Mrs Dalton Burgess's pair reared one youngster in an indoor birdroom. An egg found on April 2 of that year outside the large nest-box, was placed inside, but the hen did not incubate it. By May 4 she had laid again and was incubating. The cock became extremely savage. When the nest was inspected on June 8 it contained a chick which was judged to be about ten days old, and two eggs. The down of the chick was described as ' a golden colour.' On June 28 there were two chicks and the presence of a third was suspected. A plucked chick fledged on June 28 but the fate of its nest mates was not recorded.

In the following February Mrs Burgess recorded (*Bird Notes*, March 1922): 'The hen is now busy carrying every splinter of wood she can find into the nest, and evidently is about to lay again.' The previous year's young bird was described as a talker and a mimic; it allowed itself to be handled.

A pair of Black-capped Lories in Chicago Zoo laid annually but did not incubate conscientiously. In 1948 one egg was given to a pair of Swainson's Lorikeets with one egg of their own. The Black-cap's egg hatched between April 1 and April 4 and the chick fledged on June 3.

In England, D. G. Bloom of Mildenhall, Suffolk, bred this species in 1972. The pair had not made any previous attempt to nest, although they had been in his possession for three years. It was not until April 10, when a faint cheeping was heard coming from the nesting log, that Mr Bloom was aware that the birds were breeding. On inspecting the log he found one newly hatched chick and one egg. The food consumption increased rapidly, the amount of nectar (made from honey, condensed milk and Farlene) doubled and extra apple was eaten; a little sunflower seed and chickweed were also consumed.

The adult birds hid behind the log if anyone entered the aviary and emitted 'a painful growling screech.' The young bird joined in the chorus, as it matured, and would even jump up to bite if the nest was approached too closely. After it fledged on June 23, it was 'quite docile', in perfect feather and flying well. The breeding took place in an aviary 2.7m (9ft) long, 1.4m (4ft 6in) wide and 1.8m (6ft) high with a partly covered roof. The nesting log was hung under cover. In 1973 Mr Bloom's pair reared two nests of two chicks.

In the June 1973 issue of the *Parrot Society Magazine*, it was reported that Lady Lathbury's pair of Black-capped Lories had reared two youngsters for the second year. Other breeders of this species are Amsterdam Zoo, 1965 (1); Kelling Park Aviaries, 1967, 1968; Dudley Zoo, 1968 and 1969 and Asson Zoological Park, France, 1970 (4).

A hybrid between a male of this species and a female Blue-tailed Lory (*Eos h. histrio*) was bred in San Diego Zoo in 1932.

Dr W. D. Russell described the display of his male Black-capped Lory (pers. comm.) as follows: 'He spends a lot of time circling the hen when she is on the ground or the nest, whistling to her or pecking her. During this time his neck feathers are ruffled and he bobs up and down, sometimes jumping a few inches off the ground.'

Red-breasted Lory (*L.l. erythrothorax*) Salvadori.
DESCRIPTION: Distinguished from the nominate race by the breast, which is entirely red (ie, there is no blue on the breast, only on the abdomen). The blue of the abdomen does not extend up the sides of the breast; the blue band on the hind neck is narrower.

DISTRIBUTION: Southern parts of Geelvink Bay and the Onin Peninsula, east to south-eastern Papua and the Huon Peninsula.

IN AVICULTURE: Often imported but seldom distinguished from the nominate race.

BREEDING RECORDS: San Diego Zoo reared two in 1968, three in 1969, two in 1970, two in 1971 and three in the period 1972 and 1973.

L.l. somu (Diamond)

DESCRIPTION: Differs from *erythrothorax* only in lacking the blue on the hindneck.

DISTRIBUTION: Southern New Guinea. According to Forshaw (1973) it has been recorded from the Karimuri Basin and to the south, and from the mouth of the Purari River, from the Fly River and from the area of Lake Kutubu.

L.l. salvadorii (Meyer)

DESCRIPTION: Differs from *erythrothorax* in having a well defined blue band on the hindneck. The under wing coverts are dark blue, and the centre of the abdomen and a broad band across the lower breast, connecting with the under wing coverts, are almost black. Length: 31cm (12½in).

DISTRIBUTION: North-eastern New Guinea from Astrolabe Bay west to the Aitape area.

BREEDING RECORDS: Bred at Birdland, Bourton-on-the-Water, in 1974. At Busch Gardens, Tampa, a hybrid between a male *salvadorii* and a female *Eos bornea* was reared in 1966; four more were reared in the following year.

L.l. viridicrissalis (de Beaufort)

DESCRIPTION: Differs from *salvadorii* in being a darker, more blackish blue, on the hindneck.

DISTRIBUTION: Northern New Guinea between Humboldt Bay and the Mamberamo River.

Jobi Lory (*L.l. jobiensis*) (Meyer)

Doubtfully distinct from *salvadorii* from which it apparently differs in having the mantle and a band across the hindneck lighter. The bright red breast is described as having a rosy tinge.

DISTRIBUTION: Japen and Mios Num islands in Geelvink Bay, West Irian.

L.l. cyanauchen (*cyanuchen*) S. Müller

Blue-naped, Mysore or Biak Lory.

DESCRIPTION: Differs from *salvadorii* in lacking the red on the nape, the mauve-blue of the hindneck meeting the black of the crown and occiput.

DISTRIBUTION: The island of Biak, in Geelvink Bay, West Irian.

White-naped Lory (*L. albidinuchus*) (Rothschild and Hartert)

DESCRIPTION: Predominantly red with the forehead, crown and occiput black, followed by a patch of white on the nape of the neck. The wings are green and the under wing coverts are red; there is a broad yellow band across the underside of the flight feathers. Yellow markings on either side of the upper breast form a broken collar. The tail is red, broadly tipped with green, the underside being tipped with bronzy-yellow. The iris is said to be yellow to brownish. Length: 26cm (10½in).

The immature bird has not been described.

DISTRIBUTION: New Ireland in the Bismarck Archipelago. Nothing is known of the habits of this lory. It is completely unknown in aviculture.

Yellow-bibbed Lory (*L. chlorocercus*) (Gould)

SYNONYMS: Gould's, Green-tailed, Yellow-collared Lory.

DESCRIPTION: This lory is accepted as a distinct species but it closely resembles *domicellus*. It differs in the following respects: it lacks the violet or purple patch bordering the black cap, but it has bluish-black markings on either side of the neck, joined by the narrow yellow half collar on the upper breast. There is a broad, pinkish-red band on the underside of the flight feathers; this area is yellow in *domicellus*. The tail is red, broadly tipped above with green, not brownish-red. The base of the upper mandible is dusky. The bill and the iris are red. Length: 28cm (11in).

Immature birds are said to lack the black markings on the side of the neck, to have little or no yellow on the upper breast and variable green markings on the thighs. The bill is brownish and the iris brown.

DISTRIBUTION: Eastern Solomon Islands; absent from Bougainville. It is an inhabitant of forest canopies and secondary growth, at all altitudes. According to Cain and Galbraith (1956), in Guadalcanal it seemed to be more plentiful in the hills than in the lowlands and was commonest in lower mist forests. It also inhabits coconut plantations. It may be seen in pairs or in parties of up to about ten birds.

Vegetable matter with a high proportion of seeds has been found in the crop of this lory, also caterpillars. It also feeds on pollen, nectar and fruits.

G. W. Stevens, writing in *Cage and Aviary Birds* (July 10, 1969) stated that the Yellow-bibbed Lory is 'the favourite "pet" Parrot in the Solomons.'

'The usual method of restraining this, and indeed all other Parrots, is with a double ring of tough coconut shell, rather like a figure eight, with one half round one leg, and the other running along a length of loia vine or ratten—the old-fashioned schoolmaster's cane—with one end terminating in a box shelter on the house verandah, and the other in a nearby tree.'

It is not unusual for newly imported lories to have the ring described above still attached to one leg. As this will serve no useful purpose and could result in the lory's foot becoming entangled in a stray piece of wire mesh in the aviary, it is advisable to remove these rings.

Stevens continued: 'In confinement it quickly learns to talk and whistle, and its clownish antics are really very amusing. Sometimes this bird is kept as a free-flying pet—the best method of all, in my opinion—and returns readily to its adopted home, even when strangers are about.'

IN AVICULTURE: It would appear that this species is seldom imported but because of its similarity to the Purple-capped Lory, probably few would identify it correctly. As other parrots are exported from the area, and this lory is plentiful, it would be surprising if it was not exported from time to time. However, according to Dr Burkard, they live so high in trees they are difficult to catch.

Nothing has been written about it in aviculture; in fact, the only reference I could find to it was that one was deposited at London Zoo in 1911 by Dr P. H. Bahr, together with two Solitary Lories (*Avicultural Magazine*, 1911, p 71). *Chlorocercus* had been exhibited at London Zoo previously—as long ago as 1867, when a pair was purchased. San Diego Zoo received two specimens in 1944.

At the time of writing two pairs of this species are kept by Dr R. Burkard in Switzerland. He informed me that: 'Their behaviour is similar to all the *Lorius* species; however, they are much tamer and do not have a loud voice but a pleasant pipe and whistle. They have an extraordinary capacity for mimicry, imitating numerous voices of birds. After one week they imitated the whistle I always emit when I enter the aviary. This is one of the most beautiful and pleasant of all lories. They take lory food, fruit, greenfood and sunflower seed.'

Purple-capped Lory (*L. domicellus*) (Linné)

SYNONYMS: Purple-naped Lory.
DESCRIPTION: It is predominantly crimson, slightly darker on the mantle. The forehead, crown and occiput are black, followed by a small area of streaked, lengthened violet feathers on the nape. The wings are green with white and blue mingled on the bend of the wing; there is a broad yellow band across the underside of the flight feathers. A variable yellow band crosses the upper breast and the thighs are violet-blue. The tail is red, broadly edged with dark brownish-red. The iris varies from reddish-brown to orange. Length: 28cm (11in).

Immature birds are said to have the purple on the nape deeper and more extensive and a broader yellow band across the breast. The greater under wing coverts are margined with black. The bill is brownish.

Tom Spence, then of Fife, Scotland, noted of his pair that in the female the yellow band on the breast decreased until it was hardly discernible; she then developed two 'small purple patches on the outer horns of the crescent, recalling the similar ornamentation in Gould's Lory' (*chlorocercus*). The more massive head of the male of his pair made sexing them easy.

The young bird they bred had the yellow breast patch 'widespread and diffuse;' there were dull green bases to the red tips of the feathers of the mantle, and the under wing coverts were tipped with black and were not completely blue, as in the adult. Its bill remained black until it was four months old, when it gradually became orange.

DISTRIBUTION: The islands of Ceram and Amboina, Indonesia; introduced to Buru. This species inhabits primary forest. Very little has been recorded about its life in the wild.

IN AVICULTURE: The Purple-capped Lory has long been known to aviculturists, although it has never been imported in large numbers. Perhaps because it is one of the best known of the lories that few have bothered to record any observations concerning it. An exception was Tom Spence who imported his pair under licence in the early 1950s, when parrots could not be freely imported into Britain. He believed that his pair, together with three other Purple-caps, were 'the only specimens brought to Britain for many years.'

His pair were not kept together for many months and the female 'became exceedingly tame and quite fantastically attached to me, caressing me, grooming my eyelashes with her papillated tongue and regurgitating food into my mouth or ears. . . .'

BREEDING RECORDS: Early records, including those of alleged successes in Belgium, Japan and the USA, give no details.

The first British breeding would appear to be that recorded by Tom Spence (*Avicultural Magazine*, 1955, pp. 14–17). The hen of his pair laid several clutches before she was kept with the cock; one clutch consisted of one egg, the rest of two. The male ate the first egg she laid after he was introduced; he was cured of this habit by the substitution of a china pigeon's egg for the second. The pair was placed together in a small aviary sheltered by yew hedges and walls in the early part of June 1954. The nest-box, in the shelter, was immediately investigated and was used for roosting from the very first night.

Aviculture would be richer for more devotees with Tom Spence's ability to observe and record; however, his pair only tolerated constant interference for so long—then they mutilated the chicks. His account is worth quoting at length. 'The first egg was laid on 23rd June, and the second on the 25th. She did not begin to incubate till the second egg and even then seemed to be but little inclined for the first few days, coming off to play with the male at any opportunity. I admit to taking ridiculous liberties with this pair for I examined the eggs almost daily, taking them out to wash them and test for fertility, even floating them (albeit in water of carefully controlled temperature) to observe with delight the bobbings and stirrings of life in them. The first egg starred and chipped on the 24th day and hatched within four hours of chipping. The second egg hatched on the 26th day. I believe this was due to careless incubation in the early days when she seemed to be happy with only one egg under her. The hen did all the brooding, keeping up a constant begging call during the later stages. Her brooding position was of interest; the phalanges were clenched and raised while she rested on the angle of the flexed tibiotarsal-tarsometatarsul joint.

'The young were invested with long soft, almost white, down on the back and humeral region. This was soon lost, probably through contamination with regurgitated food. When about three weeks old the dark second down follicles and the red true feather follicles showed through the skin and by the fourth week the chick was covered in a dense dark grey short down with a whitish pattern on the neck and shoulders recalling a game chick. About this time the eyes opened and the egg-tooth was shed. The first feathers showed through on the flanks about the 60th day and the young bird left the nest on the 95th day, after a few days timid peeping out. It began to feed itself soon after.'

Only one chick survived because the parents began to resent the constant interference and 'chopped off some toes'. The 'more mutilated' of the two was removed for hand-rearing at the age of three weeks. All went well for a while then it died, apparently as a result of being given some banana.

Tom Spence commented: 'This must be an exceptionally tolerant pair of lories for they have now hatched a second clutch, indoors, with their first young one still beside them, unmolested.' When reported, the single chick of the second clutch was four weeks old. 'The first young one thrives but is a rather timid unfriendly creature.'

A year later, the news regarding this pair was disappointing. The young one from the first nest died when eight months old and those in subsequent nests were killed by the parents when about three weeks old. Finally, the hen broke her leg as a result of catching an overgrown nail in the wire netting. When the leg healed she was returned to her mate but did not breed again that year (1955).

Mrs Bonestell bred the Purple-capped Lory in California in 1939 and applied for the medal of the Avicultural Society of America but there was no notice of its award. A hen belonging to Bruyneel in Belgium which bred successfully for many years with a cock of her own species, later produced what was described as 'a gorgeous hybrid' when paired to a Red-collared Lorikeet.

In more recent years this species has been bred at Birdland, Bourton-on-the-Water and at Kelling Park Aviaries. Outside Europe, young have been reared in zoos at Dhrangadhra, India; Beira, Mozambique; and in the USA at San Diego and Pittsburgh.

Blue-thighed Lory (*L. tibialis*) (Sclater)

DESCRIPTION: Known only from the type specimen, a female purchased from the Calcutta market and presented to London Zoo in 1871. It can briefly be described as resembling *L. domicellus* but differed in having the head entirely red. Length: 28cm (11in). It would appear that this bird was an aberrant specimen of *domicellus* as nothing similar has been recorded since.

Chattering Lory (*L. garrulus garrulus*) (Linné)

DESCRIPTION: It is almost entirely scarlet—a deeper shade on the mantle—and has green wings and thighs. The bend of the wing and the under wing coverts are yellow; there is a broad pinkish-red band across the underside of the primaries.

The tail is green above, blue at the tip; the underside is bronze-red with a red patch at the base. The iris is orange-red. Length: 30cm (12in).

Immature birds have the beak brownish and the iris dark brown.

DISTRIBUTION: Halmahera and the Weda Islands.

IN AVICULTURE: This species has been known to bird keepers for many years and was exhibited at London Zoo as long ago as 1864. The Chattering is a delightful aviary bird, very lively and full of character, extremely intelligent and inquisitive; I would venture to say that there are few more intelligent parrots. Unfortunately, they are rather noisy, the vocabulary consisting of a variety of piercing and far-crying noises.

Tame birds make wonderful pets; they will learn to repeat a few words and to whistle. One Chattering Lory, hand-reared in South Africa by D. Pringle and his wife, was described by Mr Pringle as 'the most fantastic talker I have ever heard.' It associated people with the correct voices and, when given an item of food by Mr and Mrs Pringle, would render its thanks in the voice of the one who offered the food.

BREEDING RECORDS: The first recorded breeding took place in 1913 when Lord Poltimore's pair reared one youngster. In *Bird Notes* (January 1914) he wrote that the event 'was a great surprise to everyone, as no one even suspected its existence, until it was discovered one fine morning, feeding with the older inmates of the aviary.' As the latter measured 13.1m (43ft) long and 10.9m (36ft) wide it is, perhaps, not surprising that the chick's existence was not known until it fledged.

In the USA, Mrs Bonestell of California bred two in 1939. They were reared by Swainson's Lorikeets as the parents had previously killed the young which hatched. Also in California, F. H. Rudkin bred this species on several occasions, his pair being double-brooded on at least one instance.

J. F. Simoes of Lisbon, Portugal, was successful in breeding the Chattering Lory in 1960. He received two in November 1955 and two more the following year. In the spring of 1957 all four birds were placed together and one of the original birds, a male, paired with one of the new ones, probably indicating that the original two were of the same sex. The remaining two were removed from the aviary and the true pair was provided with a nest-box 91cm (35in) × 36cm (14in) square and a grandfather type box. They immediately took to the latter, which had a 9cm (4in) layer of earth and sawdust on the bottom. In order to maintain humidity a thin plastic tube was connected under the latter so that water could be injected, if necessary.

No eggs were laid in 1957 but in the following April the birds were seen mating. The hen laid two eggs which disappeared within a fortnight. In 1959 the hen laid two more eggs; neither was fertile. In November the lories were moved to a larger aviary which measured 12.1m (40ft) × 1.8m (6ft) × 1.8m (6ft) high. In 1960 the first egg was laid about April 2 and the second on April 5. One egg was clear; the other hatched on May 1. The chick was reared on nectar made from Nestlé's baby food, maizena flour, goat milk, honey, sugar and vitamins. Sunflower seed, carrots, tomatos, various ripe fruits, including banana, insectivorous food and 'lots of mealworms and earthworms.'

The chick was seen looking out of the nest on July 4 and fledged on July 7 when it was not fully feathered on the back. Had it not been for the intervention of the aviary attendant, the young bird would have been killed by the cock as it left the nest. The cock was immediately removed to another aviary.

Other breeders of this species are Natal Zoo (1964), Inge Forsberg of Sweden (one youngster reared in 1968), Phyllis Gale of South Africa (one reared in 1968, two in the nest when reported in 1969), D. G. Bloom of Mildenhall (one in 1973 and one in the nest when reported), Mrs Engelsman of Canada (two in 1973 and two in 1974), Birdland, Bourton-on-the-Water, 1965 and 1974, and Penscynor Bird Gardens, Wales, in 1971, 1974; Amsterdam, 1973; Amanzimtoti Zoo, 1966 and 1973; Leipzig Zoo, 1966 (two), 1967 (four), 1969 (four); Beira, Mozambique, 1969 (four); East Berlin, 1967 (one); Villars, France and Wroclaw, Poland.

It is of interest to note that after the youngster reared by Phyllis Gale's pair fledged the hen appeared to be 'going into a decline'. She hid behind the nest-box and was 'thoroughly miserable while the father and child had great games together in the flight. This went on for several days until 1 became alarmed for the hen. I thought I was going to lose her.' Realising that the young bird was probably a hen and the father was paying it too much attention, she removed it and the hen immediately recovered. (*Parrot Society Magazine*, April 1969).

The Chattering Lory has hybridised with a number of species. The young produced when a male was paired to a 'Red Lory' (presumably *Eos bornea*) by Mrs A. Cohen, of St Louis, USA, was described as being red with very dark green wings and no yellow in its plumage. At the age of four months it had the beak black and white skin surrounding the eye.

An inter-generic cross between a Swainson's Lorikeet and a Chattering Lory was bred, in 1912, by Mrs E. Hartley of Hastings. She described the young in *Bird Notes* (September 1912, p. 247): 'They are already larger than the father ... though they only left the nest a few days ago, being more the size and robust build of the Mother *Garrulus*, who, by the way, celebrated the occasion by immediately slaying a favourite old cock Ring-neck (Parrakeet), the only other occupant of the enclosure. They are alike in plumage, the whole of the crown extending to the line of the eye is purple, each little feather having a golden tip, and as these purple feathers extend further down the back of the neck each has a green tip, which gives a bronze hue to the whole.' The back and wings were green, also the tail which was pointed. The breast was red and the thighs and most of the remainder of the underparts green. The Swainson's had previously been mated to a Violet-necked Lory; chicks had been hatched but not reared.

Yellow-backed Lory (*L.g. flavopalliatus*) (Salvadori)
DESCRIPTION: There is a yellow patch on the mantle; in this respect it differs from the nominate race which has no yellow or some small yellow spots in that area.
DISTRIBUTION: Batjan and Obi.
IN AVICULTURE: This is, without a doubt, the best known member of the genus and, perhaps, rates with *Trichoglossus haematodus* as the lory which is most familiar to aviculturists. It makes a most delightful aviary bird provided that one

makes no attempt to keep it with other species and is prepared for a certain amount of noise. My pair is housed outside the kitchen door and immediately below my bedroom window. Throughout the night they can be heard 'conversing' in their nest-box. Every morning and evening they are offered a whole banana and never, under any circumstances, will they allow one to forget this fact. Early in the morning they are 'shouting' for their banana and, on dark winter evenings, they appear from inside their nest-box and call for their favourite fruit as soon as the kitchen light goes on, whether it is 5pm or 10pm.

It would seem that both birds are males, although on a few occasions copulation has been seen. They have been together for over 14 years and no eggs have been laid. As so often happens with common species, one cannot afford the space to obtain two hens and devote two aviaries to them, yet they are such characters that sentimental attachment precludes exchanging one or the other for a hen. Although they are compatible, they rarely sit together or preen each other.

As already pointed out (see p. 10) under no circumstances should *L. garrulus* be housed with other birds.

BREEDING RECORDS: A British aviculturist and a zoo successfully bred the Yellow-backed Lory in 1958; I cannot trace any previous records but it is difficult to believe that a species imported with such regularity had not been bred previously.

A pair at Dudley Zoo, Worcs, hatched a chick at the beginning of July 1958. The male became so aggressive that feeding had to be carried out from outside the aviary. During the rearing period the adults consumed gentles and mealworms; they were also offered boiled potato, boiled carrot, hard-boiled egg, lettuce and fruit—but they were more interested in the livefood. They consumed more fruit as the young bird grew, particularly apple and cherries, and it became necessary to supply additional nectar.

The chick fledged on September 3. Its plumage was identical to that of the adults, from whom it differed in having the beak black and the iris black instead of light brown.

A. J. Clare's pair, which also reared one youngster in 1958, were obtained the previous year and placed in an aviary 4.9m (16ft) long. Two chicks had hatched by June 27. Mealworms, gentles, fruit and seed were supplied but ignored in favour of a mixture of Complan, Farlene, Robinson's baby rice, sugar, condensed milk and Bovril.

The chicks' eyes had not opened by July 11 but their bodies were covered in quills. On August 1 the eyes had opened, the quills were opening and the body was well covered in down. Yellow feathering was showing on their backs on August 16. The young lories were seen looking out of the nest on September 3 and they fledged 13 days later. Unlike Dudley's pair, they had remained very tame and did not object to nest inspection.

In 1960 Mr and Mrs G. W. Sharratt of Chellaston, Derby, obtained a pair of Yellow-backed Lories from a pet shop. In 1963 the hen laid two eggs; they were fertile but the chicks died in the shell. In the following year, two eggs were laid, one of which hatched on April 24; the chick survived only two days. The other egg contained a chick which had died in the shell. Approximately two weeks later two more eggs were laid; one was infertile and the other hatched after 28 to 30 days.

After six weeks the chick was killed by the parents, probably because they wanted to go to nest again (they had been seen mating) and the hen laid a few days after the death of the chick.

The nest was occasionally sprayed with luke-warm water and this attention resulted in both eggs hatching. Two chicks were seen in the nest on September 11 when they appeared to be a few days old. On October 17 tragedy struck: the hen failed to appear when called. Inspection of the nest revealed that the hen had died as a result of catching her claw in the wire grid at the bottom of the box. Both the chicks were alive but after a few hours it was evident that the male was not feeding them. They were therefore taken into the house and placed in a cardboard box lined with tissue paper. They were fed with nectar made from honey and Farex, offered on the end of a spoon. Honey water and baker's apple purée were also given. At night, a baby's hot water bottle, wrapped in a woollen cloth and then in tissue, was placed in the box.

For the benefit of others who have to carry out the task of hand-rearing lories, it is worth quoting at length from the account submitted to the *Avicultural Magazine* (1965, pp. 81–2):

'The chicks were partly feathered, with black beaks and eyes, green wings without flight feathers, and the yellow on their backs was already quite plain. They gave a low-pitched cry resembling a cat purr. This continued until they were about three months old. When they were six weeks old they weighed $5\frac{1}{2}$ ounces and were still feeding well every hour until 10pm at night, the next feed being at 7am in the morning. They now took their feed from a cake-icing syringe with a fine writing tube attached, which could be placed well inside their beaks. After every feed they had their beaks wiped with moistened cotton wool, as they tended to throw their food about a lot.

'Meanwhile, a week after the chicks were removed from the nest, the cock, who had been pining for his mate, died, leaving the enclosure empty. By this time they recognised our voices and squeaked when they were spoken to, so we promptly christened them Bubble and Squeak. In all stages of their development Squeak was quick to learn and took the lead, Bubble following suit about two days later.

'27 November. Chicks gained $\frac{1}{2}$ ounce in weight. Gradually they dictated their own feeding times, and the feeds were spaced out at $2\frac{1}{2}$ to 3 hours according to their appetite.' On December 15 they were transferred to a parrot cage and were able to climb and perch immediately. At this stage they weighed 8oz each. Within two weeks they were independent. At four months their eyes were becoming lighter and their beaks were almost horn-coloured.'

A German aviculturist, H. R. Roth, bred two chicks from a pair of lories described as Yellow-backs in 1966. However, as the hen had no yellow on the back it may have been of the nominate race. At San Diego Zoo two Yellow-backed Lories were reared in 1967, two in 1969, four in 1970, four in 1971, three in 1972 and four in 1973. This species has also been bred at Birdland, Bourton-on-the-Water and in the USA, in zoos in Lexington and Manchester.

It often happens that an aviculturist records details of the first breeding of a pair of birds in his possession and not subsequent results, so that the consistency of some breeding pairs is not recorded. Paolo Bertagnolio of Rome gave details

(*Avicultural Magazine* 1974, p. 35) of one pair of Yellow-backs which had been breeding since 1967 and had reared two chicks that year (1973). A second pair, consisting of an imported male and a daughter of the original pair, reared two young from two nests, and a third pair, a male bred by the original pair and a female from the second pair, reared four young from two nests—an excellent total of eight chicks from three pairs. It is of interest that pairs two and three defied the 'one pair per aviary' rule and shared the same enclosure.

Bertagnolio recorded details of the breeding of his original pair in the *Parrot Society Magazine* (October 1967, pp. 7–8). The pair had been received the previous year. A slight difference in the size of the bill was the only detail in which they differed. They were fed on fruit, especially apple, greenfood, a sugar solution with added vitamins, Sluis insectile mixture slightly sweetened, biscuits and sunflower seed.

On April 17, 1967 there were two eggs in their nest. On May 7 the male seemed excited and nest inspection revealed two newly hatched chicks with white down. They fledged on July 18 when they differed from the adults in having the bill dark and the skin surrounding the eye light brown instead of black. There was 'a trace of dirty yellow' bordering the feathers of the hind crown.

L.g. morotaianus (van Bemmel)
DESCRIPTION: Differs from *L.g. flavopalliatus* in having a duller and less extensive patch of yellow on the mantle; the wings are said to be a darker shade of green.
DISTRIBUTION: Morotai; birds from Raou Island probably also belong to this race.

13
Phigys

Genus: *Phigys* (formerly *Calliptilus*)

The sole representative of this genus, the Solitary or Collared Lory, has only rarely been kept in captivity. It is a particularly beautiful little bird, uniquely garbed for a lory with elongated feathers on the hind neck and mantle, a feature which gives it its common name. It differs from the *Vini* species in that the feathers of the crown have no shaft-streaking and it has been suggested by Amadon (1942) that it is 'a specialised offshoot' of this genus, 'the members of which (especially the short-tailed *V. kuhlii*) it resembles in many respects. Until a more extensive study of its relationship to other lories can be made, it seems best to retain *Phigys* as generally distinct.'

It is certain, however, that it is closely related to the *Vini* species. In addition to its appearance, the fact that male and female incubate the eggs substantiates this point as, in lories, shared incubation occurs only among the members of these two genera and the closely related *Charmosyna* species.

Very few aviculturists—or, for that matter, ornithologists—are familiar with all three genera. Dr J. M. Dolan is familiar with them under captive conditions, also with *Phigys* in the wild. His opinion is that the *Vini* lories are closer to the *Charmosyna* species than to *Phigys*. However, Dr Burkard, who keeps members of all three genera (*Phigys*, *Vini australis* and *Charmosyna meeki*) believes that: '. . . the *Vini* is more similar to *Phigys* than to the *Charmosyna*.' (Pers. comm.).

Although the Solitary Lory has been bred in captivity on a number of occasions, I can find no mention of its incubation habits, except a brief reference in the Duke of Bedford's account which appeared in *The Foreigner* (1938, pp. 40–42): 'The cock and the hen took turns at sitting albeit rather irregularly, the pair being off playing together a fair amount.' Dr Burkard confirmed that incubation is shared by male and female in his breeding pairs.

Collared Lory (*P. solitarius*) (Suckow)

SYNONYMS: Fiji, Ruffled or Solitary Lory.

DESCRIPTION: The forehead, lores and crown are deep purple, also the abdomen. The distinguishing feature of this lory is the nuchal ruff of elongated bright green feathers, which can be erected from each side, forming two fans on the side of the head. The red feathers of the mantle are also elongated. The wings are dark green and the rump light green; the under wing coverts, the tail and the under tail coverts are also green. The remainder of the plumage is red. The iris is yellow or orange. The bill is orange and the legs are pinkish-orange. Length: 20cm (7½in).

The female is said to have the forehead paler and more bluish, the rear part of the crown being washed with green.

Immature birds have the feathers of the breast tipped with purple and with concealed yellowish-green spots. The red and green feathers of the hind neck are much shorter. The bill is brownish, the legs pale grey and the iris dark brown. Bahr noted that in two hand-reared wild-caught birds the beak became bright yellow when they were three months old. At five months they underwent a partial moult of the head and breast feathers and at eight months they had a complete moult. Robert Patten described the young Collared Lories bred at Taronga Zoo as having the beak slate-coloured, the feet 'grey or putty', the red band on the upper mandible narrower and duller, and the eye black. According to Amadon (1942), immature birds 'show the same sexual characters as the adults but in a less pronounced manner. Males have green in the hind-crown only near the base of the feathers, and usually concealed. In some thinly feathered male juvenals the green is more or less visible but it does not extend to the tips of the feathers as in all females.'

DISTRIBUTION: The larger Fijian islands; Lau Archipelago south to Lakemba and Oneata.

Philip Bahr wrote of this species in 1911 (*Avicultural Magazine* 1911, p. 50) that it was extremely abundant on some of the smaller islands, notably Kandavu and Taveuni but that 'In Mongooseland it is becoming extremely rare and confines its range to belts of high trees and low lying swampy places, where it is free from the attentions of this predacious little animal.'

In 1910 he was shown several nesting sites on Taveuni by a planter. They were situated low down in dead stumps which had been left in coconut palms in his plantation. As most of the sites were at ground level it is not surprising that the mongoose found the 'Kula', as the natives call it, such easy prey.

Sydney Porter's description (*Avicultural Magazine* 1935, pp. 131–135) of this species in the wild is, in some respects, conflicting. 'On the island of Kandavu the Kula is very abundant, especially around the old native buildings, and its shrill cry of 'lish-lish' is heard on every hand. I have often watched them on the flowers of the tall coco-nut palms, feeding either on the pollen or on the honey of the flowers; the birds seem to start at the bottom of the spray, running up licking the flowers quickly with their long brush-tipped tongues as they go. They often alight on the very ends of the palm fronds and dance along the mid-rib with the characteristic whisking movements of the Lory tribe until they get to the flowers at the base of the leaf.

'. . . a writer recently stated that this species is in danger of extermination. This fortunately is far from the case: in fact there is no Parrot-like bird whose prospects of survival are so bright. It is abundant on nearly all the islands and most of them, except Viti Levu and Vanua Levu, are free from the curses of bird life—the mongoose, Man, and the rats. The natives hardly ever interfere with the bird. On the islands, where the mongoose is, the bird nests far out of the reach of this pest; the white people seldom if ever shoot it, and rats and cats cannot affect it, so while these conditions continue it will never become extinct. I have never seen it far away from the regions bordering the seashore; this is no doubt owing to it finding most of its food from the coco-nut palm, a plant which depends on the sea for the distribution of its seed. . . .

'No bird has a swifter flight than this lovely Lory, the Swallow and the Swift in ordinary flight are slow compared to it. The incredible speed with which it flies from one tree to another makes it impossible for the eye to follow it. There is just a misty flash of scarlet and green. The mystery is how it manages to thread its way through the densely planted palm plantations at such a speed without colliding with the trunks.'

More recently this species has been observed by Forshaw (1973) who states: 'I have seen them feeding in the flowering coconut palms lining the streets of Suva and in August 1971 saw pairs and small parties in disturbed forest adjoining wet pasture land about 20km south of the city. . . .

'They feed on pollen, nectar, blossoms and soft fruits. Favourite feeding trees are coconut palms, drala (*Erythrina indica*), and African tulip, and when these are in bloom small flocks come and go constantly. When coming to feed in a coconut palm the lories alight out on the fronds and make their way down to the flowering stalks in a series of fluttering hops.'

The name Solitary is, of course, as inappropriate in this as in any other species of lory. They are usually found in small groups—and not singly. *In Birds of Fiji in Colour*, R. B. Sibson comments: 'They are a highly gregarious species and Latham's specific name for them, *solitarius*, is rather a wry jest. In the evenings, flights of Collared Lories speeding to their roosts through the tall trunks of the coconuts are a thrilling spectacle.

'There is something typically tropical and exotic about these small sprightly parrots, which fortunately are still widely distributed over the larger islands of Fiji, even if according to Layard, one of the earliest ornithological explorers of the islands, great numbers used to be trapped for sale to Tongans and Samoans who periodically plucked them to use their brilliant feathers for decoration.'

IN AVICULTURE: In a letter to David Seth-Smith, written in 1912, Captain T. K. Hudson described how he had brought a pair of Solitary Lories by boat from Fiji to England 40 years previously. (The description he gave established their identity beyond doubt). They were kept alive during the 15,000 mile voyage by being housed in a cage protected by glass and warmed by hot water bottles and night lights. Sadly, one bird died at Spithead and the other died shortly afterwards due to an injury.

In Philip Bahr's account of the birds encountered during 15 months in Fiji (*Avicultural Magazine*, 1911 pp. 49–56), he wrote: '. . . no success had attended any effort to keep them in captivity. They were said to become very tame, but they never lived long and died in convulsions without any previous warning. The diet recommended was mummy apple (pawpaw), honey or sugar water.'

When Bahr eventually obtained an adult specimen it unfortunately refused to feed. On a visit to the island of Taveuni in December 1910 he obtained a partially-feathered chick and a slightly older bird.

Bahr wrote: 'At first I attempted to rear these young birds on honey but they did not take very kindly to it. One of them, however, on being placed on the breakfast table, made a bee line for the porridge and commenced feeding on it with great alacrity with his brush-like tongue. Tea, with sugar and milk he absolutely could not resist, though milk and sugar alone or Nestlé's milk he was not at all partial to. Henceforward the younger bird was fed by means of a spoon on sweetened tea and milk, and became very fat and grew rapidly; porridge and gruel he would not or could not take.'

Five more young birds were taken to Bahr by a Fijian; they were infested with white mites and had to be bathed in diluted lysol. Although the weather was very warm they required a considerable amount of extra heat. One did not survive—it vomited all food—but the others became very tame. 'They were always lively and cheery, tumbling about the floor, quarrelling like monkeys and greeting others of their kind with shrill cries as they winged their way over our house.'

One unfortunately died as the result of an accident and of the five remaining, three survived the long, cold boat journey to England, one dying soon after landing. On board ship, Bahr had placed the little lories in a box and took them to bed with him to keep them warm.

'The two survivors have now assumed magnificent adult plumage with an outstanding ruff of red and green. . . .

'They feed now almost exclusively on porridge, though they are very partial to fruit, especially grapes, apples and cherries. They partake of a warm bath daily and are extremely lively. During the colder weather we are now experiencing I found that they require to be placed in a warm cupboard at night.'

These two birds were deposited at London Zoo, the first of their species to be exhibited there. In 1925 Hubert Astley possessed two specimens. I can trace no further record of this species in aviculture until the Duke of Bedford obtained it in the 1930s. A Collared Lory bred by him was exhibited at London Zoo in 1941, deposited by P. H. Maxwell, who found it quite hardy.

Writing in *Foreign Birds* in 1943 (p. 61), H. J. Indge recorded: 'A pair of Fijian Ruffed Lories would suspend themselves by one leg, grasp each other's 'hands', and swing for minutes on end. It is a matter of chance that I can record no actual breeding success. I had a pair which showed no inclination to nest, and I began to despair of them, but a friend who visited us regularly said he would like to try his hand with them, and soon after he had them installed the hen laid two eggs, both clear. She laid a further two, again clear. Not to be beaten she laid a further two, and hatched two youngsters, which died at three weeks old. For the fourth time in the season she laid a further two eggs, and this time hatched one youngster, which soon followed the way of its elder brothers.'

In post-war years this beautiful little lory has not become any better known. I believe that only Dr Burkard and San Diego Zoo has kept it. A male and a female which had been in captivity several years were received from A. Isenberg in April 1966. The female died during the following year and the male lived until April 1971. In June 1970 two were received, recently collected birds which, according to Dr Dolan, were not as active as some of the other small lories in the collection. He commented (pers. comm.) that: 'They tame down very quickly and lose their fear of people. By this I mean they have no reservations about coming up to the wire and taking a piece out of your finger!'

The noted aviculturist Sydney Porter, who collected some of the world's rarest and most desirable parrots, described this species as: 'to my mind the loveliest and most engaging of the whole Parrot tribe.'

BREEDING RECORDS: In Britain, only the 12th Duke of Bedford has succeeded with this species. A pair presented to him by Dr Derscheid in 1937 reared two young in 1939 and at least one during 1940–41. Many nests were unsuccessful, the eggs being clear or broken. The Duke of Bedford did not record details of this first breeding which was briefly described by Harold King in *Cage Birds* (January 26, 1940).

'The parents were accommodated in an outdoor aviary, and went to nest in a 'grandfather clock' type of nest box, which stood in a dish of water in the aviary shelter, the box being partially filled with peat and rotten wood.

'Two white eggs were laid, the first on August 1, 1939. They hatched on August 29, and the two young left the nest in a very healthy condition.

'Hatching and rearing were carried out entirely by the parents, and the food supply consisted of Allinson's baby food, grapes, pears and apples.

'The young differ from their parents in the following details: eyes, feet, and beaks are black instead of orange; their crown and feet are darker blue and purple; the feathers on the nape and upper mandible are shorter, which makes the bands of red and green look narrower.

'The young hen is more heavily washed with green on the head than the old hen. When flying, an arc of orange spots is shown on the upper tail coverts.' When the description was made, the young birds were about six months old.

In 1940 the Collared Lory was bred at Taronga Zoo, Sydney. Several birds were received from Fiji in 1938. The following year one pair was placed in an aviary which measured 7.5m (25ft) × 1.5m (5ft) × 2.1m (7ft) high. A hollow log 45cm (18in) long was hung in the flight and by October 16 one egg had been laid. Due to disturbance caused by picnickers near the aviary, incubation was frequently interrupted. On November 13 both birds appeared agitated and inspection of the nest revealed a broken egg with a dead chick inside. On August 14 1940 a nesting log was hung in the flight under cover and the disappointment was great when a broken egg was found in the pond in the flight on September 2.

On September 23 an egg was laid in the log. A chick hatched on October 21; the other egg was infertile. A week after hatching the chick was described as 'a ball of white fluff.' Eight days later it was covered with grey down. Robert Patten, Curator at Taronga Park, recorded (*Avicultural Magazine* 1941, p. 73) that 'On 12th November it was possible to detect the development of the pin feathers coloured red and green, and on 18th November more colour was evident, but the dirty condition of the nest was now causing us some anxiety. Fearing, however, that our intrusion might have unfortunate results, we decided to leave well alone and hope for the best.

'On 23 November the feathers were more vivid in colour; the head being covered with dull green feathers. On 2nd December the breast and sides were the last portions to be clothed.'

The chick fledged on December 21, after nine weeks in the log. It was reared mainly on nectar, the fruit (apple, banana, pear and pawpaw) remaining untouched on some days. Lettuce and freshly cut lucerne were also eaten. The nectar provided was made with Mellin's food, condensed milk, a few drops of tomato juice and Marmite.

Patten's remarks about the conditions inside the log are of interest: '. . . it was a constant source of worry and anxiety to find the nesting log in such a filthy and insanitary condition; at times the young bird was actually standing in a liquid slime of excreta which would later become firm again. The astonishing thing, however, was that throughout the long period in the nest the young bird remained quite clean and eventually left it in excellent condition.'

During 1943–4 two pairs nested at Taronga, each rearing one youngster.

It would appear that in recent years this species has been bred only in Switzerland. In January 1977 Dr R. Burkard informed me: 'I have bred this species several times during the last 12 years. My experience is that they usually have two eggs but often only one is fertilised. If both are fertilised the parents usually raise only one of the youngsters; the other dies in the egg or shortly after leaving it. In captivity (at least, in my case) they do not breed until their fifth year. I now have birds of the third generation.'

14
Vini

Genus: *Vini*

The *Vini* lories are among the most beautiful of all birds. Of the five species, one is unknown in aviculture and three were represented in collections in the 1930s and early 1940s on a very few occasions and are never again likely to be available. The fifth, *Vini asutralis*, is being bred in San Diego Zoo at the time of writing. Two dealers in England advertised '*Vini* lorikeets' during the 1960s but although trappers offered the birds, they never materialised.

Two distinguishing features of the members of this genus are the feathers of the crown (long, narrow and shaft-streaked) and the very fine bill, which I find reminiscent of that of the Hanging Parrots (*Loriculus*).

Due to their island habitats, the population of these species has always been small; major destruction of their habitat would quickly lead to their extinction.

Blue-crowned Lory (*V. australis*) (Gmelin)

SYNONYMS: Blue-crested or Samoan Lory.
DESCRIPTION: Mainly dark green, brighter on the rump. A large bib-shaped patch, extending from the lores and below the eye, to the upper breast, is red, also a small patch on the abdomen, followed by a small patch of purple. The crown is dark blue with shaft-streaks of bright mauve-blue. The thighs are purple and the under tail coverts are yellowish-green. The bill and legs are orange and the iris is red with an inner ring of brown and another of yellowish-white. Length: 19cm (7½in).

Immature birds have shorter blue feathers on the crown and less red on the throat; the red on the lower breast is merely indicated and there is no purple patch on the thighs or abdomen. The bill is tipped with brown and the iris is also brown.

DISTRIBUTION: Samoa (apparently absent from Tutuila), Tonga (including Tongatabu, Eua, Hapai and Vavau islands) and nearby islands in central Polynesia and Lau Archipelago, Fiji. It is said to be erratically distributed, being found where coconut palms, *Erythrina* and *Hibiscus* trees are flowering. It is found in groups of 6 to 12 birds or in larger flocks. Its flight is swift and direct and it is apparently able to fly from one island to another.

This species was discovered at Tongatabu during Captain Cook's third voyage (1776–80) to the Friendly Islands. Mivart quoted Rev S. J. Whitmore who described it as 'very abundant on all the islands during a part of the year. The natives believe this bird migrates; but all I have been able to learn on the subject is, that they are seen passing in flocks from the western to the eastern islands. A few may be found all the year round; but during several months of the cooler season the coconuts swarm with them. They appear to feed chiefly on the nectar of the coconut flowers; but when the *Erythrina indica* (a tree very common near the coast) flowers, about July and August, they may be seen *about* it in great numbers.'

IN AVICULTURE: Judging by the lack of references in the avicultural literature, this species was entirely unknown until recently. San Diego Zoo received five in November 1970, three of which unfortunately died in the following year. It is also kept by Dr R. Burkard in Switzerland.

The Blue-crowned is the only member of the genus which I have seen alive. Undoubtedly, the other *Vinis* are equally enchanting; but the opportunity to confirm this is never likely to arise. My acquaintance with this lory was brief but memorable. I will never forget my first sight of it at San Diego Zoo. Here is housed the largest—and for me, the most interesting—collection of parrots in the world; and one aviary there drew me towards it again and again—that containing the breeding pair of Blue-crowned Lories.

Only the male was apparent in the aviary on all my visits but one. The female was caring for the young bird in the nest-box and I saw her but briefly. The male followed her back into the box, landing on the nail which formed the perch. I never tired of watching him jumping rapidly along the perch and running across the floor to the feeding dish. All the movements of this species are rapid and rather jerky, resembling those of *Charmosyna* species.

BREEDING RECORDS: San Diego's pair nested successfully in 1973; previously the hen had produced three clutches of infertile eggs. The first chick hatched on March 29, after an incubation period of 23 days; a second hatched two days later. Both were reared—the first in captivity. A third, hatched on July 10, was also reared. In 1974 chicks were hatched on February 15 and 16. The first died on March 27; the other was reared, also one from a second clutch.

Dr R. Burkard informed me in January 1977 that he had bred this species on two occasions, when the pair used a nest-box situated on the floor which measured 91cm (3ft) long and 7.7cm (3in) in diameter. He found that: 'In a group only the dominant pair breeds successfully. The difficulty lies in distinguishing the sex, which can only be judged by their behaviour. As male and female spend much time in the nest-box together, he was unable to state whether incubation was shared.

Kuhl's Lory (*V. kuhlii*) (Vigors)

SYNONYMS: Kuhl's Ruffed Lory, Ruby Lory.
DESCRIPTION: The elongated feathers of the crown are green with paler green shaft-streakings; the nape feathers are blue with mauvish shaft-streakings. The rest of the upperparts are green, darker on the wings and yellowish-green on the back and rump. The underparts, including the lores, throat and cheeks are scarlet and the thighs are purple. The under tail coverts are green. The tail feathers are

green at the tip, dark purple on the outer web, red on the inner web. The bill is orange and the iris is red with an inner ring of yellow. Length: 19cm (7½in).

Immature birds are said to have the underparts barred with greyish-purple and to have less red in the tail. The bill is dusky-brown and the iris is brown.

DISTRIBUTION: Rimitara, Tubuai Islands; introduced to Washington, Fanning and Christmas Islands in the Line Group.*

According to Forshaw (1973) this species was introduced to Washington and Fanning Islands some time before 1798. In 1874 Thomas Street, a member of a USA survey expedition, met a party of natives on Washington Island who had come from islands to the south to harvest coconuts. They had a number of tame Kuhl's Lories with them which probably resulted in them being introduced to Washington. In December 1957 six were introduced to Christmas from Washington; three were still present in early 1959.

This lory is quite common on Washington and Fanning Islands where it frequents coconut palms, whose nectar is said to be its main food. It has been reported that it prefers the deep, wet, main forest areas and is confined to the valleys because the coconut palms do not grow in the mountains. The breeding season apparently starts in January.

The range of this species is said to have decreased greatly, the deep, isolated forests of Rimitara perhaps being the only suitable habitat left. The population on Tubuai is apparently very small.

IN AVICULTURE: This exquisite little lory was first seen in Europe in 1879 when Miss Hagenbeck took one to Germany. Unknown in aviculture at the present time, it has very rarely been kept in collections. In 1930 A. A. Prestwich recorded in the *Avicultural Magazine* (p. 30) that A. W. Robinson of San Francisco had received several Kuhl's Lories. He added: 'This miniature lory has apparently only been imported into England once, and that some fifty years ago.' One was exhibited at London Zoo in 1936. Jean Delacour wrote of it: '. . . only those who have seen the specimen now in the possession of the London Zoo can have an idea of its delightful ways. Tame and gentle, it plays like a kitten; it is indeed the most wonderful pet I ever saw.' (*Avicultural Magazine*, May 1936).

In 1942 W. Sheffler of Los Angeles had this species in his collection. A female imported into England in 1935, owned by P. H. Maxwell, died in 1943.

BREEDING RECORDS: Kuhl's Lory was bred by Gilbert Lee in California, probably in the 1930s. J. Delacour reported (*Avicultural Magazine*, 1937, p. 135) that the pair had 'been nesting repeatedly for several years, but only one young one was so far reared, all the others dying after a couple of days. Mr Lee is now trying a new and more insectile diet, which they probably require.'

Taronga Park Zoo, Australia, received five specimens in April 1940, one of which died soon after arrival. The remaining four (two adult and two young birds) were housed together in a large aviary. The curator at Taronga described the adults as 'the envy of all who view them.'

---

*W. R. Ogilvie Grant (1913) wrote: 'It seems that the true home of *V. kuhlii* is the Society Group in the islands of Tahiti, Bora-Bora, etc, where it is probably now extinct. These islands lie 200 miles north of the Tubuai Islands.'

The older pair nested in November 1942 and February 1943, two eggs being laid on each occasion. One egg of the second clutch was fertile but complete incubation did not result. In 1943 the pairs were housed separately. The older pair nested in November; one egg was broken and a hatched dead chick was found on the ground beneath the nest. In January 1944 the female laid again; two chicks hatched but one died soon after; the same result was obtained in October 1944 and January 1945. In 1946 the birds nested in February. When the log was inspected on April 3 it contained a chick which was judged to be two to three weeks old, with red and green showing on the pin feathers.

On April 26 the nesting log was damp and dirty and was replaced by a new log. The young lory's feet and legs were washed with warm water before it was replaced in the new log. During the next few days it was noticed that the young bird's claws were inclined to bunch up. On April 29 it was found on the ground and was replaced in the log. Next day it was running around on the ground and seemed much stronger. Two days later a log was placed on the aviary floor and the young bird was put inside. It was not seen to feed itself until June 1. Its colouring was much duller than the adults', with bill and legs of a dark slaty colour and the iris very dark, almost black.

The incubation period was not established and although the report of the breeding by R. A. Patten (*Avicultural Magazine*, 1947, pp. 40–3) did not state whether the male and female shared incubation, it did state: '. . . during incubation if anyone entered the aviary the cock and hen would go into the flight and stop there until all was quiet, then they would both enter and stop in the nesting log, so it appeared that both shared in feeding and caring for their offspring.'

Food offered during the rearing period was cow's milk, Mellin's food and brown sugar with a little tomato juice, supplemented with a concentrated mixture of vitamins, cod liver oil and orange juice. Apple, banana, paw paw, pear and grapes were also offered.

Stephen's Lory (*V.stepheni*) (North)

SYNONYM: Henderson Island Lory.
DESCRIPTION: It is green above with paler green shaft-streaking on the crown; the rump is a yellowish shade of green. The underparts are scarlet except for the variable band of green and purple across the breast. The thighs and lower abdomen are purple; the under tail coverts are yellowish-green and the tail is greenish-yellow. Red and green are the colours of the under wing coverts. The bill and feet are orange; the iris is said to be yellowish. Length: 19cm (7½in).

Immature birds are green below with purple and red markings on the throat and abdomen and dark green tail. The bill is brownish and the iris dark brown.
DISTRIBUTION: Henderson Island, Pitcairn Group, central South Pacific Ocean. Nothing is known of the habits of this species which was discovered in 1907. G. R. Williams, whose paper on the birds of the Pitcairn Islands was published in 1960, found that it was not very common.

Tahiti Blue Lory (*V.peruviana*) (P. L. S. Müller)

SYNONYMS: Indigo Lory, White-throated Lory.

DESCRIPTION: In its coloration, this is among the most distinctive and unusual of all the lories. It is predominantly deep mauvish-blue with shaft-streaking of a paler blue on the crown. A large patch of white extends from the lores and throat to the ear coverts and extends to the upper breast. The bill is orange, the legs orange-yellow and the iris yellowish. Length: 18cm (7¼in).

Immature birds have greyish-white markings on the chin and dark greyish-blue underparts. The bill is black, the legs dark orange-brown and the iris dark brown.

DISTRIBUTION: Cook and Society islands and the westernmost islands of the Tuamotu group. It has long been extinct on Tahiti and other settled islands perhaps as a result of rats and other vermin introduced by man. An attempt to reintroduce it to Tahiti, probably in the early 1930s, was made by the American Eastham Guild.

Forshaw (1973) states that there is no reliable information on its present status, largely because of the difficulty of gathering reports from so many widely scattered islands, adding '. . . it seems to be extinct or very rare on the larger, more accessible islands and this is cause for concern.' These birds had been seen in Bora Bora in coconut palms along the coast in 1907. Forshaw spent three days of intensive searching on that island in 1971—but failed to find it. It is possible that it was an irregular visitor but he felt that it was a resident but had been exterminated by rats.

Forshaw gives the nesting site as a hollow in a tree or in a rotting coconut still adhering to the palm but another visitor to one of the islands where it was found, stated, less credibly, that this species constructs a nest in coconut trees using grass and small sticks. He also observed that they preferred dry habitat and bred during the dry season from May to July.

It would appear that this little lory, one of the most beautiful of all birds, may be in danger of extinction in the near future; however, there is no precise information on its present status.

IN AVICULTURE: In 1936 Eastham Guild brought a number of Tahiti Blue Lories to England, most or all of which were destined for the Duke of Bedford's collection, together with some Ultramarine Lories. J. J. Yealland, curator at that time, wrote (*Avicultural Magazine*, 1940 p. 309) that they had travelled well and were in excellent health. On the voyage they had received diluted condensed milk sweetened with moist sugar and any fruit obtainable. This nectar was gradually changed (see p. 16); apple, pear, grapes and occasionally tomato were offered. Yealland wrote that the birds ate the fruit like wasps, hollowing out the inside and leaving the skin—'as if their delicate beaks were not strong enough to break it.' They also drank tomato juice but the only greenfood which interested them was groundsel, of which they took the pollen from the flowers.

After about six months the lories became ill, one by one, and a number died; it was not until the nectar was diluted with its own volume of water that the losses ceased.

Dr Derschied in Belgium received a few *peruviana* at the same time as the Duke of Bedford. They were very active and did well on a diet of condensed milk mixed with an infants' food and sweetened with demerara sugar. They also ate apple, grapes and pear and were very fond of chickweed, eating the leaves, buds, flowers and even the unripe seeds. However, they became overweight on this diet, even although in the evening the nectar was replaced by sugared water. Unlike the Ultramarine Lories in the same collection, they relished mealworms; each bird was given one a day. A little coconut milk was offered occasionally.

They were kept in large indoor flights for most of the year, being housed in outdoor aviaries only during 'the best of the summer.' One egg was laid before 1937 and in the early winter of that year, two pairs were each provided with a tall hollow log with an inside diameter of 9cm (4in). They nested readily but when the nests were inspected a few weeks later, only small fragments of eggshells were found. The two hens produced at least a dozen soft-shelled eggs between them, causing egg-binding, which was aggravated by their overweight condition. Lime water and cuttlefish bone was added to the food in an attempt to prevent the production of soft-shelled eggs, but this did not have the desired effect, and it was concluded that housing the lories indoors was the cause of the trouble. A heating plant was installed in a range of outdoor aviaries with well-lighted brick shelters but, unfortunately, one hen died before being installed and the other hen died a few months later, both as a result of egg-binding.

Both John Yealland, curator at that time of Dr Derscheid's collection, and the Duke of Bedford recorded that some males behaved most viciously towards their mates. Clipping one wing solved the problem in Dr Derscheid's birds. The Duke of Bedford wrote (*Avicultural Magazine*, 1937, p. 349):

'. . . many cocks are apt to turn savagely on their hens with very little warning after living with them on apparently affectionate terms and feeding them.' One pair was separated for this reason and it was not until the male was feeding the female through the wire of the adjoining aviary that they were re-united.

BREEDING RECORDS: When provided with a grandfather-clock nest in the shelter of the aviary the hen laid two eggs. According to the Duke of Bedford, the cock and hen took 'turns in sitting'—thus it seems that this genus differs from most other lories in that incubation is shared. Two eggs were laid; one was damaged and the other hatched. In his account of the breeding (*Avicultural Magazine*, 1938 pp. 34–38) the Duke of Bedford described the down colour as black but corrected this later (p. 91) to grey. The chick matured quickly and left the nest 'about eight weeks after the first egg had been laid.' Dates are conspicuous by their absence throughout this breeding account and it would certainly appear that this estimate was incorrect for, if not, the chick spent less than five weeks in the nest. On fledging the chick was described as 'fine, strong and well-grown as anything in the Parrakeet line that I have ever reared . . .'. Its plumage was blue-black with streaks and blotches of greyish-white where the 'bib' would later appear. The beak and feet were blackish. The adult birds were allowed four mealworms per day while the chick was being reared and would have eaten more.

The Duke of Bedford received the medal of the Avicultural Society for the first breeding of the Tahiti Blue Lory which he described as 'the greatest triumph

Blue-streaked Lory
(Eos reticulata)
Photo: Thomas Brosset

Violet-necked Lory
(Eos squamata squamata)
Photo: Thomas Brosset

Above: Fairy Lorikeets *(Charmosyna pulchella rothschildi)*, male (right) and female. *Left:* Blue-crowned Lory *(Vini australis)*. *Below:* Collared or Solitary Lory *(Phigys solitarius)*. Photos: above, Thomas Brosset; others, San Diego Zoo.

Above: Green-naped Lorikeet *(T.h. haematodus)*. Photo by Horst Mueller. **Below:** Guenby Lory *(Eos squamata guenbyensis)*. Photo by Horst Mueller.

Left: upper photo: Edward's Lorikeet *(T.h. capistratus)*. Photo by R.H. Grantham. **Left, lower photo:** Mount Apo Lorikeet *(T.johnstoniae)*. Photo by San Diego Zoo.

Varied Lorikeet
(*Glossopsitta
versicolor*).
Photo: Eric Hosking

Little Lorikeet
(*Glossopsitta
pusilla*).
Photo: San Diego Zoo.

Dusky Lories *(Pseudos fuscata)*, adult female (left) and newly fledged youngster
Photo: Thomas Brosset

Goldie's Lorikeet (*G. goldei*) is a difficult bird to sex. Photo by Horst Mueller.

Gua-lories, genus *Neopsittacus.* Photo by Horst Mueller.

Tahitian Lory
(*Vini peruviana*).
Photo by Horst Muller.

Yellow-backed Lory
*(Lorius garrulus
flavopalliatus)*
Photo: R.H. Grantham

The Purple-capped
Lory (*L. domicella*) is
one of the best-known
lories.
Photo: Peter Oderkerken

Opposite:
Upper photo: Black Lory (*Chalcopsitta atra*).
Bottom left: Yellow-streaked Lories (*Chalcopsitta sintillata*). Bottom right:* Duivenbode's Lories (*Chalcopsitta duivenbodei*).
Photos: upper and bottom left, Thomas Brossett; bottom right, R.H. Grantham.

The Buru Red Lory
(*Eos bornea cyanonothus*) differs
from the nominate race
in that its colouration is
a slightly darker red.
Photo by Horst
Mueller.

Mitchell's Lory (*T. h. mitchelli*) is fairly fre-
quently improved.
Photo by Horst
Mueller.

A pair of Papuan Lorikeets (*Charmosyna papou*). Photo by Horst Mueller.

A pair of 36-day-old Perfect Lories (*Trichoglossus euteles*). Photo by San Diego Zoo.

The Red Lory (*E. b. bornea*) is a beautiful bird. Photo by Horst Mueller.

The Blue-thighed Lory (*L. i. erythrothorax*) is also known as the Red-breasted Lory. Photo by Horst Mueller.

Red-fronted Lory (*Chalcopsitta sintillata sintillata*,), also known as Yellow-streaked Lory. Photo by Horst Muller.

A very young Black Lory (*Chalcopsitta atra atra*). Photo by San Diego Zoo.

Green-naped
Lorikeet
(*Trichoglossus
haematodus
haematodus*).
Photo by Thomas
Brosset.

Left: Scaly-
breasted Lorikeet
(*Trichoglossus
chlorolepidotus*).
Photo by R.H.
Grantham.
Right: Weber's
Lorikeet
(*Trichoglossus
haematodus
weberi*). Photo by
San Diego Zoo.

Swainson's Lorikeet (*T. h. haematodus*). Photo by Horst Mueller.

Musk Lorikeets (*Glossopsitta concinna*). Photo by Horst Mueller.

Meyer's Lorikeet (*Trichoglossus flavoviridis meyeri*). Adult at left, 33-day-old youngster immediately below, 48-day-old youngsters bottom photo.
Photos: left, Thomas Brosset; others, R.H. Grantham.

of my avicultural career.' Two chicks were hatched in a later nest and fledged during the middle of March, 1938. A third clutch was infertile.

It would appear that no other aviculturist has achieved success in breeding this species. In the USA, Mrs Gilbert Lee's pair hatched chicks but they were not reared.

Ultramarine Lory (*V. ultramarina*) (Kuhl)

SYNONYMS: Goupil's Lory, Marquesas Lory.

DESCRIPTION: This exquisite little lory must surely be among the most unusually and beautifully attired of all birds, dressed entirely in delicate shades of blue, mauve and white. The forehead is deep skyblue, also the upper parts; the rump and the upper tail coverts are bright skyblue; the tail is pale blue tipped with white. The crown is mauve with shaft-streaking of pale blue; the lores and part of the cheeks are white, the remainder of the face and upper breast being white and mauve in a unique pattern of almost triangular white marks on a mauve background. The abdomen and under tail coverts are mauve and there is a patch of white above the thighs. The under wing coverts are dull blue. The bill is yellowish-orange, darker at the base of the upper mandible. The legs and iris are orange. Length: 18cm (7½in).

Forshaw (1973) states that immature birds are dark blue with scattered white markings on ear coverts, breast and abdomen and pale blue on the sides of the abdomen. The iris is dark brown aud the bill black. The young bird bred by the Duke of Bedford was described as having the white areas on the breast and abdomen bluish-black with only a faint splash of greyish-white and a trace of the same colour behind the eye. The bill and feet were black.

Of interest is the fact that the Whitney Expedition obtained an albino from Huapu Island.

DISTRIBUTION: Nukuhiva and Huapu, Marquesas Islands.

Nothing is known of its habits in the wild. Due to its limited habitat and the fact that this is being gradually decreased in extent, the survival of this species must be seriously endangered, especially on Nukuhiva where an international airport is planned.

15
Charmosyna

Genus: *Charmosyna* (Wagler)

Of the 14 exquisite, dainty lorikeets which comprise this genus, probably only six have been kept in captivity outside their native countries. They are perfect subjects but few aviculturists have had the opportunity to discover this fact; I therefore count myself extremely fortunate to have kept two species, one large (*papou*) and one small (*pulchella*). For charm and beauty they are rivalled only by the *Vini* lories. Mivart (1896) wrote of the *Charmosynas*: 'In shape these birds seem to us more elegant than any other of the Lories, while in brilliance and coloration they are inferior to very few.'

Most species are small and cryptically coloured, thus they are easily overlooked in the wild; for this reason it is difficult to assess just how rare some species are. The fact that they are difficult to locate almost certainly accounts for their rarity in aviculture, because some species are apparently quite plentiful in their natural habitat.

They are more slender in form than the *Vini* species but the two genera are obviously closely allied. Both scratch indirectly (over the wing)* but most *Charmosyna* species differ in being sexually dimorphic and in having the tail more graduated with narrow, pointed feathers. The Papuan Lorikeet also has elongated primaries and *josefinae* has primaries slightly elongated.

What little experience has been gained with the smaller members of this genus in captivity indicates that they are particularly susceptible to candidiasis; vitamin A should therefore be added to the nectar. In the experience of Dr R. Burkard, candidiasis is less likely to occur if the birds are provided with the following food which has a high vitamin content but is not sticky: one to two large spoonfuls of honey, one raw egg with shell, one apple (or pear or banana) and 10 drops of Protovit, blended in a mixer. Millet seed and 'baby food' are swelled in warm water, then blended with the other mixture.

Palm Lorikeet (*C. palmarum*) (Gmelin)

DESCRIPTION: Predominantly light green, paler and more yellowish below. The area around the bill, including the chin and lores, is red. The mantle is tinged with brown. The under wing coverts are greyish-green; there is no yellow on the underside of the wing. The central tail feathers are broadly tipped with yellow,

*All other lories known to aviculturists scratch directly.

the lateral ones narrowly yellow-tipped. The bill is orange and the iris yellow; the feet are orange-yellow. Length: 17cm (7in).

The female has less red, or none at all, surrounding the bill. The olive tinge on the mantle is absent. Immature birds resemble the female.

In 1781 Latham described *C. pygmaea*, the Pygmy Lorikeet which apparently differed in its smaller size 15cm (5.8in) and the lack of red feathering surrounding the bill. The unique type is figured in Mivart's *Monograph*. Mivart, who had seen the specimen, did not agree with Layard that it was a female *palmarum* but did not give his reasons.

DISTRIBUTION: New Hebrides, Duff Group, Santa Cruz and Banks islands. G. W. Stevens, resident for some years in the Solomons and New Hebrides, informs me that: 'The Palm Lorikeet is found in the Reef Islands, in the southern tip of the Solomons. It may not be recorded from there but I have seen it. It is decidedly not easy to see. I have seen just two pairs and, on both occasions, although I was actively looking for birds, I found them by accident. Their colouring is an almost perfect disguise.'

Meek's Lorikeet (*C. meeki*) (Rothschild and Hartert)

DESCRIPTION: Almost entirely green, darker above, more yellowish on the underparts and under wing coverts; the mantle is strongly tinged with brown. The ear coverts and the sides of the neck are streaked with darker green. There is a variable band of yellowish-white on the underside of the secondaries. The tail is green above, tipped with yellow or orange and the legs are orange. Length: 16cm (6½in).

The immature bird has not been described.

DISTRIBUTION: Solomon Islands: Kulambangra, Bougainville, Guadalcanal and Malaita. Predominantly a bird of the mountains, it is found in small parties or large flocks and has been observed in the company of the Duchess Lorikeet (*C. margarethae*). Its flight has been described as 'swift and direct.'

Red-throated Lorikeet (*C. rubrigularis rubrigularis*) (Sclater)

SYNONYM: Red-chinned Lorikeet.

DESCRIPTION: Mainly green, more yellowish below and bluish-green on the ear coverts which are streaked with paler green. The chin and a streak at the side of the lower mandible is red. The under wing coverts are yellowish-green and there is a yellow band across the underside of the flight feathers. The tail is green, tipped with yellow, the inner webs of the feathers being red at the base. The bill and iris are orange and the legs are yellowish-orange. Length: 17cm (6¾in).

The immature bird has not been described.

DISTRIBUTION: New Britain and New Ireland (Bismarck Archipelago). In 1966 this species was reported to be abundant in flocks of as many as ten in mountain forests above 500m. It frequents the upper branches of flowering trees, often in company with honeyeaters.

Krakar Lorikeet (*C.r. krakari*)

DESCRIPTION: It differs from the nominate race in the more extensive area of red which reaches to the upper throat and is bordered by yellow, and in being slightly larger.
DISTRIBUTION: Karkar Island, off the north-eastern coast of New Guinea.

Golden-banded Lorikeet (*C. amabilis*—formerly *aureicincta*) (Ramsay)

SYNONYMS: Red-legged Lorikeet, Red-throated Lorikeet.
DESCRIPTION: Mainly green, paler below, with the front part of the cheeks, throat and the thighs red; a narrow band of yellow borders the red throat. The ear coverts are streaked with bluish-green. The three outer tail feathers are red at the base of the inner web; the tail is yellow at the tip and black in the centre on the underside.
  The bill and feet are red; the iris is said to be dark buff. Length: 18cm (7in).
DISTRIBUTION: Fiji: Viti Levu, Ovalau and Taveuni.
  It would appear that this species is near extinction. In 1912 Dr P. H. Bahr was told by a planter that it was 'still common in the mountain forest of Taviuni.' In 1926 Dr Casey Wood, an authority on the birds of Fiji, thought that it was probably extinct on Ovalau and was 'to be seen occasionally' in Viti Levu and Taveuni.' In the latter island they were rarely seen away from the high mountains of the interior. Not long after, the infamous Whitney expedition visited Fiji, collecting skins for American museums. Sydney Porter recorded (*Avicultural Magazine*, 1934, p. 328): 'I have it officially from someone in Fiji who was connected with the expedition that 47 birds were shot, and I was told that since the expedition's visit it had not been seen. In spite of journey's into the interior I failed to find it.'
  It is to be hoped that this was not an accurate assessment of the number of birds taken by the Whitney expedition which found *aureicincta* only on Viti Levu; in Amadon's account (1942) of birds taken during that expedition, he lists ten of this species. It is not yet extinct, however. Forshaw (1973) quoted Blackburn who pointed out that due to its small size and the fact that it inhabited the outer canopy of mountain forest, it is difficult to locate; his observers failed to find it on Taveuni but two birds were seen in the Nausori Highlands in Viti Levu.
  Mivart (1896) mentions Layard's account of observing flocks of this species in Taveuni in company with Solitary Lories. Mivart quoted Charles Pearce who obtained specimens from 'a large tree bearing branches of yellow blossoms, from this they extracted a honey-like fluid; they had not previously made their appearance, and only remained while the tree was in flower. The flock consisted of about twenty individuals; the stomach contents contained nothing but the fluid extracted from the blossom, and a little pollen from the stamens of the flowers.'

New Caledonian Lorikeet (*C. diadema*) (Verreaux and Des Murs)

SYNONYM: Diademed Lorikeet.
DESCRIPTION: Known only from two females collected before or during 1860.

The male has never been described. The female was green, paler on the forehead, lores and underparts; the crown was deep blue and the cheeks and throat were yellow. The thighs were tinged with violet-blue and the vent was red. The tail was green above and yellow below, the lateral feathers being marked with yellow and blackish near the base and tipped with yellow. The bill and feet were orange. Length: 18cm (7in).

DISTRIBUTION: New Caledonia.

Buru Lorikeet (*C. toxopei*) (Siebers)

SYNONYMS: Blue-fronted Lorikeet, Toxopeus's Lorikeet.

DESCRIPTION: Mainly green, more yellowish on the underparts and under wing coverts. The forehead is green and the forepart of the crown blue; the chin and throat is greenish-yellow. The tail is green, narrowly tipped with dull yellow; the underside is dusky yellow with red markings at the base of the inner web. The bill and the legs are orange and the iris yellow-orange. Length: 16cm (6½in).

The female has a fainter and less extensive area of blue on the crown and a more pronounced yellow band across the underside of the secondaries.

Immature birds are darker and duller, more greenish on the throat and with a well defined yellow band on the underside of the wing.

DISTRIBUTION: The island of Buru, Indonesia.

This species is known only from seven specimens caught alive in central Buru by Toxopeus.

Pleasing Lorikeet (*C. placentis placentis*) (Temminck)

SYNONYMS: Beautiful Lorikeet, Red-flanked Lorikeet.

DESCRIPTION: Mainly green, more yellowish below. In the male the forehead and forepart of the crown are yellowish-green, the cheeks are vermilion and the ear coverts are violet, streaked with a lighter shade. The sides of the breast, flanks and the under wing coverts are vermilion and there is a dark blue patch on the rump. A yellow band crosses the underside of the flight feathers. The tail is green above, tipped with orange-yellow, and yellow below with red and black markings at the base. The bill is red and is apparently heavier in build than in other *Charmosyna* species. The iris is yellow or orange and the legs are orange-red. Length: 17cm (6¾in).

The female is easily distinguished by the absence of red in the plumage, which is replaced by green. The ear coverts are bluish-black conspicuously streaked with yellow; the forehead and crown are green.

Immature birds resemble females except young males which have some red on the lores and greenish-yellow on the forehead. According to Hartert (1901), young males differ from adult females in having the blue patch on the rump absent or only indicated. The iris is yellow and the legs orange-brown.

DISTRIBUTION: Pandjang, Ceram, Amboina and Ambelau in the southern Moluccas, on the Kei (Kai) and Aru Islands and southern New Guinea east to the Gulf District, Papua.

Flocks of this species on Ceram have been observed visiting coastal districts to feed on flowering coral trees (*Erythrina indica*). The diet is said to consist of pollen, nectar and possibly soft fruits. Its flight is swift and direct and it utters a shrill, harsh screech as it flies.

The nest has been found in a 'crow's nest' fern (two eggs) and this species has even been seen to excavate a tunnel, presumably for nesting, in a large arboreal termite mound.

IN AVICULTURE: The Pleasing Lorikeet has been collected on very few occasions. Walter Goodfellow collected a single specimen for Mrs Johnstone in 1908. Reporting the event in the *Avicultural Magazine* (1908, p. 334), H. D. Astley wrote that one male was brought 'which made one long for more!' In 1926 Goodfellow did obtain three more and Mayer collected one in the following year. H. Whitley had a single specimen in his collection at Paignton about 1931, and the Duke of Bedford kept a pair.

Halmahera Pleasing Lorikeet (*C.p. intensior*) (Kinnear)
DESCRIPTION: The rump colour of the male is more violet than in the nominate race and the forehead is greener, less yellowish. It is slightly larger, ie, 18cm (7¼in).
DISTRIBUTION: North Moluccas, including Obi, and Gebe in the Western Papuan Islands, West Irian.

C.p. ornata (Mayr)
DESCRIPTION: The mantle is slightly darker than in the nominate race, the blue rump patch is larger than in all other races and, in males, the red extends further down the throat.
DISTRIBUTION: Western Papuan Islands, except Gebe; north-western New Guinea.

Sclater's Lorikeet (*C.p. subplacens*) (Sclater)
DESCRIPTION: It differs from the nominate race in lacking the blue patch on the rump.
DISTRIBUTION: New Guinea, east of Hall Sound in the south and the Sarmi district of West Irian in the north.

Solomon Islands Pleasing Lorikeet (*C.p. pallidior*) (Rothschild and Hartert)
SYNONYM: Bougainville Pleasing Lorikeet.
DESCRIPTION: According to Forshaw (1973) it differs from *subplacens* in having the general plumage paler, particularly the blue ear coverts of the males. However, Iredale (1956) states that it is 'smaller, paler green above, ear coverts brighter blue.'

DISTRIBUTION: Woodlark Island, east of New Guinea in the Bismarck Archipelago; Bougainville and Fead in the Solomon Islands.

In Bougainville it has been recorded in secondary growth, especially around village gardens and in coconut plantations.

Gilliard and Lecroy (1967) state: 'This species was abundant in the crown of the lowland tropical forest from sea level to about 1,000 feet. Almost all our specimens were shot while feeding from the blossom of an extremely tall tree growing in the forest edge near a native garden. There was much inter flock fighting among the blue-cheeks as they fed on nectar; attacks on intruding myzomelas were noted frequently.'

Red-marked Lorikeet (*C. rubronotata rubronotata*) (Wallace)

SYNONYMS: Red-rumped Lorikeet, Red-spotted Lorikeet.
DESCRIPTION: It is mainly green, more yellowish below and on the sides of the neck. The forehead and forepart of the crown are red in the male; the ear coverts are purplish-blue faintly streaked with a brighter shade. The under wing coverts and the sides of the breast are red and there are variable red markings on the upper tail coverts. The underside of the secondaries is marked with a variable yellow band. The tail is green above, dusky yellow below; the lateral feathers are broadly tipped with yellow and marked with red at the base. The bill and legs are red and the iris is orange. Length: 17cm (6¾in).

The female has no red on the head and the ear coverts are green streaked with yellowish-green. The under wing coverts and the sides of the breast are pale green.

The immature has not been described.
DISTRIBUTION: The island of Salawati and north-western New Guinea.

Of the three species of *Charmosyna* found in this part of New Guinea, this is apparently the least common. It is found in lowland forests up to about 850m and has been seen feeding in the tops of flowering trees in the company of other lorikeets and honeyeaters.

Kordo Lorikeet (*C.r. kordoana*) (A. B. Meyer)
DESCRIPTION: The male differs from the nominate race in having the red on the crown paler and more extensive; the ear coverts are more blue than purple.
DISTRIBUTION: Biak Island in Geelvink Bay, West Irian. Mayr and de Schauensee (1939) state that this species was seen only 'in small, chattering flocks among high coconut trees that grew around the houses of Korrido, near the shore.'

Striated Lorikeet (*C. multistriata*) (Rothschild)

SYNONYM: Many-striped Lorikeet.
DESCRIPTION: Predominantly green, more yellowish on the forehead, throat and

the side of the head; the hind crown is brown, also the nape which is variably spotted with orange-yellow. The entire underparts are green, darker on the breast, and streaked with greenish-yellow. The ventral area is red. The tail is olive-green above tipped with dusky yellow and marked with red at the base; the underside is olive-yellow. The beak is orange with the upper mandible grey except at the tip. The iris is red and the legs are bluish-grey. Length: 18cm (6¾in).

The female apparently resembles the male. Immature birds are darker green on the head, with smaller orange-yellow spots on the nape and duller streaks on the underparts.

DISTRIBUTION: Western New Guinea on the southern slopes of the main ranges between the Snow Mountains and the upper Fly River. This rare lorikeet is known only from a few localities between 200 and 1800m.

Wilhelmina's Lorikeet (*C. wilhelminae*) (A. B. Meyer)

DESCRIPTION: Mainly green, more yellowish below. The crown and nape are purple-brown, the nape being streaked with blue. There is a faint olive patch on the hind crown. The breast is streaked with yellow and the under wing coverts are red. In the male there is a broad red band across the underside of the flight feathers. The lower back is red and the rump is purplish-blue. The tail is green with red markings at the base. The bill and iris are orange and the legs are grey.

The female lacks the red on the lower back and on the underside of the flight feathers. The under wing coverts are green. Length: 13cm (5in); it is the smallest member of the genus.

Immature birds have little or no blue streaking on the crown or yellow streaking on the breast. The male has the back dull purple.

DISTRIBUTION: New Guinea from the Arfak Mountains, West Irian, east to the Huon Peninsula and south-eastern New Guinea. It is an uncommon bird in the mountain forests between 500m and 1800m.

IN AVICULTURE: Almost unknown to aviculturists, this species was collected on at least two occasions by Walter Goodfellow. A single specimen which he obtained in 1908 died on the voyage home but the following year he was successful in collecting a pair for E. J. Brook.

Fairy Lorikeet (*C. pulchella pulchella*) (G. R. Gray)

SYNONYM: Fair Lorikeet.
DESCRIPTION: The male is mainly red below and dark green above; the rump is dull blue, sometimes marked with green. The thighs and a large patch on the nape are purplish-black. The breast and, in some specimens, the lower flanks, are streaked with yellow. The under wing coverts are green and red; the tail is green at the base, red in the centre shading to yellow at the tip, with the underside bright yellow. The bill is orange, also the legs; the iris is orange. Length: 18cm (7in).

The female can be distinguished by the yellow patches on the side of the rump.

Immature birds have the breast tinged with green and little or no yellow streaking. The dull blue on the rump is only faintly indicated; the thighs and the nape patch are a mixture of green and black. There is a yellow band across the underside of the flight feathers. The bill is brownish, the legs brownish-grey and the iris brown.

E. J. Brook stated that he was unable to sex the bird bred by his pair when it was young. It lacked the golden marks on the breast, having instead a blotchy band of green. Small green feathers were 'blotched about all over the breast down to the vent.' The green of the back was continued up the nape to the top of the head.

DISTRIBUTION: New Guinea, in the mountains from the Vogelkop, West Irian, east to the Huon Peninsula and southern Papua.*

This species has been observed in pairs, small parties and large flocks and is said to feed on pollen, nectar and flowers, sometimes in company with other lorikeets and honey-eaters.

IN AVICULTURE: The Fairy Lorikeet is one of several New Guinea lories which was collected privately in the early years of the century and did not reappear until the early 1970s—in this case 1973 and the sub-species *rothschildi* (qv). Goodfellow collected four in 1908 for Mr and Mrs Johnstone and three in 1909 for E. J. Brook. The latter thought that: 'Probably no member of the Parrot tribe is more graceful and beautiful' than this species (*Avicultural Magazine* 1914, p. 29).

'. . . Always interesting with its vivacious, impulsive movements, always on the move as if ready for any fun that may present itself, it is at the same time quite safe with other inmates of the aviary.' Brook's pair was housed with tanagers and sunbirds.

BREEDING RECORDS: Brook's pair nested successfully after they had been in his possession for five years. Previously the one egg which, according to Brook, formed the clutch, was always infertile. This had caused him to lose interest in their nesting activities, thus he could not give the length of the incubation period. All he could write of its breeding was: 'We found that there was a young bird in the nest, evidently just after it was hatched, and it remained in the log exactly two months; it is now flying and feeding itself.'

Rothschild's Fairy Lorikeet (*C.p. rothschildi*) (Hartert)

DESCRIPTION: It differs from the nominate race in having a broad band of green as a background to the yellow streaks of the upper breast. The abdomen is purplish-black and the patch on the nape of the same colour is extended to reach the eyes. The rump is green. The male has the under tail coverts red washed with yellow.

The female can be distinguished by the greenish-yellow patch on the side of the rump and the greenish-yellow under tail coverts. The areas of red are duller and less extensive and the blackish-purple markings on the head are less clear

---

*Some taxonomists recognise the sub-species *bella*. Peters (1937) gives its range as the mountains of central and eastern New Guinea: Gebroeders, southern Snow Mountains, Mount Goliath, Sattelberg, Huon Peninsula, Morobe district, Wharton Range, Arcora River, Aroa River.

cut and more widely diffused; the abdomen is more black than red in most specimens I have seen, possibly due to a tendency to melanism.

DISTRIBUTION: New Guinea in the Cyclops Mountains and northern slopes of mountains above the Idenburg River, West Irian.

IN AVICULTURE: I know of no instance of this distinctive subspecies in aviculture prior to 1973. In August of that year Mrs S. Belford imported four 'Little Red Lories' from Singapore. On arrival they proved to be this race, three males and a female. She immediately sent for more and quickly received another 20, almost certainly the largest importation to reach England. Subsequently a few more were imported into Britain and other parts of Europe.

In August Mrs Belford asked me to care for the first four and in October I took the remaining eight. Two others went to Raymond Sawyer, in whose aviaries they attempted to nest the following year. They were not successful but it is of interest to record that they almost filled the nest-box with small pieces of cupressus about 15cm (6in) long, also with rose leaves which they had bitten off. These birds remain permanently in their large, planted outdoor aviary; the shelter is heated at a temperature of about 45°F to 50°F during the winter. At this time their nest-box was placed in the shelter yet they preferred to roost on the perches. They often helped themselves to the fruit and, perhaps, also the insectivorous mixture in the food trays.

After I had kept the Fairy Lorikeets for six months, four went to an aviculturist in Ireland. Four of the eight remaining were retained because they were suffering from candidiasis (see p. 6).

The appeal of this exquisite little bird is an instant one and not accounted for by colour alone; its grace and daintiness are accentuated in its movements. This species is an absolute joy to watch; even caging it cannot diminish its fascination. It is seen to much greater advantage in an aviary, especially a planted one. I house one pair in a small enclosure which, in summer, is covered with the purple flowers of clematis and the white ones of that pretty weed convolvulus. It has an earth floor and contains a small cupressus tree which was soon partly destroyed by the Fairies but one of their chief delights is to bathe in it after it has been hosed down. This particular pair, unlike another, will bathe in a large plastic drinker hooked on to the front of the aviary.

These birds are easily induced to bathe by spraying. While wintering in my indoor birdroom they are sprayed regularly and nothing arouses greater excitement in them than the sight of the sprayer. As soon as they feel the water on their plumage they flap their wings vigorously, whether they are perched or clinging to the wire netting, to receive the full benefit of the water. Those I have cared for have been very steady, almost fearless, and they do not retreat from the sprayer. An excess of water on their plumage makes them quite ecstatic; I have known them to descend to the floor of their compartment which is about 90cm (3ft) high, and roll over and over in the water which has accumulated during spraying, becoming so drenched that they could fly only with difficulty. Each bird will then retire to a perch and spend long periods licking and preening its mate. This is a pastime in which they normally indulge for long periods and, indeed, it is seldom except when feeding that a bird is not perched closely against its mate.

In my pairs, displaying and mating takes place throughout the year. When four birds were housed together during the winter, I have even seen the male of one pair display to the female of the other pair, but he is quickly driven away by the rightful male. The members of the pairs do not otherwise leave their partner's sides except for an occasional squabble with the opposition. I feel that any attempt to colony breed with this species would end in failure; they seem less tolerant towards their own kind than most small lories.

In 1974 the two pairs placed in small outdoor aviaries immediately took to the nest-boxes provided; natural logs were ignored. One pair spent such long periods inside the box that my hopes were aroused—but no eggs were laid that year.

As winter approached I wondered whether I dared let them stay outside but a decision was forced on me one damp November morning when the male of one pair looked unwell. He responded very quickly to an infra-red lamp and within a few hours was quite recovered. This incident made me confine all the Fairies to the birdroom for the winter. A lamp is left on at night enabling them to feed at any time. However, a close watch has to be kept for candidiasis which seems more likely to develop when the birds are housed indoors. A possible reason is that they cannot be prevented from tearing up the newspaper which covers the floor of their compartment. This results in dirty beaks—ideal for the growth of the fungus. Undoubtedly the best floor covering in these conditions would be tiles which could be washed daily.

BREEDING RECORDS: Judging by the available literature, this species has yet to breed successfully in captivity. My pair hatched a chick in 1975. At the beginning of August I noticed that either the male or the female would be in the aviary and the other bird in the nest-box; previously the pair had spent long periods together inside the nest-box—a standard oblong type made for Budgerigars. From the position of the male's tail, which could be seen through the nest entrance, it was soon apparent that the male was incubating.

On August 14 there were several hours of rain of tropical intensity. When it subsided, I found the Fairy Lorikeets sitting outside their nest-box. I therefore entered the aviary and found that the two eggs were reposing in a puddle of water. I added a handful of peat to the bare concave and, much to my relief, one of the birds started to incubate almost immediately. On August 29 and 30 I was surprised to hear very faint squeaks from their nest-box. On September 4 I suspected that the chick or chicks had died. Next day inspection revealed one egg and a dead chick which I judged to be about six days old. It had a few wisps of white down but was very discoloured and, by the time examination was carried out, it was not possible to discover the cause of death.

In 1976, while still in her winter quarters, the female laid on January 11 or 12 and January 15; no nest-box was in position. One was immediately provided and the eggs placed inside but the birds did not enter for some weeks. The pair was placed in the usual summer aviary on May 23 and the female laid two eggs during July. The male had been showing signs of senility for some months and I was therefore not surprised that he did not take his full share of incubation; thus the eggs did not hatch.

During the following winter in their usual indoor flight, they—or probably only the male—started to foul the inside of the nest-box, probably due to his age, and I therefore lined the bottom of the box daily with paper, removing the sodden paper from the previous day. Under normal circumstances, lories keep their nest-box spotlessly clean. On February 3 there was one egg in the nest-box which was quite clean and dry; three or four days later a second egg was laid and both eggs reposed on dry paper which had been shredded by the birds.

The female of a pair of Rothschild's Fairy Lorikeets belonging to Peter Paris of Cornwall laid three clutches of two eggs under the newspaper in her cage. In 1976 the pair went to Birdland, Bourton-on-the-Water, where a special enclosure was constructed for them with breeding in mind.

Duchess Lorikeet (*C. margarethae*) (Tristam)

SYNONYMS: Margaret's Lorikeet, Princess Margaret's Lorikeet.

DESCRIPTION: Easily distinguished from the other red *Charmosyna* species by the yellow band on the breast, which continues as a line on the mantle, and is bordered by a narrow line of purple-black. The male is red, with the wings and mantle dark green, also the under tail coverts; the rump and upper tail coverts are olive green and the sides of the rump are red. There is a purple-black patch on the crown and dull purple on the breast, below the yellow band. The tail is red, tipped with yellow. The bill, legs and iris are orange. Length: 20cm (8½in).

The female can be distinguished by the yellow patch on each side of the rump. Immature birds have the yellow band on the breast and mantle poorly defined and without the purple-black line bordering it. The body feathers are edged with purple-black.

DISTRIBUTION: Solomon Islands. Principally a mountain bird, the Duchess Lorikeet also inhabits coastal coconut plantations and lowland forests. They often feed in company with other lorikeets, and may gather in groups of about 40 birds to feed on pollen, nectar and blossoms. In *Zoonooz* (December 1975), Ken Stott mentioned that on Guadalcanal the Duchess Lorikeet is more typically a mountain bird, being more abundant at low levels on other islands, including Bougainville.

IN AVICULTURE: Nothing has been recorded about this species in aviculture but it is not entirely unknown; four Duchess Lorikeets arrived at San Diego Zoo in 1944, via the U.S. Navy. (There are no zoo records for this period and their histories are unknown.)

Josephine's Lorikeet (*C. josefinae josefinae*) (Finsch)

DESCRIPTION: The coloration of this species is similar to that of the Papuan Lorikeet, except the tail which is mainly red and not elongated, accounting for almost half of the bird's total length. The male is mainly scarlet, with dark green wings and mantle. There is a black patch on the crown (extending to the nape) which is streaked with pale mauve. The thighs, lower flanks and lower abdomen are dull black and there is a small dusky blue patch on the rump. The central tail feathers are red, tipped with yellow, the lateral feathers being green on the outer webs and tipped with yellow; underside of tail is yellow. The bill, legs and iris are orange. Length: 24cm (9½in), of which the tail accounts for 11cm (4½in).

The female has the lower back yellow, not red. Immature birds have the black feathers of the abdomen and nape tinged with green; the thighs are bluish-black.
DISTRIBUTION: The mountains of western New Guinea from the Vogelkop, West Irian, east to the Snow Mountains. It inhabits forested areas between 800m and 2,000m, occasionally being found much closer to sea level, and has been observed in pairs or small groups. One observer found them feeding in flowering trees in company with Fairy Lorikeets, and another noted that they were attracted by the large white flowers of a vine. Pollen, nectar and possibly soft fruits constitute the diet. Pollen and flower buds were found in the crops of birds collected in the Weyland Mountains. Like other *Charmosyna* species, it has been described as difficult to detect, being quiet and inconspicuous, flying silently or occasionally uttering a soft call-note.

Sepik Lorikeet (*C.j. sepikiana*) (Neumann)
DESCRIPTION: The male can be distinguished from the nominate race by the more extensive area of black on the abdomen; the black patch on the nape is streaked with pale grey. The female has the lower back and flanks yellow.
DISTRIBUTION: Mountains of the Sepik region, western New Guinea.

Cyclops Lorikeet (*C.j. cyclopum*) (Hartert)
DESCRIPTION: Differs from the nominate race in lacking, or having a faint, black patch on the abdomen and the mauve streaking on the crown.
DISTRIBUTION: Cyclops Mountains, West Irian.

Papuan Lorikeet (*C. papou papou*) (Scopoli)

DESCRIPTION: The male is dark green on the wings, mantle and the upper part of the tail. The head, under wing coverts and underparts are scarlet with a darker sheen on the upper breast. There is an almost square patch of colour on the crown, which is dark blue at the front, becoming black; a crescent-shaped black patch decorates the nape. There is another black patch on the abdomen which meets the black of the front of the thighs, which are yellow at the back. There is a patch of dark blue on the rump. An unusual feature is the elongated tips to the primaries. The tail is the most beautiful feature of the Papuan Lorikeet, measuring more than 20cm (8in) and tapering almost to a hair's breadth. It is dark green above with patches of red and yellow on one side of the web and a yellow tip on the upperside. The under side is orange-yellow. The feet are pinkish; the beak is orange and the iris is the same colour with a very narrow ring of paler orange, noticeable only on close inspection. Length: about 38cm (15in).

The female has the base of the red feathers on the sides of the rump yellow and a yellow-orange patch over the yellow spot above the thighs.

Immature birds are said to be generally duller with the feathers of the neck and breast margined with black. The black patch on the abdomen is margined with bluish-green. The blue on the rump is duller and less extensive and there is a variable yellow band across the underside of the secondaries. The tips of the primaries are not elongated and the central tail feathers are shorter. The bill is brownish-orange, the iris pale yellow and the legs brownish-orange.

DISTRIBUTION: New Guinea in the Vogelkop, West Irian.

The Papuan Lorikeet is found in pairs or small parties in mountain forests between 1,500m and 3,500m. Forshaw (1973) states that they move about in a peculiar, jerky manner, often flicking their long tail feathers. 'A flash of brilliant colours and the long tail streaming behind makes them conspicuous birds in flight, but when feeding among blossoms or flowering epiphytes attached to moss-covered branches they are easily overlooked.' He observed them in company with Musschenbroek's Lorikeets, feeding on the fruits of *Schefflera*. Pollen, nectar, blossoms, buds, berries, seeds and possibly insects form the diet.

Forshaw states that skins of this species are greatly prized as head decorations by highland people and are freely traded.

IN AVICULTURE: The nominate race is almost unknown in aviculture, although the subspecies *stellae* (qv) has been kept on several occasions. I was extremely fortunate to have a male Papuan Lorikeet in my care for nine months from September 1972, lent by a friend who had imported it a short time previously. I was immediately captivated by its tameness and delightful personality. Evidently it had been hand-reared, for it was fearless and craved attention. When spoken to it would display and then the yellow patches on the thighs would stand away from the body. It would make a soft whistling noise, lifting and waving one foot, and then the other. It was easy to induce this bird to display by whistling to it, causing it to stretch to its full height, bow and hiss and make a snapping noise with its beak.

This bird's exceptionally long tongue was a constant source of amusement. It would be literally waved around the beak and could easily reach the bird's cere. Lories use their tongue's to explore objects more than most parrots but I have never seen a lory use its tongue more frequently than the Papuan. For a short while I kept it in a cage and it would even push its slender head through the bars and stretch its tongue to its limit in an effort to reach my face.

When received, the Papuan was not in full adult plumage, the breast feathers having dark margins. The tail was not full length, thus the bird measured only about 30cm (12in). After it moulted, its tail measured 20cm (8in) to give a total length of approximately 35cm (14in). To see this bird in flight was to view one of the wonders of New Guinea's birdlife. Eventually the Papuan was bought by a friend who housed it in a 6m (20ft) planted aviary, then in a 12m (40ft) aviary which had the appearance of a garden, complete with a pool for the small wading birds. Here the Papuan could be seen flying, with the long tail streaming behind and slowing its flight. When in one of my aviaries I noticed that it never flew in a perfectly straight line, but always flew upwards before landing.

This bird was quite incredibly beautiful; it was certainly the most elegant and lovely parrot I have ever seen and I would venture to suggest that there are very few more beautiful birds in existence than the Papuan Lorikeet. Grace of form and beauty of plumage in such a degree is a rare combination.

While in my temporary possession, the Papuan Lorikeet refused fruit and small seeds. Its diet consisted of nectar made from equal amounts of honey and malt, with the occasional addition of condensed milk, with the same mixture and a vitamin preparation added to trifle sponge. It was particularly fond of the latter. On this somewhat monotonous diet it thrived—in fact, I have seldom seen a fitter and more active bird. An enthusiastic bather, it kept itself in immaculate condition. When kept in the large planted aviary mentioned, it was believed to sample a wider variety of foods, including mealworms.

Stella's Lorikeet (*C.p. stellae*) (A. B. Meyer)

DESCRIPTION: It differs from the nominate race in having a more extensive black patch on the crown and hind neck, the forepart being streaked with bluish-violet. There is no yellow in the body plumage. It is slightly larger, ie, about 39cm (15½in).

There is a melanistic phase in which the red areas are replaced by black, except on the rump and lower back.

The female has the sides of the rump and the lower back yellow.

E. J. Brook described the first young Stella's Lorikeet he bred as having yellow flanks, as in the female but the lower back was red, as in the adult male. The beak was brown. A young one bred by another pair had far more yellow on the back. It was almost identical to the adult hen and Brook believed that it was a female and that the first one reared was a male because of the 'yellow mottlings amongst the red.' He pointed out that Mivart (1896) was at fault in believing that immature birds resemble the male.

DISTRIBUTION: The mountains of south-eastern New Guinea west to the Angabunga River and the Herzog Mountains.

Rand noted the number of melanistic examples found in the Snow Mountains at certain altitudes as follows: 6,oooft—seven birds, one melanistic; 7,oooft—15 birds, all melanistic; 9,oooft—six birds, five melanistic. If further information was available it might be possible to conclude that the melanistic form predominates at higher altitudes.

IN AVICULTURE: Those collected by Walter Goodfellow for Mrs Johnstone in 1907 were probably the first to reach England. He collected five more pairs in 1908 and in September 1909 he brought back four more. Most of these were obtained by E. J. Brook.

Of their behaviour Brook recorded (*Bird Notes*, 1910, p. 67): 'Their voice is not disagreeable, it is shrill, but not piercing. One or two of the cocks made a noise just like the bleating of a lamb; this may be acquired but I think it is natural.

'The birds proceed by jumps or bounds, whether on the ground or on horizontal perch.

'I find these birds as hardy as most other Lories.

'They are an accommodating species, as several pairs will live together in the same aviary, where they make a grand show.'

Stella's Lorikeets were included in Alfred Ezra's collection at Foxwarren Park in Surrey in the 1930s, probably being those brought to England in 1933 by the collector Shaw Mayer. There were 13 examples of the red form and four of the black; this may be the only occasion on which the latter has been imported into England. Alan Lendon recorded seeing both phases in Taronga Zoo in 1953.

In recent years it would seem that Stella's Lorikeet has been represented only in the collection of San Diego Zoo, which has exhibited five specimens. I saw one, a male, which had been in the collection for five years when I visited the zoo in 1974. Subsequently a pair reached Los Angeles in 1975, one of which died soon after its arrival. The survivor was offered at $1,000!

BREEDING RECORDS: In 1910, two pairs of Brook's Stella's Lorikeets were successful in rearing young. The hen of the first pair unfortunately died when the chick was two weeks old due, apparently, to a lump of sand in the bowel. The incubation period was 'about three weeks' and the chick fledged after 'exactly two months.' Regrettably, Brook gave no further information, except regarding the plumage of the young birds.

In 1974 hybrid Stella's × Violet-naped Lories were bred at San Diego Zoo. They were described, while still feathering, as having the top of the head and the forehead red, shading into reddish-violet on the back of the head and nape. The wings were coming in green.

Mount Goliath Lorikeet (*C.p. goliathina*) (Rothschild and Hartert)
DESCRIPTION: Said to differ from *stellae* in having the tips of the long central tail feathers yellow, rather than orange-yellow, and the long upper tail coverts green, rather than red, in both sexes.
DISTRIBUTION: The mountains of central New Guinea.

In a paper published in 1954, E. T. Gilliard stated that from his observation, melanistic specimens were three or four times more numerous than normal ones. This observation has been corroborated by other ornithologists.

Rothschild (1931) wrote: 'The natives declare that one black bird might be seen in a small flock of normal plumaged birds, or one paired with a normal bird, but they have never seen a black one paired with a black one.' (That observation is unlikely to be accurate if melanistic specimens outnumbered normal ones in the ratio given.)

Wahne's Lorikeet (*C.p. wahnesi*) (Rothschild)
DESCRIPTION: It differs from *goliathina* in having a wide yellow band across the breast and a green tinge to the patch on the abdomen. The melanistic phase is known.
DISTRIBUTION: New Guinea, in the mountains of the Huon Peninsula.
Addendum: During 1976 four Fairy Lorikeets were reared at Walsrode Bird Park in Germany. Also in the collection was the Red-marked Lorikeet (*C. rubronotata*) and the Pleasing Lorikeet (*C. placentis*).

16

Oreopsittacus

Genus: *Oreopsittacus* (Salvadori)

The single species in this genus differs from all other parrots in having 14 instead of 12 feathers in the tail. In shape it resembles the smaller *Charmosyna* lorikeets, except for the upper mandible which is thinner and longer; it, also, is sexually dimorphic. It is virtually unknown in aviculture.

Arfak Alpine Lorikeet (*O. arfaki arfaki*) (A. B. Meyer)

SYNONYMS: Blue-cheeked Alpine Lorikeet, Whiskered Lorikeet.
DESCRIPTION: The male is mainly green, darker above, with the forehead and crown red; the lores and cheeks are purple with a double row of white dots or streaks below the eye. The abdomen and lower flanks are yellow or red and the under wing coverts and the sides of the breast are red. There is a yellow band across the underside of the secondaries and yellow on the sides of the under tail coverts. The tail is green with the tip and the underside rose-red. The bill is black, the iris dark brown and the legs greenish-grey. Length: 15cm (6in).
The female has the crown and forehead green. Immature birds resemble the female in this respect but can be distinguished by the narrow black edges to the feathers of the upper parts. There is less purple on the cheeks and the white streaks are less clearly defined. The central tail feathers are tipped with orange-yellow.
DISTRIBUTION: New Guinea, in the mountains of the Vogelkop.

Greater Alpine Lorikeet (*O.a. major*) (Ogilvie-Grant)
SYNONYM: Western Blue-cheeked Lorikeet.
DESCRIPTION: Slightly larger than the nominate race, it apparently has the red on the head extending beyond the eyes, and the tail tipped with scarlet.
DISTRIBUTION: New Guinea in the Snow Mountains, West Irian.

Southern Blue-cheeked Alpine Lorikeet (*O.a. grandis*) (Ogilvie-Grant)
DESCRIPTION: It differs from *major* in having the abdomen and lower flanks green.
Immature males and females have a narrow red frontal band; the green of the

upper parts is duller and the narrow black tips to the feathers are pronounced, especially in very young birds.

DISTRIBUTION: The mountains of south-eastern New Guinea, west to the Huon Peninsula and the Sepik region. It is found between 2,400 and 3,620m, according to Mayr and Rand (1937). They described it as 'one of the most frequent visitors to the flowering trees, where parties of as many as ten sometimes gathered, in company with other parrots (chiefly *Neopsittacus*), honeyeaters and flowerpeckers. They are active little birds, walking about on the small branches and twigs, reaching out here and there to nibble the center from a flower, swinging about and clinging upside down to slender twigs.

'. . . a bird, apparently alone, was walking about quickly in the smaller branches of a forest tree, hopping from branch to branch, the while whistling to itself in a very low tone and rapidly bobbing its head and body, occasionally stopping to eat a flower. A few days later, while watching a flower tree, I saw a party of five fly into the tree, and I kept them in sight for some time. Two came into a tree overhead, which was laden with small fruit. But they were continually moving about, one bird following the other. Finally, it approached the other with spread wings, showing their bright markings. The first bird fled and of the ensuant pursuit through the branches I could see little.'

IN AVICULTURE: In 1909 Walter Goodfellow collected three specimens for E. J. Brook. Their arrival was reported in *Bird Notes* for August of that year. This is the only reference I can trace to this species in captivity.

17
Neopsittacus

Genus:*Neopsittacus* (Salvadori)

The two members of this genus can be distinguished from the *Oreopsittacus* species by the heavier, broader bill and the broader tail feathers with rounded tips in adults. (Immature birds have pointed tips to the tail feathers.) There is no sexual dimorphism.

It is extremely unlikely that the aviculturist will encounter either species; I have never seen a living specimen.

Musschenbroek's Lorikeet (*N. musschenbroekii musschenbroekii*) (Schlegel)

DESCRIPTION: The crown, nape, hind neck and cheeks are olive brown, streaked with dull yellow on the crown and nape and with pale green on the cheeks; the lores are dull greenish-black. The upper parts are dark green and the underparts light green with red on the throat, breast and centre of the abdomen. The under wing coverts and a broad band across the underside of the flight feathers are red. The tail feathers are green, tipped with yellow, the lateral feathers being red at the base; the underside of the tail is bright orange-yellow. The bill is pale yellow, the iris red and the legs grey. Length: 23cm (9in).

Immature birds are duller than adults; the red areas on the underparts are lacking but the throat and upper breast are tinged with red. The iris is brownish-yellow to orange.

DISTRIBUTION: The mountains of the Vogelkop, New Guinea.

IN AVICULTURE: This species is extremely rare in aviculture. The pair owned by H. Whitley in 1933 are unlikely to have been the first but I cannot trace any earlier records for this species. Alfred Ezra had a pair in his collection at Foxwarren Park in Surrey in 1940. In 1949 the Duke of Bedford received a pair from Sir Edward Hallstrom in Australia. The former wrote: 'In build and movements they bear a considerable resemblance to the Trichoglossine Lorikeets although they do not posture in quite the same absurd fashion as the latter.' (*Avicultural Magazine* 1950, p. 211). He described the voice, as 'rather harsh and sibilant but too low in tone and too lacking in volume to be unpleasant, even in a confined space.'

In more recent years Musschenbroek's Lorikeet has been exhibited at San Diego Zoo (*N.m. major*—qv) and, in Germany, at Stuttgart Zoo (1970s).

It is of interest that those who have kept it and commented on its diet state that it is mainly a seed-eater. Alfred Ezra found that his fed 'entirely on seed'. It was the opinion of the Duke of Bedford's aviary attendant that they did not possess a brush tongue and G. E. Whitmore, into whose possession they passed, was of the same opinion.* They refused liquid food, other than sweetened bread and milk, when young were in the nest, living on seed, apple, pear and grapes.

BREEDING RECORDS: The first and, perhaps, to date, the only successful breeder of Musschenbroek's Lorikeet, was Sir Edward Hallstrom. Two young were reared during 1953. Walter Turner submitted to the *Avicultural Magazine* (1954, p. 77) the following observations made by Sir Edward:

'The Musschenbroek's and Double-eyed Dwarf Parrots were most difficult to rear. Although the Musschenbroek's, when first caught, is a seed-eater, it cannot rear the youngsters on seed, and after losing several young birds I drove nails into the perches nearest the door, and every morning pushed an apple on to each nail, and the birds were thus able to feed the young ones with soft food. It was also impossible to encourage the Musschenbroek's to go to the floor of the aviary for water, and as a result the water was put on the same level as the food—about 5ft from the ground.'

According to Sir Edward (*Avicultural Magazine* 1956, p. 117) one of the main difficulties in breeding from his pair was that they would 'rush into their nest-box, although they may be placed as far as 25ft from the front of the aviary, sometimes with fatal results to the youngsters.'

'A number' had been reared and the pair had two chicks in the nest at the time Hallstrom's report was made.

The Duke of Bedford's pair—in which the male was brighter in colour and slightly larger—hatched a chick in 1950 but failed to rear it. Two eggs were laid in June and the male spent most of his time in the nest with the hen. When the nest was inspected on July 10 a chick was found. It was covered with grey down and estimated to be about ten days old. It died a few days later; the cause of death was not determined. The pair nested again and on September 2 the probable presence of a chick was reported. Nothing further was reported of this pair, except that they were sold because they were 'unsatisfactory as breeders.' Subsequently they became quite well known at shows.

Southern Musschenbroek's Lorikeet (*N.m. major*) (Neumann)

DESCRIPTION: Differs from the nominate race in having the streaking on the cheeks bright greenish-yellow. The plumage is paler throughout, especially on the underparts, the red of which is nearer to scarlet. It is slightly smaller.

DISTRIBUTION: The mountains of south-eastern New Guinea from the Sepik region and the Huon Peninsula to southern Papua.

This lorikeet is an inhabitant of mid-mountain forest at altitudes as low as 1,250m. Forshaw (1973) observed them on the Hagen Range, feeding on *Schefflera* fruits. They inhabited the mid and upper storeys of the trees, running along stout

---

*It should be pointed out, however, that in certain small species the 'brushes' are almost impossible to observe. This applies to the Iris Lorikeets in my possession. I have not even seen the 'brushes' of a very tame, hand-reared bird, but have seen those of another specimen.

branches in a 'rodent-like manner.' When disturbed they flew off shrieking loudly; the flight was swift and direct. This species is known to feed on nectar, pollen, blossoms, fruit, seeds and berries, also insects and their larvae, possibly ingested on fruits or blossoms.

Forshaw, also Mayr and Rand (1937), observed Musschenbroek's Lorikeets in company with Stella's Lorikeets. Mayr and Rand described it as common at 2,000m on the eastern slope of Mount Tafa. It inhabited the tops of the lower trees in the heavy forest, where it was the only *Neopsittacus*. About 20 were seen in one 'big flower tree' in company with the Stella's. At a lower altitude, 1,250m, one bird taken had its gullet filled with seeds.

IN AVICULTURE: San Diego Zoo received two Musschenbroek's Lorikeets from the collection of Edward Marshall Boehm (New Jersey, USA) in 1965; they had been collected in the Schraderberg area of south-east New Guinea. These birds were not offered seed, only nectar and blossoms. One died in December 1969 and the other in June 1971, when it was discovered that both birds were females.

N.m. medius (Stresemann)
DISTRIBUTION: Snow Mountains, West Irian.
Doubtfully distinct from *N.m. major*.

Alpine Lorikeet (*N. pullicauda pullicauda*) (Hartert)

SYNONYMS: Emerald Lorikeet, Southern Alpine Lorikeet, Victoria Alpine Lorikeet.
DESCRIPTION: It can briefly be described as resembling Musschenbroek's Lorikeet except that almost the entire underparts are red, only the flanks and thighs being green. The upper parts are green, except the head; the crown and nape are streaked with yellowish-green, the nape being tinged with olive-brown. The cheeks are streaked with greenish-yellow. The under wing coverts and a broad band across the underside of the flight feathers are red. The tail is green on the upper surface, darker than in *N. musschenbroekii* and without the yellow or orange tips; it is marked with red at the base and the underside is dull olive-green. The bill is orange. Length: 18cm (7in).

Immature birds are less brightly coloured, especially on the underparts where the area of red is much less extensive. The streaking on the head is less clearly defined and the bill is brownish.
DISTRIBUTION: The mountains of south-eastern New Guinea, west to the Sepik region.

It is found in the same regions (except the Vogelkop) as the Musschenbroek's Lorikeet but at higher altitudes, usually from 2,400m to 3,800m. The food taken is similar to that of the latter species.

Mayr and Rand (1937) recorded that 'Sometimes flocks of 28 to 30 gather together in the top of a pine tree, apparently to feed on the fruit; they came in two's and three's, with much twittering and squeaking as they moved about, and when they left they went in small parties, not as a flock. . . . These parrots, as with *N. musschenbroekii*, are adaptable in feeding habits, eating either small fruits or flowers depending on their availability.'

At 2,400m on Mount Tafa, Mayr and Rand found this species more common than Musschenbroek's. Gyldenstolphe (1955) described it as not uncommon in the cloud-forests above and around Weiga. It was 'shy and also frequented the canopy of such trees which were growing on exceedingly steep and slippery mountain-slopes. Practically every evening small flocks of this species, or of the allied *N.m. major*, passed at a considerable height above our camp-site at Weiga en route to their sleeping quarters still higher up among the inaccessible and uninhabited mountains forming the Wahgi Divide.'

IN AVICULTURE: This species is almost unknown in captivity. The only reference I can find to it is the single specimen owned by Sir Edward Hallstrom in Australia in 1953.

N.p. alpinus (Ogilvie-Grant)

DESCRIPTION: It is darker green above, with very little shaft-streaking; the breast is orange-red and the abdomen is a darker shade.

DISTRIBUTION: Snow Mountains and the ranges east to the Fly River.

N.p. socialis (Mayr)

DESCRIPTION: It differs from *N.p. pullicauda* in being darker green on the upper parts and the sides of the head; there are reddish streaks on the ear coverts and less olive-brown on the nape.

DISTRIBUTION: Herzog Mountains and the mountains of the Huon Peninsula.

Appendix of names in English, French, German and Dutch

English	French	German	Dutch
Black Lory	Lori noir	Schwarzer Lori	Zwarte Lori
Yellow-streaked Lory	Lori à front jaune	Schimmellori	Oranjegstreepte Lori
			Strepen Lori
Duivenbode's Lory	Lori de Duivenbode	Braunlori	Duivenbode's Lori
Cardinal Lory	Lori cardinale	Kardinallori	Kardinaal Lori
Black-winged Lory	Lori aux joues bleues	Blauohrlori	Koningslori
	Lori aux ailes noires		Zwartvleugel Lori
Blue-streaked Lory	Lori strié bleu	Strichellori	Blaauwgestreepte-Lori
Violet-necked Lory	Lori de Wallace	Kapuzenlori	Violetnek Lori
			Wallace's Lori
Red and Blue Lory	Lori histrion	Diademlori	Diadeem Lori
	Lori rouge et violet		
Red Lory	Lori rouge	Roter Lori	Rode Lori
Half-masked Lory	Lori aux joues bleues	Halbmasken-Lori	Blauwwanglori
			Ceram-Lori
Ornate Lorikeet	Loriquet orné	Schmucklori	Prachtlori
			Ornaatlori
Green-naped Lorikeet	Loriquet à nuque verte	Schmalbindenlori	Groennecklori
Swainson's Lorikeet	Loriquet de Swainson	Gebirgslori	
		Lori von den Blauen	Lori van de Blauwe
		Bergen	Bergen
Dusky Lory	Lori à dos blanc	Weissruckenlori	Witrug Lori
Red-collared Lorikeet	Loriquet à collier rouge	Rotnackenlori	Roodnek Lori
Cherry-red Lorikeet	Loriquet cerise	Kirshbrauner Lori	Bruine Lori
		Ponape-Lori	
Scaly-breasted Lorikeet	Loriquet écaillé	Schuppenlori	Schubbenlori
Perfect Lorikeet	Loriquet a tête jaune	Gelbkopflori	Geelkop Lori
	Loriquet eutele		
Perfect Lorikeet	Loriquet a tête jaune	Gelbkopflori	Geelkop Lori
	Loriquet eutele		
Yellow and Green Lorikeet	Loriquet vert de Sula	Sula Schuppenlori	Sulase Lori
Mount Apo Lorikeet	Loriquet de Mrs Johnstone	Mrs Johnstone's Lori	Mrs Johnstone's Lori
Varied Lorikeet	Loriquet varié	Buntlori	Bonte Lori
	Loriquet versicolore		
Iris Lorikeet	Loriquet Iris	Irislori	Iris Lori
Goldie's Lorikeet	Loriquet de Goldie	Veilchenlori	Viooltjes Lori
Musk Lorikeet	Loriquetmusqué	Moschuslori	Muskuslori
Purple-crowned Lorikeet	Loriquet de Florent	Porphyrlori	Purperkoplori
	Loriquet à tête pourpre	Blauscheitellori	
Little Lorikeet	Loriquet nain	Zwerglori	Dwerglori
	Loriquet à face rouge	Zwergmoschuslori	
Louisiade Lory	Lori à bande violette	Schwarzsteisslori	Violetstaart Lori
New Britain Lory	Lori aimable	Lieblicher Lori	Liefeliijke Lori
		Neubrittanien-Lori	
Black-capped Lory	Lori à calotte noir	Frauenlori	Zwartkap Lori
White-naped Lory	Lori à nuque blanche	Weissenackenlori	Witnek Lori
Yellow-bibbed Lory	Lori à queue verte	Grünschwanzlori	Groenstaart Lori

English	French	German	Dutch
Purple-capped Lory	Lori des dames	Schwarzkappenlori Erzlori	Vrouwen Lori Rode Zwartkop-Lori
Chattering Lory	Lori des Moluques, Noira, Babillard	Gelbmantellori	Molukken Lori
Collared Lory	Lori solitaire	Einsiedlerlori	Gekraagde Lori
Blue-crowned Lory	Lori vini à crête bleue	Blaukäppchenlori	Blauwkap Lori
Kuhl's Lory	Lori vini de Kuhl	Blaukopflori	Kuhl's Lori
Stephen's Lory	Lori vini de Stephen	Stephen's Lori	Stephen's Lori
Tahiti Blue Lory	Lori blanc et bleu de Tahiti	Saphirlori	Saifier Lori
Ultramarine Lory	Lori bleu des îles Marquises	Smaragdlori	Smaragd Lori
Palm Lorikeet	Lori des Palmiers	Zwerg lori Palmenlori	Palm Lori
Meek's Lorikeet	Loriquet de Meek	Meeks Lori	Meeks Lori
Red-throated Lorikeet	Loriquet à cou rouge	Rotkinnlori	Roodkin Lori
New Caledonian Lorikeet	Loriquet à diademe	Diademzierlori	Diadeem Lori
Buru Lorikeet	Loriquet des îles Bourou	Buru-Zierlori	Buru Lori
Pleasing Lorikeet	Loriquet joli	Schönlori	Blauwstuithoning- papegaai
Red-marked Lorikeet	Loriquet aux marques rouges Loriquet à croupion rouge	Rotbürzellori	Roodstuithoning- papegaai
Striated Lorikeet	Loriquet multistrié	Vielstrichellori	Geelgestreepte Lori
Wilhelmina's Lorikeet	Loriquet de Wilhelmine	Wilhelminenlori	Wilhelmina's Honing- papegaai
Fairy Lorikeet	Lori à croupion noir	Goldstrichellori	Zwartstiut-honing- papegaai.
Duchess Lorikeet	Lori de Marguerite	Margaretha's Lori	Margaretha's Honing- papegaai
Josephine's Lorikeet	Loriquet de Joséphine	Josephinenlori	Josephine's Honing- papegaai
Papuan Lorikeet	Loriquet papou	Papua Lori	Papoea Honing- papegaai
Arfak Alpine Lorikeet	Loriquet des Monts Arfak	Berglori Bergzierlori	Arfakse Honingpapegaai
Musschenbroek's Lorikeet	Loriquet de Musschenbroek	Gualori	Musschenbroek's Dwergpapegaai
Alpine Lorikeet	Loriquet de Victoria	Hartert's Gua	Oranjesnavel-Berglori

Bibliography

Amadon, Dean 1942.
Birds collected during the Whitney South Sea Expedition, *American Museum Novitates*.
July 24, 1942.

Cain, A. J. 1955.
A revision of *Trichoglossus haematodus* and of the Australian platycercine parrots,
Ibis, vol. 97, pp. 432–479.

Cain, A. J., and Galbraith, I. C. J. 1956.
Birds of the eastern Solomon Islands, *Ibis*, vol. 98, pp. 100–134.

Cayley, Neville W. 1938.
Australian Parrots in Field and Aviary, Angus & Robertson, Sydney.

Churchill, D. M., and Christensen, P. 1970.
Observation on pollen harvesting by brush-tongued lorikeets, *Australian Journal of Zoology*, vol. 18, pp. 427–437.

Finsch, Otto. 1900.
Notes from the Leyden Museum, vol. 22, p. 65.

Forshaw, Joseph M. 1973.
Parrots of the World, Lansdowne, Melbourne.

Gilliard, E. T., and Lecroy M. 1967.
Bulletin American Museum of Natural History, p. 195.

Greenwood, Jeremy. 1969.
Rainbow Lorikeet. *Birds of the World*, Part 7, vol. 4, IPC Magazines Ltd., London.

Gyldenstolph, N. 1955.
Arkiv för Zoologi, Bd. 8, no. 1.

Hartert, E.
1896. *Novitates Zoologicae*, vol. 3, pp. 562, 565, 595, 596.
1898. *Novitates Zoologicae*, vol. 5, p. 43.
1901. *Novitates Zoologicae*, vol. 8, p. 4.
1924. *Novitates Zoologicae*, vol. 19, p. 211.

Hickson, Sydney J. 1889
A Naturalist in North Celebes, John Murray, London.

Iredale, T. 1956.
Birds of New Guinea, Georgian House, Melbourne.

Lendon, Alan H. 1973.
Australian Parrots in Field and Aviary, Angus & Robertson, Sydney.

Mayr, E. and Rand, A. L. 1937.
Results of the Archbold Expeditions, vol. 14, Birds of the 1933–34 Papuan Expedition,
Bulletin of the American Museum of Natural History, vol. 73, art. 1, pp. 1–248.

Mayr, E. and Schauensee, R. Meyer de, 1939.
The birds of the Island of Biak, *Proceedings of the Academy of Natural Sciences, Philadelphia*, vol. 91, pp. 1–37.

Mees, G. F. 1965.
The avifauna of Misool, *Nova Guinea Zool*, series 31, pp. 139–203.

Mitchell, J. L. 1966.
  Birdkeeping in Australia, vol. 9, no. 2.
Mivart, St. George 1896.
  A monograph of the lories or brush-tongued parrots, R. H. Porter, London.
Ogilvie-Grant, W. R. 1913.
  Birds of Henderson Island, *Bulletin of British Ornithologists Club*, pp. 58–61 and 76–77.
Peters, J. L. 1937.
  Check-list of Birds of the World, vol. 3, Harvard University Press, Cambridge, USA.
Petrak, Margaret L. 1969.
  Diseases of Cage and Aviary Birds, Lea and Febijer, Philadelphia.
Rand, A. L., and Gilliard, E. T. 1967.
  Handbook of New Guinea Birds, Weidenfeld & Nicolson, London.
Rothschild, W. 1931.
  A collection of birds made by F. Shaw Mayer, *Novitates Zoologicae*, vol. 36, p. 271.
Rothschild, W. and Hartert, E. 1901.
  Novitates Zoologicae, vol. 8, p. 71.
Rutgers, A. and Norris, K. A. (eds.), 1972.
  Encyclopaedia of Aviculture, vol. 2, Blandford Press, London.
Salvadori, T. 1891.
  Catalogue of birds in the British Museum, vol. 20, Psittaci, British Museum (Natural History), London.
Seth-Smith, D. 1903.
  Parrakeets, R. H. Porter, London.
Sibson, R. B. 1972.
  Birds of Fiji in Colour, Collins, Auckland and London.
Wallace, Alfred Russel, 1922.
  (new edition), *The Malay Archipelago*, Macmillan, London.

Periodicals and publications mentioned in the text

Australian Aviculture—Journal of the Avicultural Society of Australia.
Avicultural Magazine—Journal of the Avicultural Society (Great Britain).
Bird Notes—Journal of the now defunct Foreign Bird Club.
Cage and Aviary Birds (formerly *Cage Birds*)—weekly magazine, IPC Business Press, Sutton, Surrey, England.
International Zoo Year Book—Zoological Society, London.
Foreign Birds—Journal of the Foreign Bird League (Great Britain).
Parrot Society Magazine—Journal of the Parrot Society (Great Britain).
The Foreigner—Publication of Keston Foreign Bird Farm, Keston, England, 1934–37.
Zoonooz—Monthly publication of the Zoological Society of San Diego, California, USA.

Index

GENERAL INDEX
(*Main text reference in bold type*)